A Photographic Atl
Marine
Biology

MORTON
PUBLISHING
925 W. Kenyon Ave., Unit 12
Englewood, CO 80110
www.morton-pub.com

Gary D. Wisehart
Erin C. Rempala
Michael J. Leboffe

Book Team

Publisher:	Douglas N. Morton
Biology Editor:	David Ferguson
Editorial Assistant:	Rayna Bailey
Production Manager:	Joanne Saliger
Production Assistant:	Will Kelley
Cover Design:	Bob Schram, Bookends, Inc.

Copyright © 2012 by Morton Publishing Company

ISBN: 978-089582-785-2

Library of Congress Control Number: 2011940095

10 9 8 7 6 5 4 3 2 1

Preface

The *Photographic Atlas of Marine Biology* is designed to supplement a college-level marine biology text. It presents photographs of living organisms in their natural habitat and in public and private aquaria, preserved specimens, taxidermy specimens, and photomicrographs of living, whole specimens, and sectioned and stained specimens. There is one scanning electron micrograph. The emphasis is on nearshore and intertidal organisms of North America. Organisms photographed in their natural habitat include some from Vancouver Island to the lagoons of Baja California, from Maine to Patagonia, the Gulf Coast of North America, and the Caribbean (Florida Keys, the Virgin Islands and Cayman Islands). Aquaria and preserved specimens are from a wide range of locations around the world's ocean. Photographs are by the authors except where noted.

The emphasis is on evolutionary relationships and systematics except for a few eukaryotic taxa, which are presented in functional groups. In Chapters 2 through 32, a table presents taxa names with reference to photographs of representative organisms, a general description of each taxon, species examples, approximate number of known species, and name origins. Chapters 1 and 33 differ from the other chapters. Chapter 1 is a general introduction to biodiversity, taxonomy, and phylogeny; and Chapter 33 is a summary of nearshore and intertidal habitats of North America.

In addition to photographs, there are dozens of art pieces that emphasize phylogeny and systematics, present life cycles, or show important anatomical, embryological, or morphological details. Some art pieces appear repeatedly so that chapters may be used independently and in any sequence, and to provide evolutionary perspective for the organisms of that chapter. Some of the art is modified from figures appearing in *Biology* by Neil A. Campbell and Jane B. Reece, and *Integrated Principles of Zoology*, by Cleveland P. Hickman, Larry Roberts, Susan Keen, Allan Larson, Helen I'Anson, and David Eisenhour.

This *Atlas* does not contain tools for identification. There are many identification guides available for each geographic region.

Acknowledgments

We would like to thank our colleagues and friends at San Diego City College for their patience, understanding and support. In alphabetical order, these include Donna DiPaolo, Anita Hettena, Roya Lahijani, David Singer, Minou Spradley, and Muu Vu. We would particularly like to thank Debra Reed for her involvement and Laura Steininger for her assistance.

Aerial photographs were made possible by the generous willingness of Dr. Steven J. Byers to fly one of the authors along the Southern California coast. We would like to thank Bonnie Philips and Kaye London of Cabrillo National Monument, National Park Service; Jim Milbury and Teri Frady of the National Oceanic and Atmospheric Administration; the staff of the San Diego Natural History Museum, including Philip Unitt, Curator of Birds and Mammals, who reviewed our bird identifications (any remaining errors are those of the authors), Bradford Hollingsworth, Ph.D., Curator of Herpetology, and Jimmy Rabbers, who assisted with the American alligator skull for us to photograph; and Marya Ahmad, Education Specialist/Research Associate, Tijuana River National Estuarine Research Reserve, California State Parks. Thanks also to Karsten Zengler of the University of California, San Diego, for supplying the *Thermotoga maritima* culture, and to Ann Ancibor of Pet Kingdom for making specimens available.

Some photographs first appeared in other Morton publications. We would like to thanks authors Burton Pierce, John. L. Crawley, Dale W. Fishbeck, Kent M. Van De Graaff, and Aurora Sebastiani for use of their photographs.

Thanks to Elizabeth Wisehart for her assistance in selecting many of the photographs and for her patience as a "photographer's assistant" and travel companion. Thanks to Alicia Leboffe for her "keen eyes" in spotting invertebrates at the tide pools. Thanks also go to Brian and Jamie Wick for their assistance as dive buddy, specimen collector, tour guide, and host during trips to southern Florida. And finally, thanks to Sandra Storrie for her help in locating tide pool specimens and for recruiting the assistance of Ann Ancibor.

We appreciate the efforts of Gwen Goodmanlowe, CSU–Long Beach, Sharon E. Mozley-Standridge, Middle Georgia College, Kathryn Craven, Armstrong Atlantic State University, and John Korstad, Oral Roberts University, for reviewing the manuscript and for their helpful suggestions. This work is better for their comments. Sadly, some of their excellent suggestions will have to await another edition.

Artwork is the creative product of the talented people at Imagineering Art in Toronto, Ontario, Canada. The quality of their work is exceptional and we are grateful beyond belief for their efforts, because the alternative was author-drawn stick figures.

Colleagues, marine science enthusiasts, and family members were very generous in allowing us to use their photographs. Their contributions are noted where they occur. These include photographs by Keith Baier (Baierwood); Mark Baier, M.D. (Northern Nevada Emergency Physicians at Renown Regional Medical Center); Nick Baker (Ecology Asia); Elizabeth Balser (Illinois Wesleyan University); Stephen Bouscaren (San Diego City College); John Calambokidis (Cascadia Research); Ari Friedlaender (Duke University, Nicholas School of the Environment); Elaine Humphrey (University of Victoria, Advanced Microscopy Facility); Ian and Todd Malloy (Crikey Adventure Tours); James Milbury of the Southwest Fisheries Service, NOAA; Steve Murvine; and Jennale Peacock. If we have left anyone off the list we sincerely apologize. This omission was not intentional.

Particular thanks to the Morton team for their patience (and we really mean *patience!*) and assistance: Doug Morton (President), Chrissy Morton DeMier (Business Manager), David Ferguson (Biology Editor), Carter Fenton (Sales and Marketing Manager), Joanne Saliger (Production Manager), Will Kelley (Production Assistant), and Desireé Coscia and Rayna Bailey (Editorial Assistants). The work of these Morton team members occurs behind the scenes, but it is all essential to the success of their publications. But a special thanks is owed to Joanne Saliger for her great skill in designing the layout, her aesthetic sense, and eye for detail, because her work is seen in the final product. Thanks also to Bob Schram of Bookends, Inc., for the cover design.

Any project with these time demands requires sacrifice by those close to us. We would like to thank our families for their understanding and patience. One of us can start working on the ever enlarging "honey do" list now! Another of us can start working on the ever enlarging "editor do" list.

The following institutions kindly permitted us to photograph some of their collections. We are grateful for their generosity, as it would have been difficult to obtain photographs of comparable specimens in the wild. We encourage you to visit these institutions when in their vicinity and see their entire collections.

≈ Aquarium of the Pacific in Long Beach, California
http://www.aquariumofpacific.org/

≈ Birch Aquarium at Scripps   http://aquarium.ucsd.edu/

≈ Cabrillo Marine Aquarium, City of Los Angeles Recreation and Parks   http://www.cabrillomarineaquarium.org/

≈ Chula Vista Nature Center
http://www.chulavistanaturecenter.org/

≈ Denver Museum of Nature and Science
http://www.dmns.org/

≈ Denver Zoo   http://www.denverzoo.org/

≈ Downtown Aquarium (Denver, Colorado)
http://www.aquariumrestaurants.com/
downtownaquariumdenver/default.asp

≈ Ellie Schiller Homosassa Springs Wildlife Park
http://hswsp.com/main.html

≈ Grand Cayman Islands Turtle Farm
http://www.caymanturtlefarm.com/

≈ Hatfield Marine Science Center of Oregon State University
http://hmsc.oregonstate.edu/

≈ J. N. "Ding" Darling National Wildlife Refuge (Sanibel Island, Florida)   http://www.fws.gov/dingdarling/

≈ Mandalay Bay Shark Reef Aquarium
http://www.mandalaybay.com/entertainment/
shark-reef-aquarium.aspx

≈ Manatee Park, Lee County Parks & Recreation, Florida
http://www.leeparks.org/facility-info/facility-details.
cfm?Project_Num=0088

≈ Monterey Bay Aquarium
http://www.montereybayaquarium.org/

≈ Oregon Coast Aquarium, Newport   http://aquarium.org/

≈ Oregon Zoo (Portland)   http://www.oregonzoo.org/

≈ San Diego Natural History Museum http://www.sdnhm.org/

≈ San Diego River Park Foundation
http://www.sandiegoriver.org

≈ Santa Monica Pier Aquarium
http://www.santamonicapier.org/fun/2010/8/30/
santa-monica-pier-aquarium-general-information.html

≈ Sea World San Diego
http://seaworldparks.com/seaworld-sandiego

≈ Tijuana River National Estuarine Research Reserve
http://trnerr.org/ or http://www.parks.ca.gov/?page_id=669

≈ Torrey Pines State Natural Reserve
http://www.torreypine.org

≈ Ty Warner Sea Center at the Santa Barbara Museum of Natural History   http://www.sbnature.org/twsc/2.html

Finally, we encourage readers to point out changes that will increase this *Atlas'* utility and any errors encountered. You may contact us through the publisher.

Gary ≈ Erin ≈ Mike

Contents

Extreme halophiles

Green turtle

1 Introduction to Marine Biodiversity, Taxonomy, and Phylogeny

The number of organisms alive on earth is unknown. Estimates range from a few million to as many as 50 million. Even the actual number of described and catalogued species is debated with estimates running from 1.2 million to 1.9 million. Whatever the true number, it is clear that a very large proportion of earth's total species count is marine. An estimated 80 percent of marine species have not yet been identified.

Throughout history humankind has sought order in the diversity of life, and various schemes have been used to organize and group species using some type of **taxonomy**. With the wide acceptance of evolutionary theory culminating in the publication of *On the Origin of Species by Means of Natural Selection* by Charles Darwin in 1859, taxonomies began to be constructed grouping organisms based upon ancestral relationships. That sounds nice in principle, but in practice, determining evolutionary (ancestral) relationships is difficult on a good day.

General Principles

An organism's actual ancestral history and the science of reconstructing evolutionary histories are both called **phylogeny**. A major goal of studies of fossils, comparative anatomy, morphology, physiology, molecular biology, genomes (genetic composition), and biogeography is to

use the data collected to construct phylogenies. Figure 1-1 shows a phylogeny of life. Domain Bacteria is on the left, Archaea on the right, and Eukarya in the middle.

An aid in organizing information about all known species and in adding new species when they are discovered is to use a standardized system for assigning names and for grouping organisms sharing common ancestors. This is called **classification**. Science is a community activity, and while individuals may develop procedures, processes, and methodologies, their general value elevates if the community of scientists adopts them. The general methods adopted by biologists for classification of species is to first give each unique species a name consisting of two parts: the first name is always capitalized and is the generic (genus) name, while the second is the specific epithet and is only capitalized if it is derived from a proper noun such as a person's name or a named geographic feature. Combined, they name the species and both names are italicized or underlined. An example is the polar bear, *Ursus maritimus*. Carolus Linnaeus, the "father" of classification, first developed this system in 1758. Biologists still generally accept his method in modern, modified form.

Linnaeus introduced many of the classification categories used today. Modern categories include, Domain, Kingdom, Phylum/Division, Class, Order, Family, Genus,

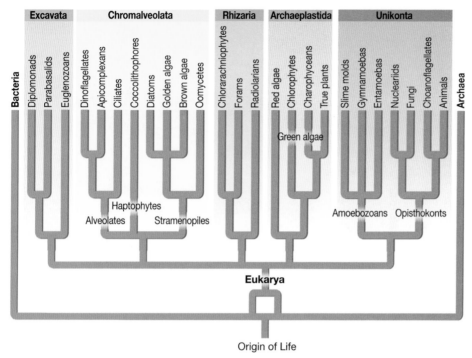

1-1 A Tree of Life ≈ This is a proposed phylogeny of life illustrating ancestral connections between all major groups of living things. Biologists currently use three Domains to encompass all known life forms: Bacteria, Archaea, and Eukarya. In this diagram, time progresses from bottom to top along the Y-axis, with the top representing today. Each line leads to a currently existing group of organisms at the top. These groups are said to be extant as opposed to extinct. The bottom line presumes an ancestor common to all life. The bottom line branches and then leads to the Bacteria on the left and Archaea on the right. From this original branch, two lines lead to the Eukarya with its various groupings shown in color at the top of the page. Two connecting lines indicate that Eukarya are derived from both Bacteria and Archaea and not from a single ancestral type. In addition to this diagram presenting a hypothetical and controversial phylogeny, it also overemphasizes the Eukarya. See Appendix A for definitions of terms, clades, and taxa in this figure.

and Species. These are in sequence from most general category containing large numbers of organisms to most specific containing a single kind of organism. The science of classification, its theoretical study and underlying principles is termed taxonomy. The study of relationships in an attempt to understand phylogenies is termed **systematics**. Taxonomic categories such as Phylum and Family should not be confused with **taxa** (**taxon**, singular) such as Animalia (the Kingdom name containing animals) and Delphinidae (the Family name containing dolphins). Each is a taxon and collectively they are taxa.

As our understanding of phylogenies changes, so do classification categories and methodologies. For example, in recent years the category Domain was added as evidence accumulated that the Kingdom as the most inclusive level is insufficient.

All species are a composite of anatomical, morphological, physiological, and molecular characteristics inherited from distant ancestors and those evolved in that species. Those characteristics inherited from past ancestors are called **ancestral characteristics** or **symplesiomorphies** and those not shown by ancestors, which evolved more recently, are called **derived characteristics.** Organisms that share derived characters are called a **clade** and the characters they share are called **shared derived characters** or **synapomorphies.**

There are several methods used to classify organisms and to graphically represent phylogenies. Traditional evolutionary systematics has the longest history in biology and is heavily dependent upon anatomical, morphological, and biogeographical data. This approach maintains that the production of new species (**speciation**) may occur in two

fundamentally different patterns. The first occurs when one species gives rise to another and the first species no longer exists. The second is when one species gives rise to another and both species continue to exist as contemporaries evolving along their own evolutionary path and leaving their own ancestors. Thus, when a traditional phylogenetic tree is constructed (Figure 1-2), a line represents a series of speciations and species, while a branch point represents a major split in evolution that produces separate ancestral paths. A major criticism of this approach is that the process lacks objectivity and resulting groups may include descendants of more than one ancestor (**polyphyletic**), others contain some members of an ancestor but are missing others (**paraphyletic**), and finally, some groups contain an ancestral form and all of its descendants (**monophyletic**). As a result, this approach does not strictly show phylogenies.

An alternative approach increasingly used and gaining wider and wider acceptance within the biological community seeks to use only groupings that are monophyletic. Practitioners maintain that the traditional approach does not present testable hypotheses while this approach does. This method concentrates on branch points only and as a result is called **cladistics** (*cladus*—branch). The graphical representations of these phylogenies are called **cladograms** (Figure 1-3). Besides monophyletic groupings, this approach also focuses on similarity of characteristics that result from a common ancestor. These are called **homologous characteristics.** In practice, it is often difficult to determine if a similarity results from common ancestry or from adaptations to the same environment (analogous characteristics).

Anatomical structures are considered homologous if they derive from the same embryological structures and

1-2 Animal Kingdom

Phylogeny ≈ In modern format, this figure is a traditional phylogeny in the form of a tree. These phylogenetic trees often result in groupings that are polyphyletic or paraphyletic and therefore do not always well represent ancestral relationships and an accurate phylogeny. Realize that all phylogenies presented in this *Atlas* are provisional and are subject to change as new data accumulates (in this sense, they are really groups of hypotheses subject to continued testing), and many relationships are currently unresolved. All phylogenies are a single interpretation of the available data. See Appendix B for definitions of terms used at branch points in this figure.

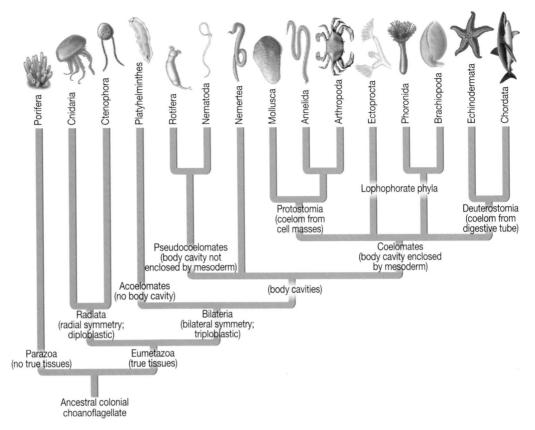

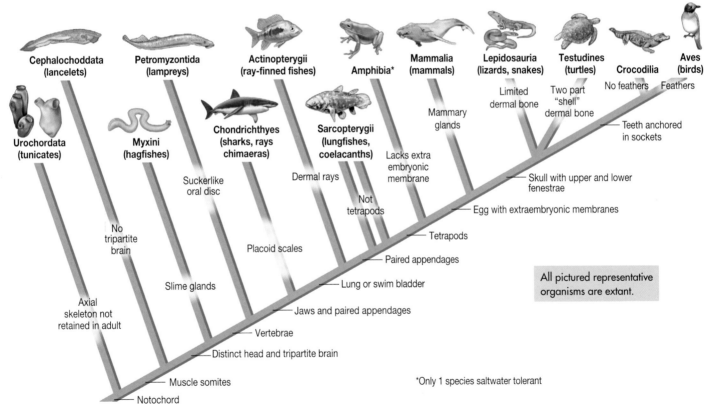

1-3 Chordata Cladogram

1-3 Chordata Cladogram ≈ In cladograms, branch points indicate a difference between groups diverging at the branch. The emphasis is on homologous characteristics or homologies, and possession of shared derived characters for those along the same branch. Notice that all organisms shown in this figure possess the common shared derived character of a hollow nerve cord running along the back (**dorsal** surface), and a skeletal element that runs along the length of the body (**axis**). The first branch separates all organisms that do not maintain this axial skeleton during their entire life from those that do. The cladograms used in this *Atlas* have labeling, which will help you identify common derived characters and differences between clades. Realize that all cladograms presented in this *Atlas* are a single interpretation of the available data. See Appendix C for definitions of terms.

occupy the same position in the body relative to other body parts. Molecular homologies are determined by the degree of similarity in structure. For example, the sequence of amino acids in a protein with the same function in several organisms would be compared. If sequences are significantly different, they are not considered to be homologous. If similar, they would be considered homologous.

The fundamental difference between traditional systematics and cladistics is that the traditional method looks for differences to place organisms in *different* groups, while cladistics depends upon similarities (homologies) to place organisms in the *same* group.

In Figure 1-3, the Crocodilia and Aves (birds) are monophyletic and are called **sister groups**. They share common ancestry more recently than either does with Testudines (turtles). The Testudines are said to be an **out-group** to the Crocodilia and Aves.

The principles presented in this section will be used frequently throughout this *Atlas*, as phylogenies and cladograms are presented for marine organisms.

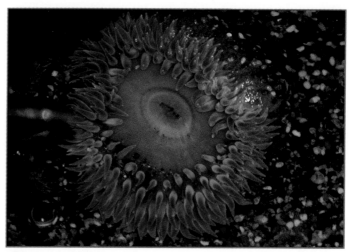

■ **1-5 Giant Green Anemone** ≈ This is a common intertidal and subtidal anemone species that lives along the Northeastern Pacific basin. Its common name varies by region. One name is the giant green anemone because it may reach up to 30 cm across its tentacles and stand more than 35 cm high in sublittoral (low tide down to the edge of the continental shelf) areas of its distribution. It is in the genus *Anthopleura*.

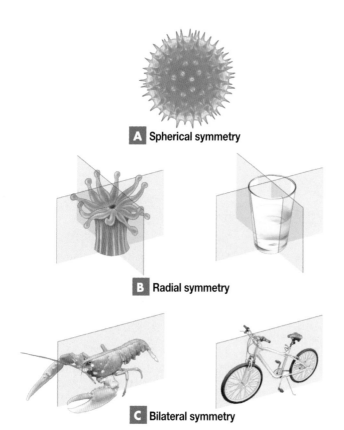

A Spherical symmetry

B Radial symmetry

C Bilateral symmetry

■ **1-4 Symmetry** ≈ Three basic symmetries are shown: a basketball has spherical symmetry; a tire, pie, or vase has radial symmetry; an automobile and airplane have bilateral (*bi*—two, *lateral*—side) symmetry. Within each of these basic types are a host of modifications that make symmetry much more diverse and complex than what is represented here. However, being able to distinguish between these types will serve the marine biology student well, whether using a key to identify organisms or focusing on evolutionary relationships between diverse taxa.

Methods of Systematics and Cladistics (With an Emphasis on Animals)

Traditional and modern methods use comparative studies to provide information to help resolve phylogenetic and systematic relationships. Data can be collected from the following areas of study:

≈ morphological (*morph*—form, *logi*—discourse)
≈ reproductive cycle
≈ anatomical (*anato*—cut open)
≈ physiological (*physio*—nature, *logi*—discourse, and here it means the study of functions and vital processes of an organism and its organs)
≈ biochemical (*bio*—life, + chemical)
≈ ecological (*eco*—operation of a household, *logi*—discourse)
≈ biogeographical (*bio*—life, *geos*—earth)
≈ embryological (*embryo*—embryo, *logi*—discourse).

A fundamental, morphological character used is shape. In Figure 1-4, three different shapes are shown. These are only representative and variations exist. For example, many sea anemones (Figure 1-5) generally show radial morphology, but more specifically, a variation called bi-radial symmetry.

Reproductive cycles (Figure 1-6), number of chromosomes, and the pattern of chromosomal pairing are also used in establishing ancestry.

Additionally, embryological development patterns in multicellular organisms, particularly animals, have been widely used. Figure 1-7 shows a development pattern

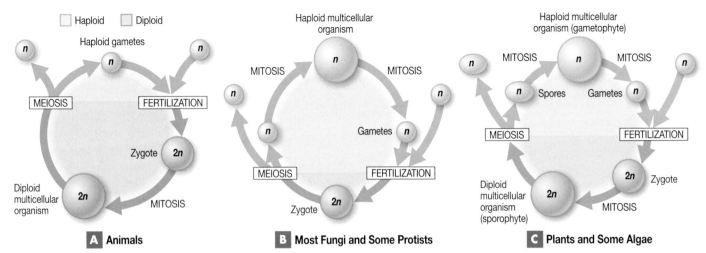

A Animals	**B** Most Fungi and Some Protists	**C** Plants and Some Algae

Legend: ☐ Haploid ☐ Diploid

A Animals: Haploid gametes — MEIOSIS — FERTILIZATION — Zygote 2n — Diploid multicellular organism 2n — MITOSIS

B Most Fungi and Some Protists: Haploid multicellular organism — MITOSIS — MITOSIS — Gametes n — MEIOSIS — FERTILIZATION — Zygote 2n

C Plants and Some Algae: Haploid multicellular organism (gametophyte) — MITOSIS — MITOSIS — Spores — Gametes — MEIOSIS — FERTILIZATION — Diploid multicellular organism (sporophyte) 2n — Zygote 2n — MITOSIS

■ **1-6 Life Cycles** ≈ This figure applies to organisms in the Domain Eukarya. Notice that life cycles vary between animals, plants, fungi, and algae (and even within the algae). At the level shown here, there is little variation within the animals and plants (defined as multicelluar, nonmotile autotrophs). Life cycles have two major stages based upon the number of the gene-containing structures in the nucleus of their cells (**chromosomes**). During the stage shown in pink, there is only one of each kind of chromosome present (this condition is called **haploid**). During the second stage shown in blue, there are two of each kind of chromosome present (this condition is called **diploid**). Haploid is also represented as **n** and diploid as **2n**; "n" is the basic number of chromosomes present for the species (constant for each species), and 2n indicates two of each kind, meaning the chromosomes are paired. Notice how all life cycles alternate between haploid and diploid stages. Each life cycle has two forms in common. The first is a single cell capable of fusing with another cell type. This cell is haploid and is called a **gamete** or sex cell. The second is a diploid cell produced by gametes fusing. This cell is diploid and is called a **zygote**. In addition, plants and animals share another common feature. They both have a multicellular, adult diploid form. You are such a form, as is the tree outside your window. Finally, all three life cycles share three common processes. The first produces more cells and is called **mitosis**. It occurs in various phases of the three life cycles. The second process takes a cell with pairs of chromosomes (2n) and reduces the number of chromosomes to the n number. This process is called **meiosis**. It occurs at a single stage in all three life cycles and takes the organism's life cycle from diploid to haploid. The final process takes a cell with one of each kind of chromosome and doubles the number of chromosomes. This process is called **fertilization**. Here, two different types of gametes (usually sperm and egg) fuse to produce the zygote and combine their chromosomes to produce a diploid cell.

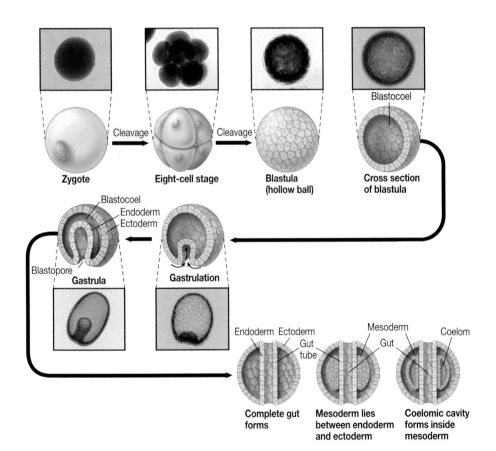

Zygote → Cleavage → **Eight-cell stage** → Cleavage → **Blastula (hollow ball)** → **Cross section of blastula** (Blastocoel)

Gastrula (Blastocoel, Endoderm, Ectoderm, Blastopore) ← **Gastrulation**

Complete gut forms (Endoderm, Ectoderm, Gut tube) — **Mesoderm lies between endoderm and ectoderm** (Mesoderm, Gut) — **Coelomic cavity forms inside mesoderm** (Coelom)

■ **1-7 Animal Development** ≈ This figure shows a developmental pattern that has been extensively used to establish phylogenies. Here you see a complete pattern of development typical of animals from flatworms through whales. Pay attention to detail. Cleavage specifically refers to mitosis (Figure 1-6). **Gastrulation** is the process where a ball of cells (**blastula**) pushes into its hollow center (**blastocoel**) forming a cavity. As gastrulation proceeds, various **germ layers** are formed. Which layers and how they are formed has been extensively used to interpret evolutionary relationships. Notice that a three-layered embryo is shown. The outer layer is **ectoderm** (*ecto*–outer, *derm*–skin), the inner layer is **endoderm** (*endo*–within), and the middle layer is **mesoderm** (*meso*–middle). There are many variations on this pattern.

seen in animals as diverse as flatworms through mammals. The embryological homologies used to determine ancestry include:

≈ methods of fertilization (internal, external, etc.)

≈ formation of the zygote (fertilized egg) and the pattern followed in restoring a paired number of chromosomes

≈ early cell division (cleavage) pattern

≈ number and size of cells formed by cleavage divisions

≈ each embryonic cell's developmental potential

≈ invagination formation (gastrulation) and position relative to other embryological structures

≈ formation of specific embryological tissue layers

≈ absence or presence of a body cavity and the method of its formation.

Figure 1-8 shows that even when a body cavity exists, there are clade associations with the pattern of its formation. Figures 1-9 through 1-11 summarize some of the patterns and their association with a few taxa. Proposed phylogenies may be better understood and remembered when arguments for their associations are known, including the basic premises used to justify them. These developmental patterns are important parts of the traditional and cladistic arguments favoring proposed contemporary animal phylogenies.

■ 1-8 Development of a Body Cavity

≈ In this figure, the development of the third embryo layer (the mesoderm) and its association with a body cavity are shown. Although there are variations from these patterns, they are viewed as the basic patterns in animals from flat worms to humans. The difference between (**A**) and (**B**) is found in the position and method of development of the first mesodermal cells. Note their position relative to the first opening into the gastrula called the **blastopore**. Three basic outcomes can occur in (**A**). The first is for the mesoderm to fill the blastocoel. The second is for the mesoderm to cover only the outer part of the blastocoel. The third is for the mesoderm to line all surfaces of the blastocoel. All of these patterns where the mesodermal cells arise near the blastopore are collectively known as **protostomial** (*proto*–first, *stom*–mouth). As we survey the protostomes, the importance this developmental pattern has played in our understanding of phylogeny will be obvious. In (**B**), the pattern of mesoderm development results in the blastocoel being covered on all surfaces, but the mesoderm arises further from the blastopore than in protostomes. These organisms are called **deuterostomes** (*deutero*–second).

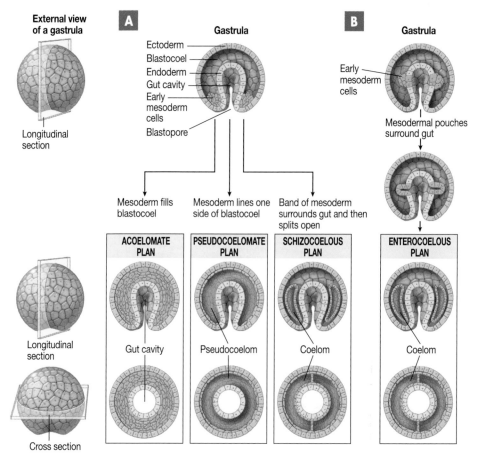

1-9 Animal Phylogeny ~ Compare this graphic with Figure 1-8. Major animal taxa are shown in a phylogeny using major embryological developmental pathways as a means of establishing evolutionary relationships. Three groups are shown based upon color. Beige shows animals that have no distinct embryological layers (germ layers) or only two (ectoderm and endoderm). Other embryological patterns are indicated. Blue shows animals with three germ layers and a protostomic pattern of mesoderm development. Other embryological patterns are also indicated. Green shows animals with three germ layers and a deuterostomic pattern of mesoderm development. Other embryological patterns are also indicated.

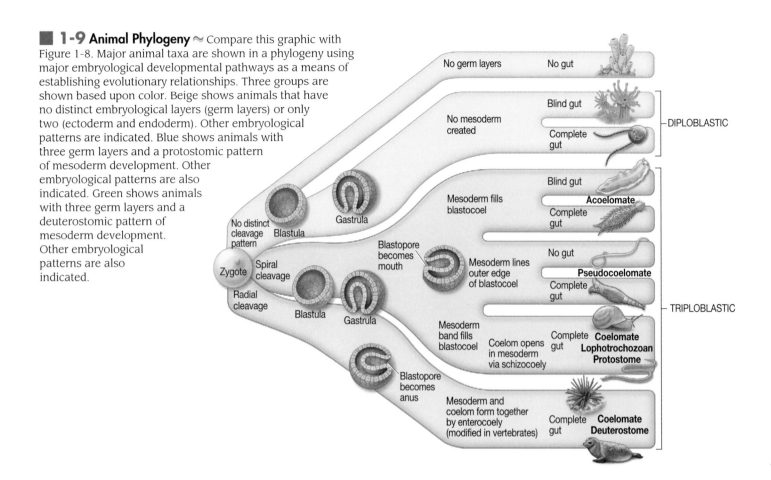

	PROTOSTOMES		DEUTEROSTOMES	
	Spiral cleavage	Cleavage mostly spiral	Radial cleavage	Cleavage mostly radial
	Cell from which mesoderm will derive	Endomesoderm usually from a particular blastomere designated 4d	Endomesoderm from pouches of primitive gut	Endomesoderm from enterocoelous pouching (except vertebrates)
	Primitive gut, Mesoderm, Coelom, Blastopore	In coelomate protostomes the coelom forms as a split in mesodermal bands (schizocoelous)	Mesoderm, Coelom, Primitive gut, Blastopore	All coelomate, coelom from fusion of enterocoelous pouches (except vertebrates, which are schizocoelous)
	Anus, Annelid (clamworm), Mouth	Mouth forms from or near blastopore; anus is a new formation. Embryology mostly determinate (mosaic). Includes phyla Platyhelminthes, Nemertea, Annelida, Mollusca, Arthropoda, Phoronida, Ectoprocta, Brachiopoda, minor phyla	Mouth, Anus	Anus forms from or near blastopore, mouth is a new formation. Embryology usually indeterminate (regulative). Includes phyla Echinodermata, Hermichordata, Chordata

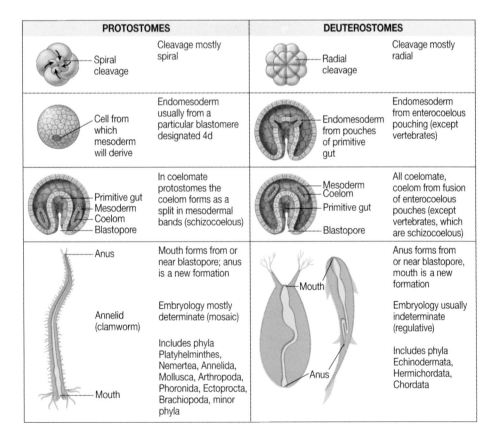

1-10 Protostome versus Deuterostome Development ~ Details of protostome and deuterostome development are shown. For cleavage pattern,* note the alignment of the contact point between neighboring cells. In deuterostomes, the contact points align vertically on the embryo and are described as radial. In the protostomes, contact points are staggered and are said to spiral. The fate of the blastopore also varies between protostomes and deuterostomes, becoming the anus in the deuterostomes and mouth in the protostomes. Finally, origin of mesoderm cells varies between both groups. Note phyla typical of each type.

*Cleavage patterns include determinate (mosaic) and indeterminate (regulative). Determinate occurs when the tissue and/or organ fate of blastomeres (cells of the embryo) is prescribed very early during development. Indeterminate is where the fate is *not* prescribed early in development.

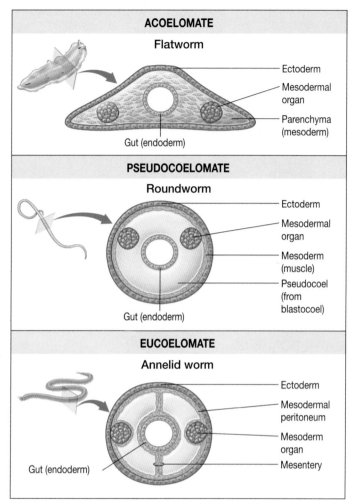

■ **1-11 Body Cavities** ≈ Consequences of protostome and deuterostome development are shown. **Acoelomate** (*a*–without, *coelom*–cavity), **pseudocoelomate** (*pseudo*–false) and **eucoelomate** (*eu*–true) body plans may result from the protostome pattern. Sample marine organisms are shown with each type.

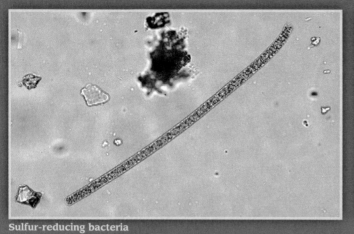

Sulfur-reducing bacteria

Unidentified marine
Gram-negative bacterium

2 Marine Bacteria and Archaea

Ribosomal RNA (rRNA), DNA, and protein comparisons suggest strongly that there are three major clusters of organisms inhabiting our world. The three groups are so significantly different that a category higher (more inclusive) than Kingdom was created to house and differentiate between them. This category is the **Domain,** and the three Domains are Bacteria, Archaea, and Eukarya (Figure 2-1 and Table 2-1). Prior to this, Bacteria and Archaea were housed in the Kingdom Monera, which included all **prokaryotes** (nonnucleated cells). Some evidence suggests that Bacteria and Archaea are distantly related and occupy different clades in the tree of life. If true, the term "prokaryote" has outlived its usefulness.

Unlike most of the other groups you will see throughout this book, Bacteria and Archaea are not easily identified visually—even with a microscope. Because they are so small and structurally simple (Figure 2-2), identification requires running multiple biochemical tests and matching the results to published descriptions of possible organisms. Depending on the organism, this can take weeks, and because of strain variability the match may not be a perfect one. The best a microbiologist can say is that, "Based on the test results, this organism best matches the accepted description of Organism X." Therefore, all identifications are provisional.

For the most part, the Bacteria and Archaea covered in this chapter will not be identified to species (the exceptions being pure cultures obtained from a reputable source). Some will be identified to a functional grouping, such as "sulfur-reducing bacteria." Otherwise, organisms will simply be described by structure.

Figure 2-3 is an artist's rendition of a generic bacterial cell illustrating structures visible with the electron microscope. Compared with eukaryotes, the interior of Bacterial (and Archaeal) cells is relatively simple. There is no nuclear envelope forming the nucleus and housing the single chromosome. Instead, the region occupied by the chromosome is called the **nucleoid** (*oid*—resembling) and is made of a single, circular molecule of double-stranded DNA (dsDNA). Nor are there membranous organelles, such as Golgi bodies, endoplasmic reticulum, and vacuoles. Instead, the functions carried out by all of the complex eukaryotic cytoplasmic organelles occur in the cytoplasm or are associated with the cytoplasmic membrane. **Ribosomes** (the structures that perform protein synthesis) differ in size from their eukaryotic counterparts and are free in the cytoplasm, often seen in chains called **polyribosomes** (*poly*—many). The cytoplasm also houses various storage (such as lipid, polysaccharide, or phosphate) or waste (such as elemental sulfur) granules. Many Bacteria have small, circular DNA

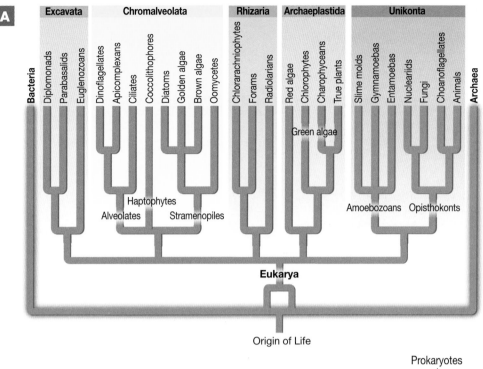

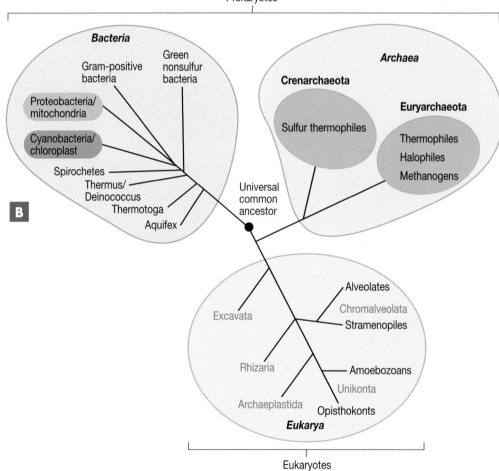

2-1 Phylogeny of the Three Domains of Life ≈ (A) The subjects of this chapter are shown at either end of this phylogeny. The connecting lines between Bacteria and Archaea at the base is intended to show that Eukarya arose as a result of endosymbiosis between an ancient fermenting archaean and an aerobically respiring bacterium, forming mitochondria. (See Appendix A for definitions of terms, clades, and taxa in this figure.) (B) Don't let the single branches for Bacteria and Archaea in (A) fool you. There is great diversity within these domains! It's just that the differences are less obvious (biochemical rather than structural) than those seen in Domain Eukarya. And undoubtedly, much remains to be discovered.

Characteristic	Bacteria	Archaea	Eukarya
Genetic			
Genome surrounded by nuclear membrane	No	No	Yes
Membrane-bound organelles	No	No	Yes
DNA molecule covalently bonded into circular form	Yes	Yes	No
Introns common	No	No	Yes
Operons present	Yes	Yes	No
Plasmids present	Yes	Yes	Rare
mRNA processing (poly-A tail and capping)	No	No	Yes
Metabolism			
Oxygenic photosynthesis	Yes (some)	No	Yes
Anoxygenic photosynthesis	Yes (some)	No	No
Methanogenesis	No	Yes	No
Nitrogen fixation	Yes (some)	Yes (some)	No
Chemolithotrophic metabolism	Yes (some)	Yes (some)	No
Cell Structure			
Cell wall of peptidoglycan	Most	Never	Never
Ester-linked, straight-chained fatty acids in membrane	Yes	No	Yes
Ether-linked, branched aliphatic chains in membrane	No	Yes	No
Ribosome type	70S	70S	80S

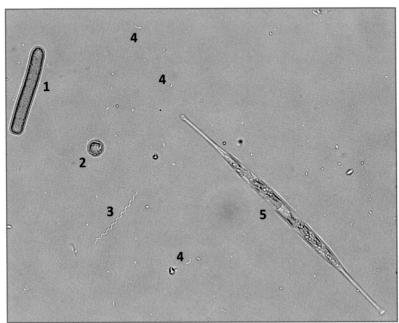

■ **2-2 Comparison of Eukaryotic and Nonnucleated Prokaryotic Cells** ≈ Prokaryotic cells are nonnucleated and generally smaller than eukaryotic cells. In this micrograph, 1, 3, and 4 are prokaryotes; 2 and 5 are eukaryotes. Number 1 is a chain of cyanobacterial cells. Each cell is about 10 μm wide and the whole chain is about 70 μm in length. Number 2 is a eukaryotic flagellate about 10 μm in diameter. Number 3 is a long, thin bacterium approximately 60 μm long and 1 μm wide. The cells labeled 4 are more typical Bacteria. They range in size from about 3-5 μm long by 1 μm wide. Number 5 is a diatom and is over 200 μm in length.

molecules called **plasmids** not associated with the chromosome. These carry genes for a variety of nonessential, but useful functions (such as antibiotic resistance). In addition, some cells are capable of producing highly resistant resting stages called **endospores** (*endo*—within, *spora*—seed). Spore shape, location in the cell, and whether it expands the cell are useful features for identification (Figure 2-4).

Outside of the cytoplasm is a typical **cell membrane** made of a phospholipid bilayer with proteins and other molecules embedded in it. External to that, most Bacteria have a **cell wall** made of a complex polymer called peptidoglycan (*peptide*—protein, *glycan*—sugar). The rigid, but porous, wall keeps cells from bursting when in an environment that would cause water to enter them and lead to their **lysis** (bursting). There are two major structural wall types (Figure 2-5), designated as either **Gram-positive** or **Gram-negative** (Figure 2-6), depending on their reaction to a Gram stain (named after Christian Gram, its developer). Gram-positive walls have a thick peptidoglycan layer and appear violet after a properly performed Gram stain. Gram-negative cells have a thin peptidoglycan layer

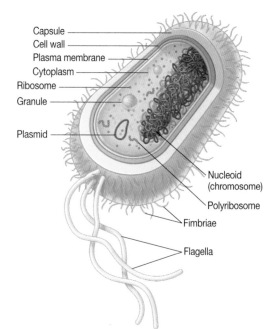

- Capsule
- Cell wall
- Plasma membrane
- Cytoplasm
- Ribosome
- Granule
- Plasmid
- Nucleoid (chromosome)
- Polyribosome
- Fimbriae
- Flagella

■ **2-3 Bacterial Cell Structure** ≈ Note the relative simplicity of internal structures. Note also the chromosome is a circular molecule of double-stranded DNA, and that there are additional small pieces of DNA (plasmids) in the cytoplasm. See text for details.

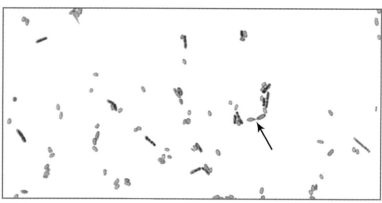

■ **2-4 Bacterial Endospores** ≈ Some Bacteria (most notably *Bacillus* and *Clostridium* species) are capable of producing highly resistant resting cells called endospores. These allow the microbes to become dormant during unfavorable conditions and germinate when conditions are better. Endospores can survive many decades before germinating. In this micrograph, the cells (grown in the laboratory) were stained using a special technique that shows endospores. The metabolically active and growing (vegetative) cells are red; the endospores are green. Some vegetative cells have yet to sporulate; others (arrow) are in the process. Each vegetative cell will produce one endospore and then release it by bursting. Most of the endospores shown have been released. Spore shape and location in the cell while forming are useful identifying characteristics. These endospores are elliptical in shape and (without a lot of examples to choose from) appear to be centrally located. The cells are approximately 5 μm in length.

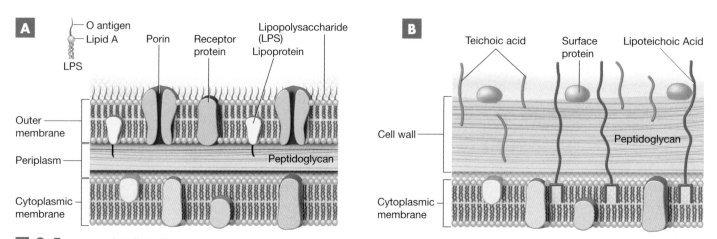

A
- O antigen
- Lipid A
- LPS
- Porin
- Receptor protein
- Lipopolysaccharide (LPS)
- Lipoprotein
- Outer membrane
- Periplasm
- Peptidoglycan
- Cytoplasmic membrane

B
- Teichoic acid
- Surface protein
- Lipoteichoic Acid
- Cell wall
- Peptidoglycan
- Cytoplasmic membrane

■ **2-5 Bacterial Cell Walls** ≈ The Gram-negative wall (**A**) is composed of less peptidoglycan (as little as a single layer) and more lipid (due to the outer membrane) than the Gram-positive wall (**B**).

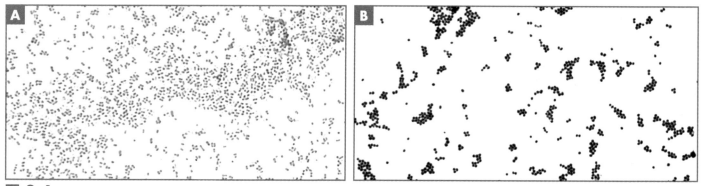

■ **2-6 Gram-Stain Reactions** ≈ When a Gram stain is properly done, Gram-negative cells appear pink and Gram-positive cells appear a deep violet. (**A**) Shown is a Gram stain of *Escherichia coli*, an intestinal bacterium of mammals (including humans). Its presence in coastal waters is an indicator of human sewage or mammalian pet or marine mammal fecal contamination. Cells are about 2-3 μm by 1 μm. (**B**) These are Gram-positive *Staphylococcus aureus* cells. *S. aureus* is an opportunistic pathogen of humans.

surrounded by another phospholipid bilayer membrane (called the **outer membrane**) and stain pink. In Figure 2-5B, you can see that the cytoplasmic and outer membranes are similar, but not identical, in composition. Archaea also have cell walls and are Gram-negative, but they do not contain peptidoglycan.

Some cells produce a gooey material of varying composition called a **capsule** (Figure 2-7). Capsules are used for attachment to surfaces and reduce dehydration. Some also have thin, rod-like protein projections called **fimbriae** (*fimbria*—fringe) that are used for attachment to surfaces or to other cells. These are only visible with the electron microscope. Most motile Bacteria have **flagella** (some without flagella demonstrate gliding motility), which are constructed and operate differently from their eukaryotic counterparts—they rotate rather than thrash back-and-forth. The number and position of flagella are usually characteristic for each species (Figure 2-8).

Unlike eukaryotes that undergo mitosis and cytokinesis (Figure 1-6), most Bacteria and Archaea reproduce by a type of cell division called **binary fission** (*binaries*—two together, *fission*—to split). None of the chromosomal activity associated with mitosis is observed, though the chromosome does replicate and each daughter cell receives a copy. Figure 2-9 shows a cyanobacterial cell undergoing binary fission.

Most Bacterial cells are in the 1 to 5 µm size range (about a thousand times smaller than the head of a pin). However, within the last couple of decades bacterial species have been described that are as much as four-times the size of a *Paramecium*! The first, *Epulopiscium fishelsoni*, was initially described as a protist, but biochemical analysis (ribosomal RNA) showed it clearly is not a eukaryote.

Found as an obligate symbiont of surgeonfish, it has a unique method of reproduction. Instead of simply dividing, it produces multiple offspring cells within its cytoplasm that are released when the parent cell lyses. It gives birth!

All organisms require certain resources from their environment and survive within a certain range of temperatures, acidities, salinities, and oxygen concentrations.

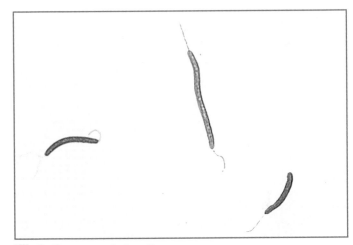

■ **2-8 Bacterial Flagella** ≈ Bacterial flagella are extremely thin (approximately 20 nm) and difficult to see with the light microscope. The easiest way to see them is to apply a stain that coats them and makes them thick enough to be visible. This light micrograph is actually a composite of three micrographs to bring the three cells together. They were observed in the same sample and when alive were spiral-shaped (approximately 25-30 µm long) and highly motile. After staining for flagella, the cells died and their spiral "relaxed" and now are seen only as gentle curves. The flagella are the fine, hair-like structures at the ends of the cells. It seems the "normal" condition for this species is for flagella to be at both ends, but the number is questionable. Only one flagellum stained on the cell on the far right. There probably was one on the other end, but we suspect it broke during slide preparation. Flagella are very delicate! The cell on the far left has *two* flagella on its left end. More study would need to be done to establish if the norm for this species is one flagellum at each end or two (or more?).

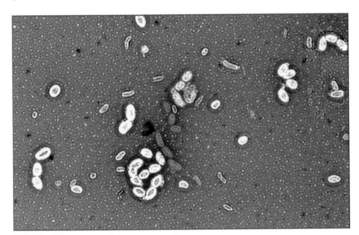

■ **2-7 Extracellular Capsule** ≈ Some bacterial cells produce a slimy or gooey extracellular capsule. This capsule stain preparation made from a layer of surface slime found in an estuary appears to show several different bacterial species (based solely on their shapes); these stain pink. The ones with a white halo around the pink cells have produced a capsule. These are mostly the plump cells with tapered ends and are between 2–4 µm long. Capsules are important in marine species as a mechanism of attachment to a surface.

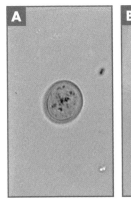 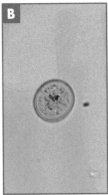 

■ **2-9 Binary Fission in a Cyanobacterium (Provisionally Identified as *Chroococcus*)** ≈ These three photos show a cyanobacterium undergoing binary fission, the style of cell division characteristic of most Bacteria. Unlike eukaryotes, mitosis does not occur. The time between (**A**) and (**C**) was approximately two hours. It is not known how long the process would have taken in its natural environment.

Successful cultivation of Bacteria and Archaea requires providing them with all their essential needs. Table 2-2 summarizes Bacterial and Archaeal nutritional types based on energy and carbon source. Viewing organisms in this way is useful not only for the ecologist studying their roles in nature, but also for the microbiologist interested in cultivating the organisms for study in the laboratory. Energy can be supplied by two sources: light and chemicals. If light is used, the organism is categorized as a **phototroph** (*photo*—light, *troph*—nourish). **Chemotrophs** (*chemo*—chemical) get their energy from chemicals. Some organisms are able to make all their biochemicals when supplied with carbon dioxide (CO_2) as the only carbon source. These are known as **autotrophs** (*auto*—self). Others, known as **heterotrophs** (*hetero*—other), can only survive when supplied with organic carbon; that is, molecules minimally containing carbon and hydrogen. Heterotrophs vary greatly in their carbon needs. Some can survive using a single organic compound (such as glucose), whereas others may require a majority of their biochemicals (such as amino acids, sugars, and many others) preformed from the environment. Terms for energy and carbon source are frequently combined. For instance, an organism that requires organic carbon and gets its energy from those molecules would be classified as a **chemoheterotroph**. An organism that can use CO_2 as its sole carbon source and light as its energy source is a **photoautotroph**.

All organisms require oxygen as part of their biochemicals, but not all need or can even tolerate molecular oxygen (O_2). Table 2-3 summarizes aerotolerance categories and Figure 2-10 illustrates their growth in a medium where oxygen is only available at the top.

■ Table **2-2** ≈ Nutritional Types of Bacteria and Archaea

Energy Source	Category	Examples of Organisms
Light	Phototroph	Cyanobacteria, and purple and green sulfur bacteria
Chemicals	Chemotroph	*Bacillus*, *Clostridium*, *Vibrio*, nitrifying bacteria, sulfur-oxidizing bacteria, *Halobacterium*
Carbon Source	**Category**	**Examples of Organisms**
CO_2	Autotroph	Cyanobacteria, purple sulfur bacteria, sulfur-oxidizing bacteria, nitrifying bacteria
Organic molecules	Heterotroph	*Bacillus*, *Clostridium*, *Vibrio*, sulfur-reducing bacteria

■ Table **2-3** ≈ Aerotolerance Groups of Bacteria and Archaea

Aerotolerance Group	Category	Examples of Organisms
Obligate Aerobe	Requires O_2 for metabolism (aerobic respiration)	Some *Bacillus*, *Beggiatoa*, *Thiothrix*, nitrifying bacteria, *Oceanospirillum*
Obligate Anaerobe	O_2 is not used; cannot grow in the presence of O_2	*Clostridium*, *Desulfovibrio*, *Thermotoga*, green sulfur bacteria
Facultative Anaerobe	Will grow in the presence of O_2 and use it (for aerobic respiration), but can grow in its absence	*Vibrio*, some *Bacillus*
Microaerophile	Requires O_2 but at lower than atmospheric concentrations	Microbial mat species

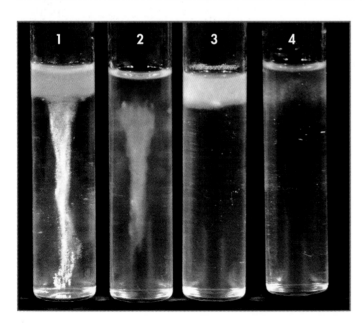

■ **2-10 Aerotolerance Categories** ≈ Shown are four tubes of a liquid growth medium containing an ingredient that removes free oxygen (O_2), making most of it anaerobic. Only where the medium is pink (the top 1 cm or so) has enough oxygen diffused in from the air to be considered aerobic. (The pink comes from a chemical that turns pink in the presence of oxygen and is colorless in its absence.) The white cloudiness is microbial growth. Tube 1 shows growth of a facultative anaerobe, an organism that will use oxygen if available but can grow in its absence. It grows better in the aerobic zone than in the anaerobic region. Tube 2 shows an obligate anaerobe, an organism that can only grow in the *absence* of oxygen. Therefore, the cloudiness is only seen below the aerobic zone. Tube 3 shows an obligate aerobe, one that requires oxygen and can't grow without it, and so the growth is restricted to the top 1 cm or so. Tube 4 only shows growth just below the aerobic zone. These organisms are microaerophiles (*micro* = small, *aero* = air, *phile* = loving); that is, they require oxygen at a concentration less than atmospheric levels.

For this book, four regions of an estuary and a sandy beach were sampled and cultivated on a Petri plate containing a nutrient-rich medium made with artificial seawater and grown at room temperature. Some plates were cultivated aerobically, others anaerobically. Any cells whose nutritional and environmental needs were met grew and reproduced. Eventually, enough cells were produced from the original cell(s) so that a visible mass of cells, called a **colony** (*colonia*—settlement), was seen on the plate. Figures 2-11 through 2-13 show the field sites and the colonies obtained from them. The different **colony morphologies** (*morphos*—shape) are a good first indication that different

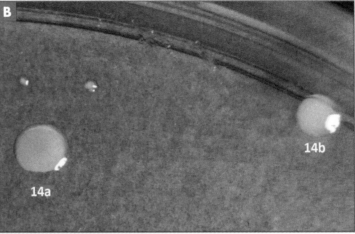

■ **2-11 Beach Sand** ≈ (A) This photo shows the location where a beach sand sample was taken from the intertidal zone. (B) This is a close-up view of bacterial colonies recovered from the sample after growing aerobically for 72 hours at room temperature. About four different colony shapes (morphologies) are seen. (Compare this diversity with the plates shown in Figure 2-12.) The first clue that two organisms are different species is that their colonies have different morphologies. Colonies 14a (3 mm in diameter) and 14b (4 mm in diameter) were selected for Gram staining and are shown in Figure 2-14.

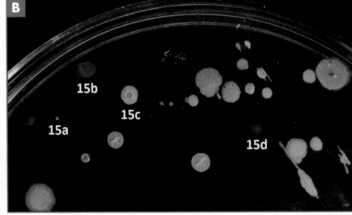
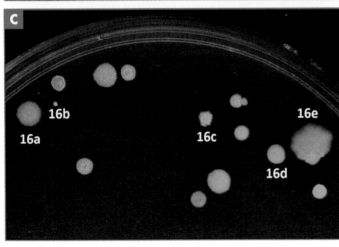

■ **2-12 Light and Dark Fine Sand** ≈ (A) This site was in the estuary and had fine-grained sand. A trowel was used to dig into the sand, where it revealed clearly defined layers: a top, lighter layer and a dark, deeper layer. (B) This plate shows colonies recovered from the light layer after 72 hours of aerobic growth at room temperature. Look at the diversity! Colony 15a is less than 1 mm in diameter, round and smooth. Colony 15b is gray in color and irregular in shape. Colony 15c is buff colored, about 4 mm in diameter, and has interesting elevations on its surface. Colony 15d is grayish, transparent, and has a wavy edge. Gram stains of these colonies are shown in Figure 2-15. (C) These colonies were recovered from the dark layer after 72 hours of aerobic incubation at room temperature. Colony 16a is grainy and yellowish with a diameter of 6 mm. Colony 16b is white, opaque, and about 1 mm in diameter. Colony 16c is buff colored, has a wavy edge, and a bumpy surface. Colony 16d is yellowish, round, and about 3 mm in diameter. Colony 16e is large, granular, and grayish. It grew so fast it overgrew a yellow colony at its bottom edge. Gram stains of these selected colonies are shown in Figure 2-16.

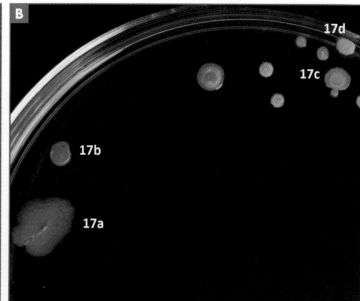

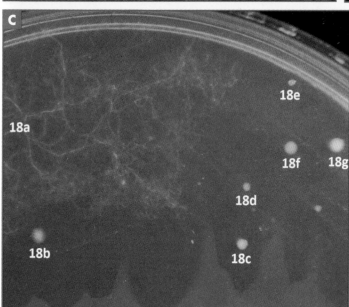

■ **2-13** **Dark Mud** ≈ (A) This photo is looking straight down on estuarine mud. The lighter, surface layer (at the edges) is a few millimeters thick. It was scraped away to show the dark mud below it. Samples were taken from a depth of several centimeters into the dark mud. (B) These colonies were recovered after 72 hours of aerobic growth at room temperature. Colony 17a is large (>10 mm), grainy, and irregular in shape. This is a common colony morphology for the genus *Bacillus*. Colony 17b is also irregular in shape and is flat except for a raised edge and center. Colony 17c is beige, flat with a raised center, and is about 4 mm in diameter. Colony 17d is yellowish and has a diameter of about 3 mm. It has a thin, irregular edge. These colonies were Gram stained and are shown in Figure 2-17. (C) This plate was from the same dark mud sample, but was incubated anaerobically at room temperature for five days. Colony 18a illustrates rhizoid (root-like) growth. Colony 18b is about 2 mm in diameter, whitish, and with a denser center. Colony 18c is cream colored, circular, and opaque. Colony 18d is circular, less than 1 mm in diameter, and translucent. Colony 18e is grayish with a small lump in its center. Colony 18f is circular, about 1 mm in diameter, and translucent. Colony 18g is opaque, white, and circular with a diameter of 1.5 mm. These selected colonies were Gram stained and are shown in Figure 2-18.

species are growing. However, even though there is obvious diversity in the colonies, we cannot be naïve and think that we recovered all the Bacteria and Archaea in the samples. A nutrient medium—even a nutrient-rich one—lacking a single growth requirement is enough to prevent growth of a microbe in a sample. In fact, based on microscopic evidence and identification of unique DNA sequences from samples, it has been estimated that as many as 99% of Bacteria and Archaea have yet to be cultivated!

After initial differentiation based on colony morphology has been made, microscopic features such as cell shapes, cell arrangements, and Gram reaction are useful in further differentiating between species. Common cell shapes include spheres (**cocci**, *sing.* **coccus**; *kokkos*—berry), rods (**bacilli**, *sing.* **bacillus**; *baculus*—stick), and spirals (**spirilla**, *sing.* **spirillum**). Less common, but still frequently encountered,

are flexible corkscrews (**spirochaetes**; *spiro*—spiral, *chaete*—long hair) and curved rods (**vibrios**; *vibrare*—vibrate). Species often show characteristic cellular arrangements. Common cellular arrangements are pairs, chains, and irregular clusters. Others simply grow as single cells. Figures 2-14 through 2-19 show cell shapes and arrangements from some colonies in Figures 2-11 through 2-13 as well as other samples collected from various marine and estuarine sites. All were photographed at 1000x and are reproduced here at the same relative sizes.

Bacteria

It is pretty safe to say that the species growing on the plates in Figures 2-11 through 2-13 are chemohetero-trophic bacteria, though photoautotrophs cannot be

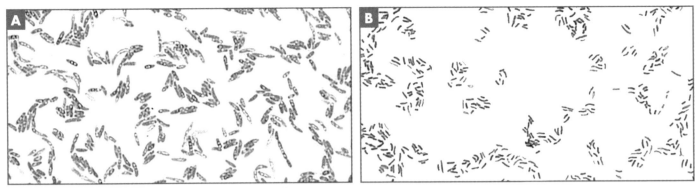

■ **2-14 Gram Stains of Beach Sand Colonies Shown in Figure 2-11** ～ **(A)** These Gram-negative rods have tapered ends and are approximately 1.5 × 0.5 μm in size. The whitish dots inside the cells are storage granules. **(B)** These are slightly curved Gram-negative rods. They are approximately 2-3 × 0.5 μm.

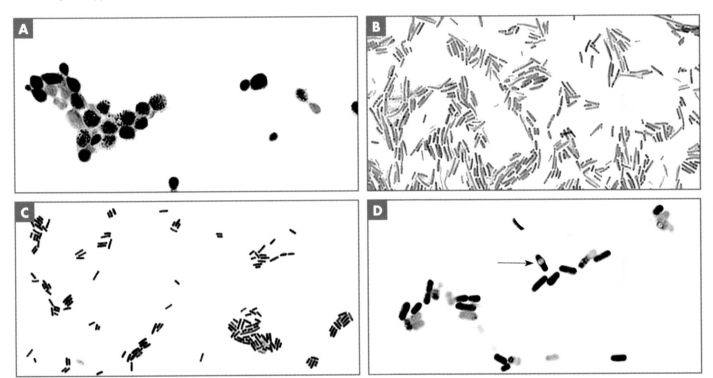

■ **2-15 Gram Stains of Light Fine Sand Colonies Shown in Figure 2-12B** ～ **(A)** These are large, Gram-positive coccobacilli. Sometimes, Gram-positive cells stain Gram-negative as they age. Recall that these were incubated 72 hours. Gram stains are best made on colonies 24 hours old. **(B)** These Gram-negative rods are 3–5 μm long by 0.5 μm wide. **(C)** These slender, Gram-positive rods are approximately 2 × 0.5 μm in size. **(D)** Notice the endospore in the cell indicated by the arrow. Aerobic, Gram-positive, endospore-forming rods can provisionally be identified as members of the Genus *Bacillus*. Typically, only younger cells of *Bacillus* species stain Gram-positive and become Gram-negative with age, as shown here. These cells are approximately 3 × 1.5 μm in size and the endospores are round.

ruled out as they were incubated in sunlight from a window. Chemoheterotrophs may be obligate aerobes, microaerophiles, facultative anaerobes, or obligate anaerobes (as seen in Table 2-3). They may perform aerobic respiration, anaerobic respiration, or some type of fermentation. These metabolic strategies are summarized in Table 2-4.

A few marine chemoheterotrophs from the genera *Vibrio* and *Photobacterium* are able to emit light by a process known as **bioluminescence** (*bios*—life, *lumen*—light). Many of these organisms maintain mutualistic relationships with other marine life. For example, *Photobacterium* species living in the flashlight fish receive nutrients

from the fish and in return provide a unique device for frightening would-be predators, communicating, and luring prey. Not surprisingly, natural selection has favored flashlight fish predators that locate their prey by the bioluminescence they emit! It is an energetically costly process for the bacterium. It is estimated that a single *Vibrio* cell burns the energy yield from between 150 and 1,500 glucose molecules per second emitting light! It is also known that luminescence from *Vibrio* occurs only when a certain minimum (threshold) population size is reached in a phenomenon called **quorum sensing**. This system is controlled by a genetically produced **autoinducer** (*auto*—self, *in*—into,

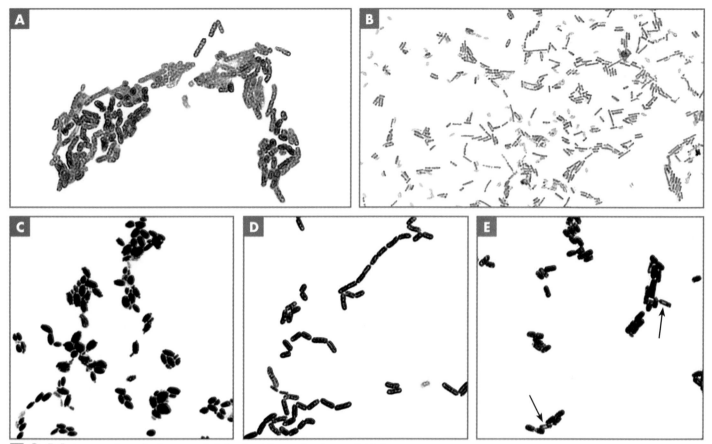

■ **2-16 Stains of Dark Fine Sand Colonies Shown in Figure 2-12C** ≈ (A) Sometimes, endospores are not as obvious as the one in Figure 2-15D and a spore stain is done to verify their presence. This is a spore stain of a Gram-positive rod. Notice the green endospores and the whitish storage granules in the vegetative cells (which may be mistaken for endospores in a Gram stain). This is provisionally identified as a *Bacillus*. (B) These large, plump rods vary in size from 2 × 1.5 μm to 3 × 2 μm. It is unusual to have cells of such different sizes in a population. It is possible there was more than one species growing in Colony 16b. (C) This is an endospore-stained preparation of slender, Gram-positive rods. Again, these are provisionally identified as *Bacillus*. (D) These Gram-positive rods grow in chains. No endospores were observed, but the absence of endospores is equivocal: Is the organism incapable of producing endospores or can it produce endospores and just isn't? (E) This is another specimen provisionally identified as a *Bacillus*. Notice the rods are shorter and fatter than the specimens in Figures 2-16A and 2-16C, and more slender than Figure 2-15D. The endospores (arrows) are also elongated and thinner than those of Figure 2-16A.

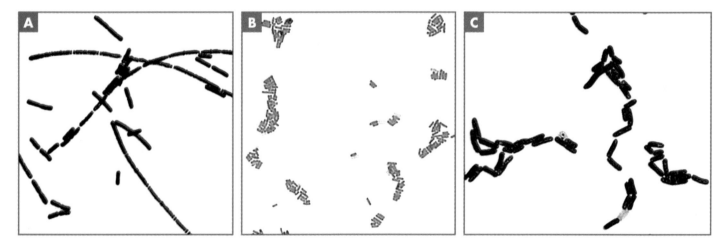

■ **2-17 Gram Stains of Aerobic Mud Colonies Shown in Figure 2-13B** ≈ (A) These Gram-positive rods grew in long chains. Cells are approximately 4–7 × <1 μm. (B) These slender, Gram-negative rods are approximately 2 × 0.5 μm in size. (C) Here we see Gram-positive rods with no indication of endospores and no storage granules growing in pairs or short chains. The cells are 4-6 × >1μm. Compare these carefully with Figure 2-17A to see their differences. *(continued)*

■ 2-17 Gram Stains of Aerobic Mud Colonies Shown in Figure 2-13B ~

(continued) (D) These cells resemble those in Figure 2-17C, but they grow in longer chains and the colonies are different in morphology, so they likely are not the same species. But this does give an indication of how difficult identification based on structure is with bacteria! (E) This Gram-positive coccus growing in clusters is from a different aerobic mud plate than the one shown in Figure 2-13B. The cells are approximately 1 μm in diameter.

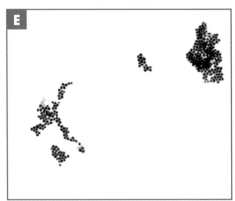

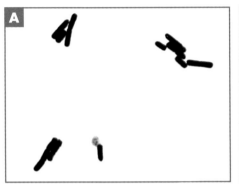

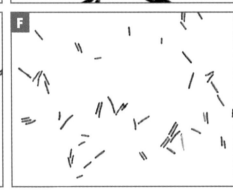

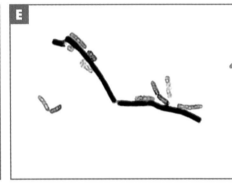

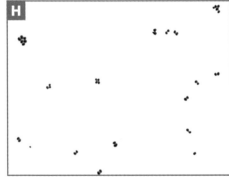

■ 2-18 Gram Stains of Anaerobic Mud Colonies Shown in Figure 2-13C ~

(A) More plump, Gram-positive rods! Compare these to the cells in Figures 2-17C and 2-17D. Then, go back to Figure 2-13 and compare the colonies. Very different! (B) These Gram-negative rods appear to produce endospores. Anaerobic, endospore-forming bacteria are probably in the genus *Clostridium*, which is composed of Gram-positive cells, at least when they are young. Remember that these were stained after five days of incubation (making them old).

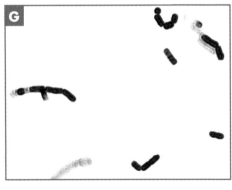

(C) These Gram-positive rods in chains do not appear to produce endospores, but some cells are losing their ability to stain Gram-positive. Notice how the rods are not of uniform width. (D) These long, slender Gram-negative rods are approximately 6 × 1 μm and form short chains. (E) It is usually safe to assume that a colony not touching any other growth on a plate is composed of a single species. However, Colony 18e is apparently an exception. This Gram stain shows two clearly different cell types, based on Gram reaction, cell size, and arrangement. The Gram-positive rods are 7 × 1 μm, form chains, and show no evidence of storage granules. The Gram-negative rods are 5 × 1 μm, grow in singles and pairs, and have abundant storage granules. (F) These are long, slender Gram-negative rods, measuring 6 × <1 μm. There is no evidence of spores. They superficially resemble the cells of Colony 17b, but they are longer and the colonies have different morphologies. (G) More short, plump Gram-positive rods! These measure 4 × >1 μm. (H) These Gram-positive cocci grow in pairs. Each cell is approximately 0.5 μm in diameter. They are from the same mud, but a different anaerobic plate than the one shown in Figure 2-13C.

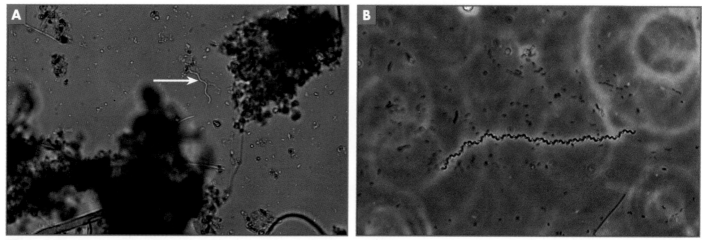

■ 2-19 Other Cell Morphologies Shown in Wet-Mount Preparations ≈ Bacterial cells can have a helical shape. **(A)** If the helix is loose and the cells are fairly thick, it is a spirillum (arrow). **(B)** Spirochaetes are much more tightly coiled and are flexible. They also have a unique arrangement of flagella (called axial filaments) that run on the inside of the spiral. Axial filaments are only visible with the electron microscope.

■ Table 2-4 ≈ Basic Types of Heterotrophic Metabolism

Metabolism	Summary Reaction	Relative Energy Yield	Examples
Aerobic Respiration	Glucose + $6O_2$ → $6CO_2$ + $6H_2O$	Highest	*Bacillus, Vibrio, Azotobacter*
Fermentation	Glucose → Acid, Gas and/or Alcohol	Lowest	*Bacillus, Vibrio, Clostridium, Thermotoga*
Anaerobic Respiration	Carbohydrate + SO_4^- → CO_2 + H_2S + H_2O	Intermediate	Sulfur-reducing bacteria (*Desulfovibrio, Desulfobacter*)
	Carbohydrate + NO_3^- → CO_2 + NO_2^- + H_2O	Intermediate	Nitrogen-reducing bacteria

Photograph by Burton Pierce

■ 2-20 Bioluminescence ≈ Some species of *Vibrio* and *Photobacterium* are capable of producing light from chemical reactions. These colonies were photographed in the dark. They are only visible because they are emitting their own light.

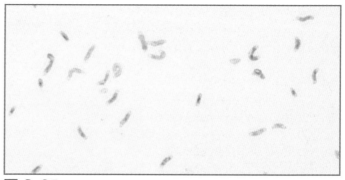

■ 2-21 *Thermotoga maritima* ≈ *T. maritima* is a Gram-negative bacterium that was first isolated in a geothermal marine region in Italy. It grows over a temperature range of 55–90°C, with an optimum of 80°C. Its genome has been sequenced and, surprisingly, approximately one-quarter of its genes were obtained by lateral gene transfer with Archaea species. Cells are 0.5 μm wide by 1.5–11.0 μm long. Note the light, oval regions at the end of cells. These are the "togas."

ducere—to lead) that must be in sufficient concentration to trigger the bioluminescence reaction. Figure 2-20 shows a bioluminescent species grown in the laboratory.

Another noteworthy bacterial chemoheterotroph, *Thermotoga* (Figure 2-21), is a **hyperthermophilic** (*hyper*—above, *therm*—heat, *philic*—loving) Gram-negative rod. It lives in hydrothermal vent habitats and can withstand

temperatures up to 95°C! It ferments a variety of carbohydrates and is also capable of fixing N_2 (converting N_2 to ammonia).

Cyanobacteria (*cyan*—dark blue) are photoautotrophs (though some are photoheterotrophs. Like the true plants and other eukaryotic autotrophs, they perform **oxygenic** (*oxy*—oxygen, *genic*—to produce) photosynthesis in which oxygen is a waste product (Table 2-5). They are easily seen without staining because of their combination of photosynthetic pigments, which confer on them a bluish-green color (and sometimes others). They were formerly known as "blue-green algae" but they are not eukaryotic. All are Gram-negative, though their peptidoglycan is thicker than most other Gram-negatives. When they are single-celled, they are about the size of bacteria. But when they are found in chains, called **trichomes** (*tricho*—hair), they are easily visible at moderate microscopic magnification. Many trichomes are capable of gliding motility (by an as yet undetermined mechanism) and some are enclosed in a **mucilagenous sheath.**

Cyanobacterial trichomes often have specialized cells, including **heterocysts** (*cystis*—bag, bladder), which are nitrogen-fixing cells, and **akinetes** (*a*—without, *kinetos*— movement), which are resistant spores. **Nitrogen fixation** is the important ecological process by which nitrogen gas (N_2) (a form not usable by most autotrophs and, therefore, doesn't enter food chains) is converted into an ammonium ion (NH_4^+)—which is usable by most autotrophs and, therefore, enters the food chain. Cyanobacteria are the primary nitrogen-fixers in marine environments (see *Azotobacter* below). Figures 2-22A–H illustrate some common forms and cyanobacterial variability. All micrographs are unstained wet-mount preparations.

Cyanobacteria such as *Lyngbya*, *Oscillatoria*, and *Synechococcus*, among others, combine with various chemoheterotrophic and photoautotrophic bacteria and are responsible for forming microbial mats in shallow waters. The mat communities become stratified according to oxygen and sulfur gradients (not unlike in a Winogradsky column) and host a complex, stratified community of microbes. As the layers age, they become calcified and then **petrified** (*petra*—rock). **Stromatolites** (*stroma*—layer; -*lite* from *lithos*—stone) are fossilized microbial mats and contain some of the earliest known fossils (Figure 2-22I).

Azotobacter is a free-living, Gram-negative chemoheterotrophic aerobe. Other than cyanobacteria, *Azotobacter* is the only significant nitrogen-fixer in marine sediments. Figure 2-23 shows a non-marine *Azotobacter* isolated from soil.

Chemoheterotrophs and oxygenic photoautotrophs are the "vanilla" of microbial metabolism. That is, they do what plants and animals do and are therefore quite familiar to us. But, microbial diversity is nowhere greater than in their metabolic abilities. Following are examples of some of that diversity organized by functional groups. These demonstrate that just as our society can obtain electrical energy from flowing water, coal, oil, natural gas, nuclear fission, etc., cells can obtain energy from a variety of sources: light, organic chemicals, and a multitude of inorganic chemicals.

Chemoautotrophs obtain their energy from inorganic chemicals. For instance, ammonia (NH_3) and nitrite (NO_2^-) can serve as energy sources for the chemoautotrophic nitrifying bacteria (**nitrification** is the process of making nitrate—NO_3^-). Some nitrifiers use ammonia as an energy source and convert it to nitrite; others then use the nitrite as an energy source and convert it to nitrate. *Nitrosococcus oceani* is widely distributed in marine environments and is a major marine nitrifier. *Nitrosomonas marina* (Figure 2-24), another oceanic species, has the ability to break down urea—$(NH_2)_2CO$—producing CO_2 for autotrophic growth and NH_3 for energy production—highly efficient! *Nitrobacter* species get energy from converting nitrite to nitrate. *N. winogradskyi* has been isolated from ocean samples and *N. vulgaris* from brackish waters.

Sulfur-oxidizing bacteria constitute another chemoautotrophic group, but they get their energy from sulfur compounds, such as hydrogen sulfide (H_2S) and elemental sulfur (S^0), which are commonly found in marine sediments. Examples include the genera *Thiobacillus*, *Beggiatoa* (Figure 2-25), and *Thiothrix*. All are Gram-negative, but *Beggiatoa* and *Thiothrix* are distinctive because they form long filaments, move by gliding, and store sulfur granules in their cytoplasm. Many species are also capable of heterotrophic growth.

An especially interesting group of chemoautotrophic sulfur-oxidizing bacteria are Gram-negative **endosymbionts** (*endo*—within, *sym*—with, *bios*—living) of the annelid tubeworm *Riftia* found at hydrothermal vents (Figure 2-26). The worm absorbs H_2S from the surroundings and supplies it to the chemoautotrophic bacteria (which can

■ Table **2-5** ∼ Basic Types of Autotrophic Metabolism

Metabolism	Sample Summary Reaction	Examples
Oxygenic Photosynthesis	$6CO_2 + 12H_2O \rightarrow C_6H_{12}O_6 + 6O_2 + 6H_2O$	Cyanobacteria
Anoxygenic Photosynthesis	$CO_2 + 2H_2S \rightarrow CH_2O + 2S + H_2O$	Green and purple sulfur bacteria
Chemoautotrophic Metabolism Nitrifying Bacteria	$CO_2 + NH_3 + O_2 \rightarrow CH_2O + HNO_2 + H_2O$ (unbalanced; CH_2O represents carbohydrate)	Nitrifying bacteria (*Nitrobacter*, *Nitrosomonas*)
Sulfur-oxidizing Bacteria	$CO_2 + H_2S + O_2 \rightarrow CH_2O + S^0 + H_2O$ (unbalanced; CH_2O represents carbohydrate)	Sulfur-oxidizing bacteria (*Thiobacillus*, *Beggiatoa*)

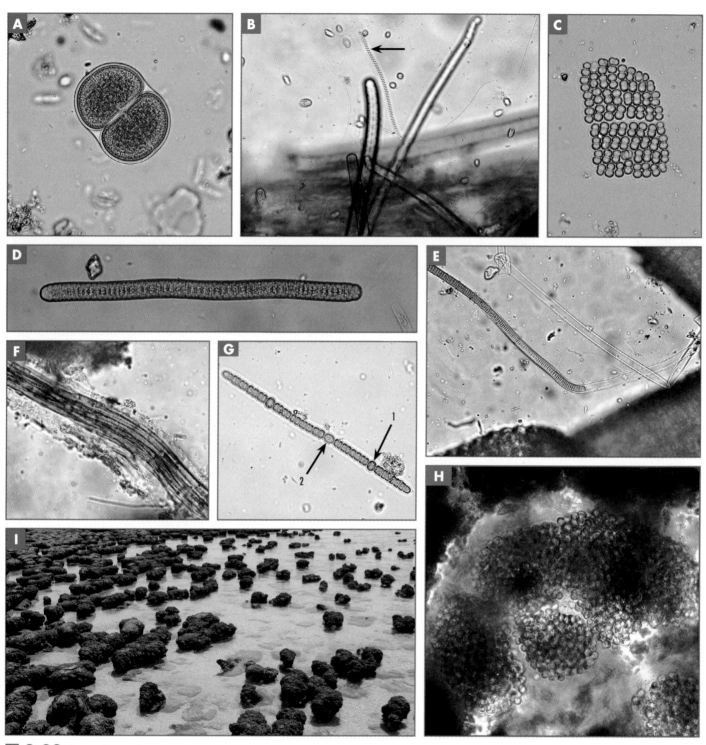

2-22 Cyanobacteria ~ (**A**) This marine species of *Chroococcus* was about 23 μm across. The two cells are beginning to divide transversely (note the faint cleavage furrow running from the upper left to the lower right in each cell) and will become a tetrad, the most complex arrangement for this species. (**B**) *Spirulina* (arrow) is perhaps the most distinctive cyanobacterium because of its helical shape. The width of the helix varies, but can obtain sizes up to 12 μm. This genus is sold in health food stores as a dietary supplement. (**C**) Cell division in two perpendicular directions produces the planar arrangement characteristic of the genus *Merismopedia*. The cells are enclosed in a mucilaginous sheath and are approximately 1–2 μm in diameter. (**D**) *Oscillatoria* trichomes are formed from disc-shaped cells that are approximately 10 μm long (that is, across the trichome). These cyanobacteria demonstrate gliding motility. (**E**) *Lyngbya* trichomes are distinguished from *Oscillatoria* by the extracellular sheath. The trichomes are approximately 20 μm in width. (**F**) *Microcoleus* trichomes are found bundled in a sheath. (**G**) The trichomes of the gliding cyanobacterium *Anabaena* may possess thick-walled spores called akinetes (1) and specialized, nitrogen-fixing cells called heterocysts (2). Trichomes are of variable lengths but are approximately 20 μm in width. (**H**) This colonial cyanobacterium is provisionally identified as *Synechocystis*. (**I**) Stromatolites are fossilized microbial mats made of layers of cyanobacteria, sediments, and minerals stacked upon one another. Fossil stromatolites have been dated to 3.5 billion years before the present. Shown are modern marine microbial mats that are "living" stromatolites; that is, they haven't yet fossilized. They were photographed at Shark Bay, Western Australia, and are in the 1 m height range.

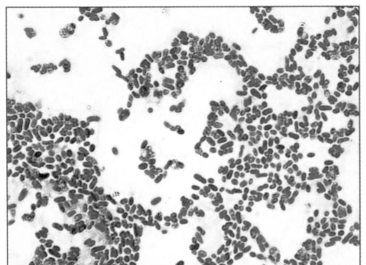

■ **2-23** *Azotobacter* **Gram Stain** ≈ Plump, Gram-negative rods characterize the free-living, nitrogen-fixing *Azotobacter.* These cells were grown in culture.

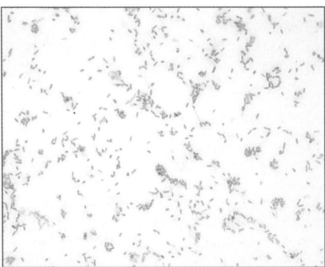

■ **2-24** *Nitrosomonas* ≈ *Nitrosomonas* is a genus of Gram-negative nitrifying bacteria found in seawater, brackish water, and freshwater, as well as soils. The cells are straight rods 0.7–1.5 μm wide by 1.5–2.4 μm long. They are aerobic chemoautotrophs that obtain energy by converting ammonia to nitrite. This specimen was obtained from soil grown on a medium containing ammonia as the only nitrogen source and carbon dioxide as the only carbon source.

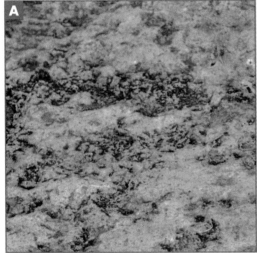

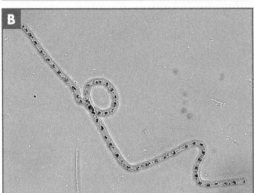

■ **2-25 Sulfur-oxidizing Bacteria** ≈
(A) This whitish material is a microbial mat found at the edge of an estuarine lagoon. Among its many inhabitants are sulfur-oxidizing bacteria. The smell of sulfur was heavy in the air! (B) This is a light micrograph of an organism provisionally identified as *Beggiatoa*. Sulfur-oxidizing bacteria get their energy from H_2S and produce sulfur as a waste product, which shows up as the dark granules inside the cell.

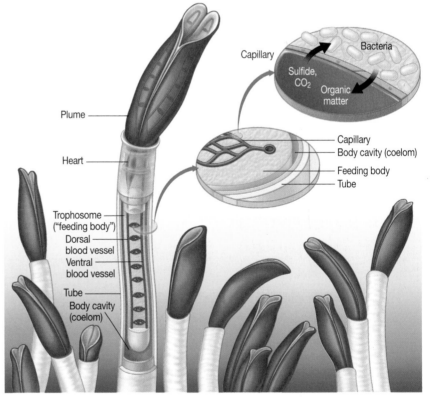

■ **2-26 An Artist's Representation of the Hydrothermal Vent Tubeworm** *Riftia* **and its Sulfur-oxidizing Bacteria** ≈ *Riftia* is an annelid worm (Chapter 12) that lives near hydrothermal vents and harbors endosymbiotic Gram-negative, sulfur-oxidizing bacteria in its trophosome. The worm absorbs H_2S from the surroundings and supplies it to these bacteria, which in turn get energy from the sulfur and produce organic compounds from CO_2, which can be used as food by both the bacteria and *Riftia*.

amount to half the mass of the worm!) living in an organ called a **trophosome** (*troph*—feed, *soma*—body). These, in turn, oxidize the sulfur (they extract the energy from it) and produce organic compounds from CO_2, which can be used as food by both the bacteria and *Riftia*. As *Riftia* has no digestive tract, this is an obligate mutualistic endosymbiosis. In a way, *Riftia* can be viewed as an autotrophic animal!

A second group of sulfur-oxidizing bacteria are photo-trophs. These include the purple and green sulfur bacteria that perform bacterial photosynthesis, a process that differs from plants and cyanobacteria in that different chlorophylls are used and oxygen is not a byproduct (**anoxygenic**; *an*—not). Most are freshwater, but *Allochromatium* (Figure 2-27) and others may be found in brackish water and estuaries.

Purple non-sulfur bacteria constitute a different, poly-phyletic group of photoautotrophs. Figure 2-28 shows a bloom of purple bacteria.

Sulfur-reducing bacteria are chemoheterotrophs that perform **anaerobic respiration** (see Table 2-4) using sulfate and other sulfur compounds and producing H_2S (instead of using oxygen, as in aerobic respiration, which produces

water). These are important members of anoxic (without oxygen) communities and are responsible for the odor associated with these black sediments. Figure 2-29 shows a community of sulfur-reducing bacteria recovered from anoxic mud. H_2S is toxic to most organisms, but it is removed by sulfur-oxidizing bacteria (see above), which use it as an energy source.

Lab culturing of the various sulfur bacteria requires spe-cial media. A simpler way is to re-create their environments in a **Winogradsky column**. It bears the name of its developer, Sergei Winogradsky (1856–1953), a Russian microbiologist and pioneer in microbial ecology. One of his major discov-eries was finding microorganisms (e.g., *Beggiatoa*) capable

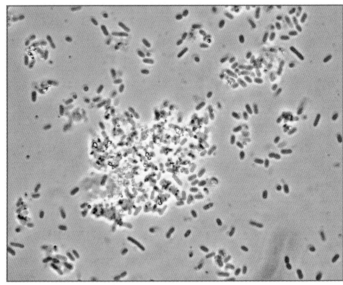

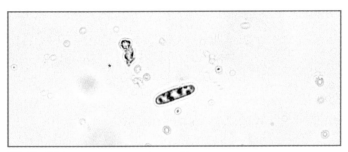

■ **2-27 Photoautotrophic Sulfur Bacterium** ≈ This organ-ism was provisionally identified as *Allochromatium*, a purple sulfur bacterium. Note the evenly distributed sulfur granules in the cytoplasm.

■ **2-29 Community of Sulfur-reducing Bacteria** ≈ This phase contrast micrograph shows several different sulfur-reducers. They are common inhabitants of dark, anoxic muds and use sulfur compounds during anaerobic respiration the way humans use oxygen in aerobic respiration.

■ **2-28 Bloom of Purple Bacteria** ≈ (A) Shown is a bloom of purple bacteria in an estuarine tide pool. For a sense of scale, the black California horn snails are approximately 3–4 cm long. (B) This is a light micrograph of the bacteria presumed to be responsible for the bloom based only on their abundance and color in the sample. The dark spots may be sulfur granules, in which case this is likely a purple sulfur bacterium.

of the unheard of type of metabolism that came to be known as chemoautotrophy. Until he made his discovery, only photoautotrophs—those that perform plant photosynthesis—were known to be autotrophs.

Winogradsky first used "his" column in the late 19th century. It was (and is) used as a convenient laboratory source to supply for study a variety of anaerobic, microaerophilic, and aerobic bacteria, including purple nonsulfur bacteria, purple sulfur bacteria, green sulfur bacteria, chemoheterotrophs, and many others.

The basis for the Winogradsky column is threefold (Figure 2-30A). The first two factors involve opposing gradients that impact the types of organisms that can grow. The first is the oxygen gradient, which gets more and more anaerobic toward the bottom. As a result, obligate aerobes, microaerophiles, facultative anaerobes, and obligate anaerobes are found in different locations in the column. The second is the H_2S gradient, which runs opposite in direction to the O_2 gradient. The third factor is the diffuse light shined upon the column. This promotes growth of phototrophic organisms at levels in the column where they are adapted to the opposing O_2 and H_2S gradients. These layers of phototrophs occur in natural ecosystems but are extremely thin because light doesn't penetrate mud sediments very far. But with the transparent column, thicker layers develop, which are more easily sampled for cultures (Figures 2-30B and 2-30C).

Archaea

Archaea are found in extreme environments with high salt concentrations, high temperatures, and/or high acidity. They are characterized as **extreme halophiles** (*hal*—salt, *philos*—loving), **extreme thermophiles**, and **extreme acidophiles**, respectively. We will concentrate on the extreme halophiles.

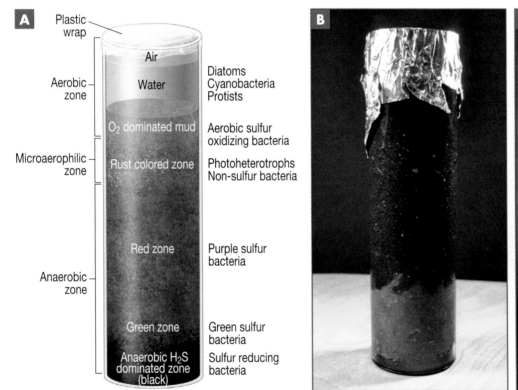

2-30 Winogradsky Column ≈ **(A)** What you put into a Winogradsky column dictates what you grow. Any well-constructed column has an oxygen gradient from top to bottom, with the aerobic zone penetrating perhaps only as much as 20% of the total depth. The remaining portion of the mud column becomes progressively more anaerobic. A gradient of sulfur compounds runs in the opposite direction. The different amounts of oxygen and sulfur compounds leads to layering of microbial communities adapted to that specific environment. This illustration is a generalized picture of the layering that you might see in a mature column. (The column often produces intermixed patches rather than distinct layers.) Starting at the top and working downward the layers are: air, water (containing algae and cyanobacteria), aerobic mud (sulfur-oxidizing bacteria), microaerophilic mud (non-sulfur, photosynthetic bacteria), red/purple zone (purple photosynthetic bacteria), green zone (green photosynthetic bacteria), and black anaerobic zone (sulfur-reducing bacteria). **(B)** Shown is a newly made Winogradsky column. The lighter gray area at the bottom is a slurry made from mud and shredded paper enriched with $CaCO_3$ and $CaSO_4$ (providing carbon and sulfur sources, respectively). Note the absence of air spaces. The black layer comprising the majority of the column is the unenriched mud. Note the absence of air spaces. **(C)** This is the same column after eight weeks. Notice the layers and colors! Also notice that the layers are not as well defined as in **(A)**. In fact, some look mixed (e.g., the rust and red portions appear mixed in some regions). But the dark, anaerobic zone above the whitish layer at the bottom is well defined. The remainder is—pardon the expression—clear as mud.

Halobacterium is a genus of motile extreme halophiles. They exhibit a variety of cell morphologies, including rods (Figure 2-31A), cocci, and other irregular forms. Most are obligate aerobes, though some are facultative anaerobes. While some can survive and grow at a salinity of 87 ‰ NaCl, most require salt in the 200 to 260 ‰ range. Think what pouring salt on a snail does to the poor snail! These organisms—in fact, all marine organisms—have to deal with the dehydrating effect of salt. *Halobacterium* is able to survive at such high environmental salt concentrations because it concentrates KCl intracellularly to achieve osmotic (water) balance.

Pigments play a major role in *Halobacterium* survival (Figure 2-31B). Metabolism is chemoheterotrophic (aerobic respiration), but in the absence of oxygen some species can become phototrophic because of the membrane-bound pigment **bacteriorhodopsin**. Absorption of light by this pigment is converted into a form usable in cellular metabolism. It is unclear if these organisms can live exclusively as photoautotrophs, but they certainly are capable of photoheterotrophic growth. **Halorhodopsin**, a second membrane-bound pigment, is used to pump chloride ions inward (to increase KCl, as mentioned above). Other pigments are involved in phototactic (*photo*—light, *taxis*—order) responses by modifying flagellar rotation. Some species produce gas vacuoles that assist in flotation. Figure 2-31C shows a Gram-stained culture of *Halobacterium* with gas vacuoles.

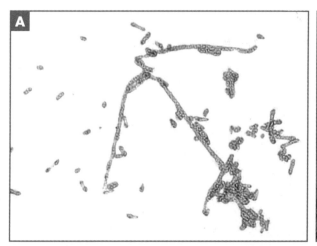

■ **2-31** *Halobacterium* ≈ (A) *Halobacterium* is really an archaean, not a bacterium. Its cells are pleomorphic (*pleion*—more, *morph*—form) rods that vary in different media and temperatures. Note the white gas vacuoles in the cells. (B) This is an aerial view of salterns in San Diego Bay. Salterns are shallow pools of saltwater used in the harvesting of salt. As water evaporates, the saltwater becomes saltier and saltier, until only salt remains, which can be sold. The colors in the pools result from differently pigmented communities of halophilic microorganisms, such as *Halobacterium*, that are adapted to different salinities as the pools dry out. (C) Shown is a pure culture of *Halobacterium*. Due to their gas vacuoles, *Halobacterium* cells float to the surface and are seen as the pink layer.

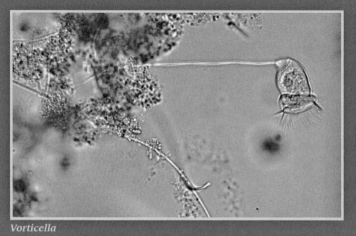
Vorticella

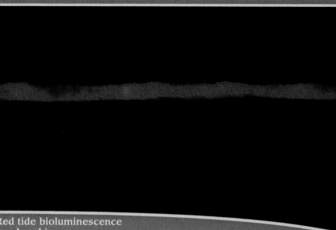
Red tide bioluminescence
in a breaking wave

3 Planktonic Heterotrophs

These single-celled organisms are **heterotrophic** (*hetero*—different, *troph*—feeder) or **detritivorous** (*detrit*—wear off, *vor*—eat) plankton. As with all **plankton** (*planktos*—wandering), they are passively carried about the horizontal and vertical aspects of the ocean by currents. **Zooplanktors** (heterotrophic plankton) include a wide array of organisms from many phyla (See Chapters 5 through 18), but this chapter presents only eukaryotic single-celled organisms. Two clades will be considered (Chromalveolata—only the Superphylum Alveolata here—and Rhizaria), but not all phyla within these clades (Table 3-1). Consideration is given to the most abundant and ecologically important of each clade (Figure 3-1).

The major eukaryotic clade Chromalveolata, Superphylum Alveolata (*alveola*—diminutive of *alveus*—cavity, hollow), are named for vesicles under the cell membrane, which help support the organisms. They also possess mitochondria, cilia, and flagella with distinct structures. Alveolata currently consists of three phyla. Only the two with the greatest known number of marine species will be considered here.

The second clade, Rhizaria (*rhiza*—root), is a very diverse group, but generally contains organisms with **pseudopods** (*pseudo*—false, *podia*—foot) of various types. These are cytoplasmic extensions of the cell. Many Rhizarians produce shells or skeletons that may be complex in structure. Mitochondria have tubular cristae. There are parasitic and flagellated members of this clade, but the best known are the amoebas. The **amoeboid zooplankton** (amoebas) are an extremely diverse group once considered distinct from other eukaryotes based upon various morphological features. Currently, their classification is largely disputed as new morphological and biochemical data have been analyzed. We will consider two clades of particular importance in the marine environment: Granuloreticulosa, in particular a major group called the **foraminiferans**, and the Actinopoda known as **radiolarians**. The Granuloreticulosa have hard shells (most consisting of calcium carbonate) and long extensions of their cytoplasm projecting through their shell. The actinopods have a shell consisting of silica and often other materials, sometimes including organic compounds. The shell has projections and cytoplasmic extensions reaching into the surrounding water.

Alveolates

Ciliophora

Ciliophora are placed within the Alveolata clade because they possess **pellicular alveoli** (flattened, membranous sacs beneath a cell membrane without vesicular products or

■ Table 3-1 ≈ Some Planktonic Heterotrophs

Major Eukaryotic Clade Superphylum Phylum/descriptive name	General Description	Examples	Approximate Number of Species	Etymology
Chromalveolata	May be photosynthetic, parasitic, saprophytic, or heterotrophic; often with a pellicle; secondary endosymbiosis with a red algae			*chroma*—color, *alveolata*—diminutive of *alveolus*—cavity or hollow
Alveolata	Alveoli just under the plasma membrane			*alveolata*—diminutive of *alveolus*—cavity or hollow
Ciliophora (Figure 3-2)	Cilia in one or more life cycle stages; heterotrophs	*Meseres, Halteria, Pelagostrobilidium, Tracheloraphis, Tiarina,* etc.	7,500–9,000	*cilium*—eyelash, *phora*—bearing
Dinoflagellata (Figure 3-3)	Typically with two flagella in a groove around the middle of the primary axis; cellulose plates	*Ceratium, Noctiluca, Prorocentrum, Scrippsiella,* etc.	4,500	*dinos*—whirling, *flagellum*—whip
Rhizaria **Granuloreticulosa**—descriptive name not a phylum (Figure 3-4)	Threadlike pseudopodia (*pseudo*—false, *pod*—foot) Locomotion and food engulfment by thin, multiply branching and rejoining cytoplasmic extensions called pseudopodia (*pseudo*—false, *pod*—foot); specific pseudopod types, reticulopodia (*reticulo*—netlike, *pod*—foot)	Foraminiferans and others	1,500	*rhizaria*—root *granulum*—little grain, *reticulatus*—netlike
Actinopoda—descriptive name not a phylum (Figure 3-5)	Locomotion and food engulfment by thin, elongated cytoplasmic extensions called pseudopodia (*pseudo*—false, *pod*—foot); specific type, axopodia (*axo*—axis, *pod*—foot)	Radiolarians and others	4,000	*actin*—ray, *pod*—foot

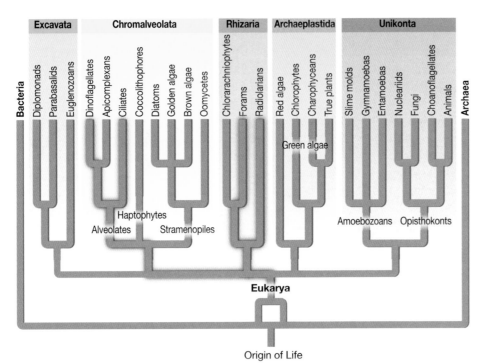

■ 3-1 Phylogeny of the Three Domains of Life ≈ The presumed evolutionary relationship between the Alveolates (Chromalveolata), Rhizaria, and other major clades is shown. This chapter describes the Dinoflagellates, Ciliates, Foraminiferans, and Radiolarians. See Appendix A for definitions of terms, clades, and taxa in this figure.

specialized structural functions) and **pinocytotic micropores** (small openings for taking in dissolved substances, generally nutrients, from the environment) on the cell surface. Molecular evidence shows strong support for the diverse Alveolata clade. Currently, the relationships between ciliate taxa are based predominantly upon cilia variation and molecular evidence.

Ciliophora is probably one of the most complex groups of microscopic unicellular organisms, with an estimated 7,500–9,000 extant species found in aquatic, marine, and terrestrial habitats. Ecologically, they are important members of marine microbial food webs. They feed predominantly via heterotrophy and can fill roles of predators, detritivores, herbivores, and parasites. Most species are solitary and motile, though both colonial and nonmotile species exist as well. Marine ciliates are typically free-living planktonic or **benthic** (*benthos*—bottom) forms, ranging in size from 10 µm–3 mm. Ciliates are typically asymmetrical (Figure 3-2), though some species display radial symmetry.

The group is named for the presence of cilia, which are usually found in patches or rows over the body, but in some species may only be found in certain areas of the cell. Cilia usually function in locomotion and feeding; they are frequently located near the **cytostome** (*cyto*—cell, *stome*—hole) (see below). The presence of numerous quick-beating cilia gives this group of organisms the ability to move faster than any other Alveolate of comparative size.

Cilia on the body can be arranged in complex structural units and function similar to muscles in contractile ciliates. Despite being unicellular and not having a mouth, ciliates have a cytostome, which is the site for ingestion via **phagocytosis** (*phago*—to eat, *cytosis*—cell). In addition to the cytostome, a mouth-like **buccal cavity** (mouth) is often found in suspension-feeding ciliates. Internally, ciliates have two different types of nuclei: a small micronucleus and a larger macronucleus (often more than one). The former is involved in cell division (mitosis or meiosis), and the later is used for all other stages of the cell's life cycle. Ciliates reproduce asexually via binary fission and sexually by fusing nuclei with another individual.

Groups such as **tintinnids** (Figure 3-2G) collect bits of particles, such as sand, and cement them together to form a rigid test, or **lorica** (sheath), outside of the cell body itself.

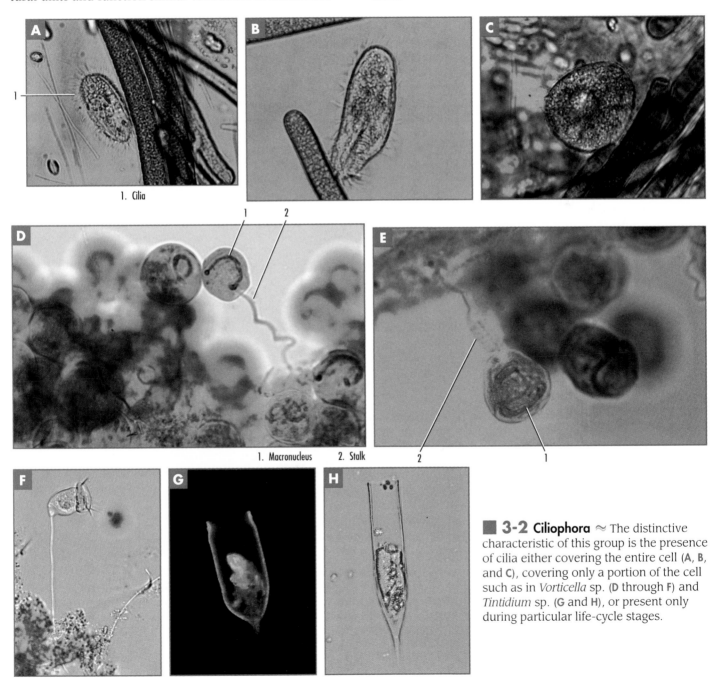

1. Cilia

1. Macronucleus   2. Stalk

■ **3-2 Ciliophora** ≈ The distinctive characteristic of this group is the presence of cilia either covering the entire cell (**A**, **B**, and **C**), covering only a portion of the cell such as in *Vorticella* sp. (**D** through **F**) and *Tintidium* sp. (**G** and **H**), or present only during particular life-cycle stages.

Dinoflagellata

As with other organisms formerly classified as Protista, the phylogeny of dinoflagellates is not well resolved. Dinoflagellates are placed in the Alveolate clade with Ciliates and Apicocomplexans (not discussed in this *Atlas*) based on molecular evidence.

The dinoflagellates (Figure 3-3) are a complex and highly diverse group of planktonic organisms found in oceanic and freshwater ecosystems. Most of the nearly 4,500 extant species are marine. Approximately half of the dinoflagellates are solely heterotrophic, while the other half is either photosynthetic or **mixotrophic** (able to live as an autotroph and a heterotroph). Heterotrophic species are mostly free-living, but a few are parasitic on fish or other single-celled plankton. Photosynthetic dinoflagellates are covered in Chapter 4.

Most dinoflagellate species have two flagella that originate at the same location, however one is typically wrapped around the central portion of the cell, and the other extends from the center toward the posterior end. Dinoflagellates typically range in size from 2 μm to 2 mm (*Noctiluca*) and typically have **tests** with plates called thecae (*theca*, sing.—case or sheath), often impregnated with vesicles of cellulose. Thecae are produced by alveoli and thus these alveoli differ from the pellicular aveoli of the Ciliophora. Species with thecae are called **armored**, whereas those without thecae are **naked**. The number and arrangement of thecal plates is a major morphological feature used in dinoflagellate taxonomy.

Most dinoflagellates have a complex life cycle with several stages, one of which has two haploid nuclei each from different cells. Reproduction is generally asexual using binary fission. However, gametes may form and sexual reproduction occur. The zygote generally undergoes meiosis, and for most of the life cycle, the organism is haploid. Some species are also able to form a resistant cyst.

Rhizaria
Foraminifera

Foraminiferans (forams) are single-celled heterotrophic, amoeboid microzooplankton found in marine and freshwater. There are approximately 1,500 extant species of foraminiferans, most of which are marine and are found in benthic habitats (Figure 3-4). However the 40 species that

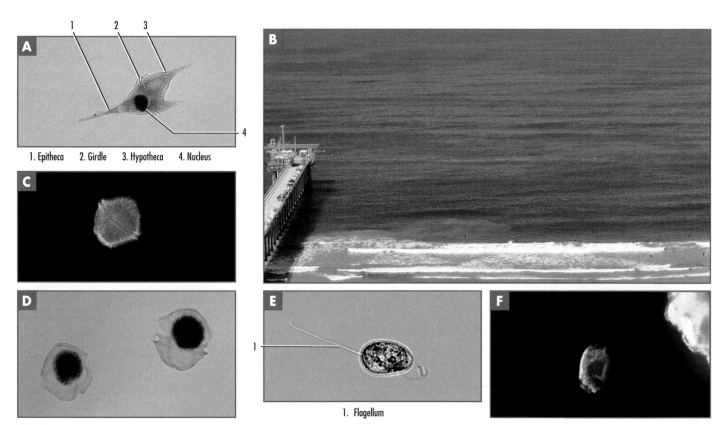

1. Epitheca   2. Girdle   3. Hypotheca   4. Nucleus

1. Flagellum

■ **3-3 Dinoflagellata** ∼ (**A**) Ceratium illustrates the typical dinoflagellate arrangement of two flagella with one running along a transverse groove and the other following behind. *Ceratium* spp. are mixotrophic (*mix*—mix, *troph*—feeder), engulfing food and possessing chloroplasts used in photosynthesis. (**B**) Some dinoflagellate species produce toxic materials, which accumulate in the water when population numbers are high, and typically occur along the western coast of North American in the late summer months appearing as a "red-tide." Bioluminescence also occurs (upper right photograph on page 27) in association with red tides. This red tide was caused by (**C**) *Lingulodinium polyedrum*, although (**D**) *Gonyaulax* spp. are more commonly associated with these events on the West Coast, while in Florida, *Karenia brevis* is typically the causative organism. (**E** and **F**) Many other flagellated unicellular organisms are found in the marine environment. However, the presence of one or more flagella is not unique to any particular clade and is minimally useful in identifying the organism.

are planktonic, such as *Globigerina*, are extremely abundant. They have calcium carbonate shells, or tests, that are well preserved and have formed fossils since the Cambrian period. Benthic forams can be so numerous that the sediment color is affected by the color of the foram species comprising it. This is the case in the pink shell beaches of Bermuda. Due to their extensive fossil record, forams are often used as index fossils to date (assign an age to) sediments. Benthic species display habitat preference and can provide clues as to the type of habitat in which they were deposited, useful not only for basic science but also for petroleum exploration. **Pelagic** (*pelagic*—of the open sea) foram tests comprise a large portion of the world's calcareous **biogenic** (*bio*—life, *gen*—to produce) **sediment** (also known as "foraminiferous ooze"). One example of this is the White Cliffs of Dover, in the United Kingdom. Chemistry of the test is useful for charting climate change. The ratio of stable oxygen isotopes changes with water temperature, and this is reflected in the test chemistry.

Foraminiferans range in size from 100 μm in the smallest planktonic species to approximately 20 cm in large deep-sea forms. Some forams house algae as endosymbionts that supply them with nutrients, while others feed on diatoms, bacteria, and other small plankton. They capture prey with movable, netlike pseudopodia (*pseudo*—false, *podia*—foot) called **reticulopodia** (*reticulo*—a network, *podia*—foot) that extend and branch out of the body wall. Movement of reticulopodia occurs by extending and contracting microtubules. Once prey is caught, it is hauled in toward the foram's cell body where it is engulfed via phagocytosis. In addition to feeding with these nets, benthic species use them for movement.

In general, forams have quite elaborate and varied skeletal structures. There are various types of tests,

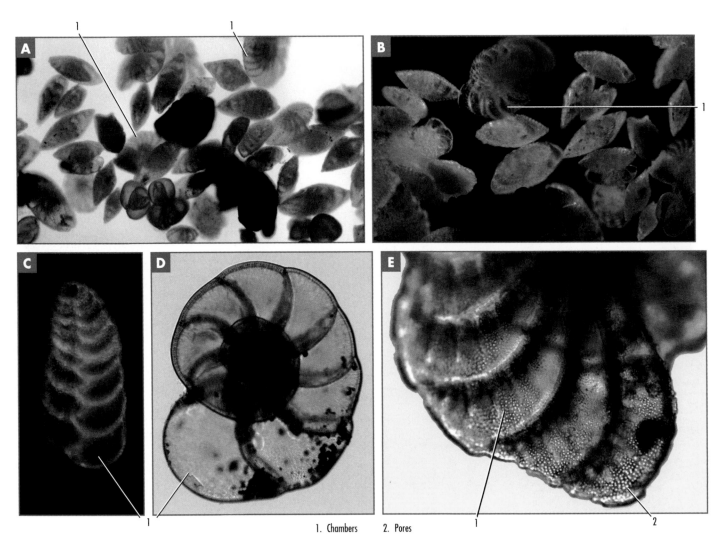

1. Chambers   2. Pores

■ **3-4 Foraminifera** ≈ **(A–E)** Shells (more properly, tests) of foraminiferans are for the most part made of calcium carbonate, although some are made of other materials. Most tests have multiple chambers and vary greatly between species. They have often accumulated in large numbers on the ocean floor. Some of these are now exposed on land in areas once covered by the ocean. **(D** and **E)** *Elphidium* sp. is a common nearshore species with a typically complex foraminiferan life cycle that may last two or more years and involve two distinct life-cycle morphologies. Note the pores in the test of *Elphidium*, through which reticulopodia once extended.

depending on the species, but calcite, or cemented particles of sand, silt grains, or sponge spicules (Chapter 5), are common. Most tests are multichambered and superficially similar in appearance to a snail shell. The lightweight, fragile test and abundant spines increase the surface area-to-volume ratio and, therefore, help planktonic species remain buoyant within the **photic** (*phot*—light) zone. Forams contain two different types of nuclei, similar to ciliates.

Radiolaria

Radiolaria (Figure 3-5) is a group rich with diverse morphologies, life histories, and a fossil history dating to the Cambrian period. Radiolarians are entirely marine, and most are planktonic, ranging in size from 30 μm–2 mm. A few colonial species are as large as 20 cm. They have durable, glassy tests (most are radially symmetrical) that become part of siliceous biogenic sediment ("radiolarian ooze") when they die and sink to the seafloor. The abundance of fossil radiolarians is useful for dating the age and type of sediment. The geographic distribution of radiolarians is limited by water temperature and salinity, and therefore abundance decreases with increasing latitude. **Euphotic** (*eu*—well, *phot*—light) radiolarians are often associated with dinoflagellate or algal endosymbionts (*bio*—life; "living within"), and their depth range is thought to be limited by decreasing light availability at depth.

Similar to the forams, radiolarians have pseudopodia, some of which form a net (cortex) around one or two tests, and other non-retractable spiny **axopods** (*axo*—axle, *pod*—foot). Functions of the cortex include: capturing smaller plankton or detritus, digestion, assistance with flotation, and location of endosymbionts. The inner cell body (medulla) contains the nucleus, stored food, and lipids, and is housed inside the elaborate, porous, organic test. There is typically another test of silicon dioxide outside of the organic test, but still within the cortex. The lightweight test, vacuoles, lipids, and spiny projections are all beneficial for planktonic species.

Radiolarians reproduce both asexually and sexually. The phylogeny of the Radiolaria has not yet been resolved. Variation in the silica test is an important morphological trait for classification purposes; however, individual species have many unique traits that have made classification difficult because they obscure more general shared characters. Molecular evidence suggests that the Radiolaria may be grouped in a clade with the Heliozoa, and the Acantharia (neither discussed in this text) and that this clade may be linked to the Alveolata.

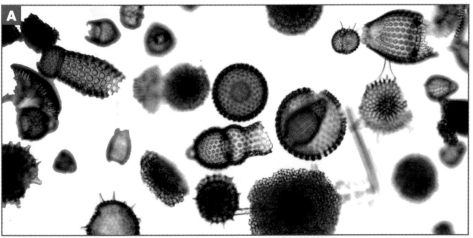

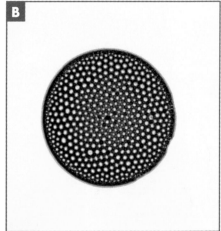

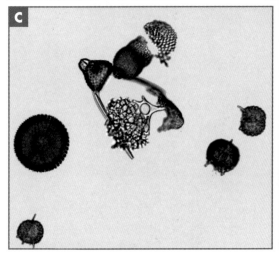

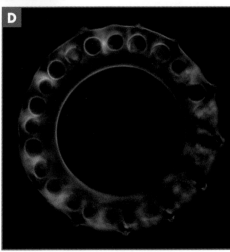

■ **3-5 Radiolaria** ≈ (A–D)
The tests (shells) of radiolarians typically are made of silica and often are very intricate in their design. Tests have a single chamber, although the chamber may have undivided segments. Holes through the test come in a variety of shapes. Radiolarians are predominantly pelagic (open ocean) organisms with life cycles not completely known.

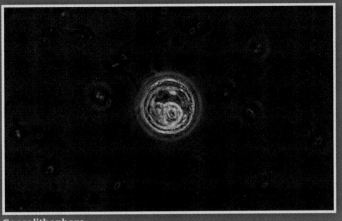
Coccolithophore

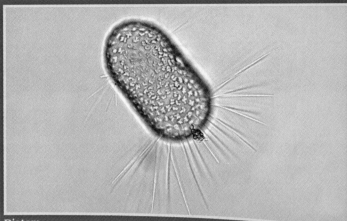
Diatom

4 Simple Eukaryotic, Planktonic, and Benthic Autotrophs

nlike most chapters, this chapter is a functional grouping of many clades, some only distantly related (Figure 4-1). The unifying feature is all are unicellular or colonial autotrophs. They are currently classified in the major eukaryotic clades: Ecavata, Chromalveolata, and Archaeplastida (Table 4-1).

Archaeplastida

Archaeplastida (*archae*—ancient, *plastos*—shaped) are characterized by having organelles called **plastids** derived from an ancient cyanobacterium that was engulfed by a heterotrophic eukaryote and subsequently maintained a stable, mutually beneficial relationship with the host cell. Eventually, the cyanobacterium evolved into a eukaryotic plastid, such as a chloroplast. This process has been termed "**primary endosymbiosis**" (*endo*—within, *sym*—with, *bios*—life). There are four main clades within Archaeplastida: the rhodophytes (red algae, which are covered in Chapter 29), the chlorophytes (green algae), the charophytes (stoneworts), and the true plants (embryophytes). Chlorophytes and charophytes are loosely referred to as "green algae," but that is not a formal taxonomic designation. Most charophytes are found in freshwater and are not covered

here. True plants are covered in Chapter 32. (Note that Figure 4-1 shows the charophytes and true plants in the same clade. Current evidence supports the origin of true plants from a charophyte ancestor.)

Most chlorophytes are freshwater. Of the 10% that are marine, only a few are unicellular. (Multicellular chlorophytes are covered in Chapter 30.) The marine unicellular chlorophytes belong to the Class Prasinophyceae. Most defining characteristics of this class are subcellular or biochemical and are beyond the scope of this text. However, motile species have flagella emerging from a depression at the anterior of the cell and they are associated with a **basal body** of complex construction. The cells are covered with organic scales and have a single, usually lobed, chloroplast with one **pyrenoid** that stores starch. All possess **chlorophyll a** as the primary photosynthetic pigment, but accessory pigments **chlorophyll b**, **lutein**, and **β-carotene** are also present. Figure 4-2 shows an unidentified prasinophyte.

Excavata

This group obtains its name from the presence in many members of a feeding groove *excavated* from one side of the cell. Among the major clades within Excavata are

33

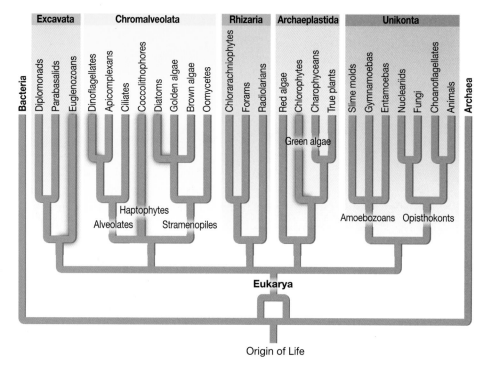

4-1 A Phylogeny of the Three Domains of Life ≈ Simple marine autotrophs are found in three of the five major eukaryotic clades: Excavata, Chromalveolata, and Archaeplastida.

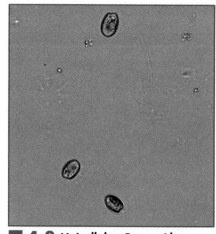

4-2 Unicellular Green Alga (Chlorophyta) ≈ Marine unicellular green algae are likely from the Class Prasinophyceae. These green, flagellated unicells were isolated from estuary water. The flagella emerging from the indented end are barely visible. Most features that differentiate prasinophyte species are subcellular or biochemical. Thus, identification of these cells was not attempted.

Table 4-1 ≈ Major Eukaryotic Unicellular Marine Autotrophs

Major Eukaryotic Clade Phylum or Class	General Description of Unicellular Representatives	Examples	Approximate Number of Species	Etymology
Archaeplastida Prasinophyceae (Figure 4-2)	Polyphyletic; cell "wall" of one or more layers of scales of varying composition; chlorophylls *a* and *b*, and β-carotene in a single lobed chloroplast; starch stored in chloroplast; one or more flagella emerging from a pit at the anterior; red eyespot present in some	*Pyramimonas, Tetraselmis, Prasinocladus*	135	*prasinos*—green, *phyte*—plant
Excavata Euglenophyta (Figure 4-3)	Mixotrophic unicells with one or more discoid chloroplasts containing chlorophylls *a* and *b*, and β-carotene; cytoplasmic paramylon granules for storage; one or two flagella; red eyespot; proteinaceous pellicle; some cells are flexible	*Euglena, Eutreptia, Trachelomonas*	1,000	*eu*—genuine, *glene*—eyeball, *phyte*—plant (presumably referring to the red eyespot)
Chromalveolata Dinophyceae *(Dinoflagellata to zoologists)* (Figure 4-4)	Unicells typically with two flagella in a groove around the middle of the primary axis; often mixotrophic, many with cellulose thecal plates; chlorophylls *a* and *c*, and fucoxanthin in autotrophic forms	*Ceratium, Noctiluca, Gonyaulax, Gymnodinium*	4,500	*dinos*—whirling, *flagellum*—whip
Bacillariophyceae (Figures 4-5 through 4-9)	Unicellular or colonial; chlorophylls a, c_1, and c_2, and fucoxanthin are present in one or more variously shaped chromoplasts; wall of silica separated into two valves; oil droplets form outside of chromoplast for storage	*Navicula, Chaetoceros, Coscinodiscus, Tabellaria, Fragilaria*	6,000	*baculus*—stick, *phyte*—plant
Haptophyta (Figure 4-10)	Two smooth flagella associated with unique microtubular feeding structure (haptonema); chlorophylls a, c_2, and a variant form of a, as well as fucoxanthin, β-carotene, and other accessory pigments; many with calcium carbonate coccoliths	*Pavlova, Coccolithophora, Prymnesium*	400	*hapt*—to grasp, *phyte*—plant

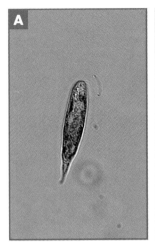

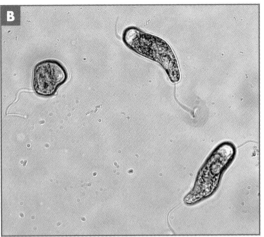

4-3 Euglenids (Euglenophyta) ≈ Euglenids are the only simple auto-trophs from the Excavata, and most are freshwater. These euglenids were taken from an estuarine sample. **(A)** One flagellum is visible at the anterior of this euglenid, as is the red eyespot. Paramylon granules (white) and chloroplasts (green) are also visible in the cytoplasm. **(B)** This euglenid species has two visible flagella. It is covered by a flexible pellicle that allows it to change shapes. Note the contracted individual at the left.

parabasalids, diplomonads, kinetoplastids, and euglenids. Of these, only the euglenids are autotrophic.

The majority of euglenids (Figure 4-3) are freshwater, but estuarine and intertidal species are known. The most easily identified are green, photosynthetic unicells. Many are also capable of heterotrophy when light is not available, making them **mixotrophic** (*mixis*—mingling, *troph*—food). One or two flagella are present and emerge from an invagination of the anterior (forward) cytoplasmic membrane. A red photoreceptor called an **eyespot** at the cell's anterior is another distinctive feature. They possess the same photosynthetic pigments as chlorophytes, but store a different carbohydrate (**paramylon**) in the cytoplasm (rather than starch in the chloroplast). The cell is covered

by a protein **pellicle** (*pellicule*—a small piece of skin) rather than a cellulose cell wall. The pellicle may be flexible, in which case the cell is capable of contorting as it moves.

Chromalveolata

The chromalveolates (*kroma*—color, *alveus*—small cavity) may or may not be a monophy-letic group. However, there is evidence to suggest that early in their evolution they under-went **secondary endosymbiosis** by engulfing a red alga, which already had a plastid derived from primary endosymbiosis. Many **extant** (living) species of chromalveolates have func-tional plastids that clearly resemble red algae, whereas others possess reduced plastids that also resemble red algae. Some have no plastids, but have red algal plastid DNA in their genome. Still others show no evidence of a red algal connection. A mystery is there for the solving if you choose to engage it! The major groups of chromalveolates are the **alveolates**, **stramenopiles** (Hetero-kontophyta), and **haptophytes**.

Alveolata

The alveolates possess cytoplasmic membranous sacs near the cytoplasmic membrane. It has been speculated that the alveoli are somehow involved in maintaining osmotic balance, but their function is not known for certain. There are three main groups of alveolates: dinoflagellates, api-complexans, and ciliates. Only the dinoflagellates have autotrophic members.

Dinoflagellates (also discussed in Chapter 3) (Figure 4-4) are typically unicellular and have two flagella: one protruding from the cell and the other positioned in a

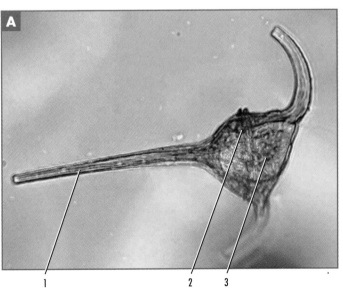

1. Epitheca   2. Girdle   3. Hypotheca

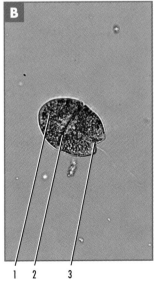

4-4 Dinoflagellates (Dino-phyceae) ≈ The anterior part of a dinoflagellate cell wall is the epitheca, and the posterior cell wall is the hypotheca. The girdle, a constricted region, separates these two regions and houses a flagellum. A second flagellum also extends from the cell. **(A)** *Ceratium* is a very common planktonic dinoflagella (more than 60 species) and is easily identifiable by horns that emerge from the hypotheca. It consistently has 17 thecal plates—5 in the epitheca, 4 in the girdle, and 8 in the hypotheca. Some plates are visible in this micro-graph. **(B)** The posterior flagellum of this unidentified planktonic dinoflagellate is visible.

groove (the girdle) encircling the cell. Most are mixotrophic, though strictly autotrophic and heterotrophic species are also known. Starch is the primary storage material of photosynthetic species and is stored outside the chloroplast. Chlorophylls *a* and *c*, as well as **fucoxanthin** (*phukos*—seaweed, *xanthine*—yellow) and other pigments are present. Many dinoflagellates house endosymbiotic brown algae.

If the dinoflagellate is armored (thecate), alveoli immediately beneath the cell membrane house cellulose plates (thecae). The number of thecae is consistent in many species. Some species are naked and the vesicles do not contain cellulose plates. On a gross cellular level, the girdle marks the separation of the anterior **epitheca** (*epi*—upon, *theca*—case) and the posterior **hypotheca** (*hypo*—below) portions of the cell (these are also referred to as valves).

Photosynthetic dinoflagellates are important primary producers and are one of the main causes of harmful algal blooms (HABs), or "red" tides (Figure 3-3). Many HABs are toxic to humans or other organisms upon contact with high levels of dinoflagellates, while others are toxic (and can be fatal) if consumed. An example of the first type is *Pfiesteria piscicida,* which releases a toxin that can kill fish. The second case occurs with paralytic shellfish poisoning (PSP) caused by a toxin produced by several dinoflagellate species. When first consumed by predatory planktonic species, the toxins are at low levels. But by the time it is passed through the food chain to mussels, clams, or oysters, it has been biomagnified[1] until it reaches levels where it is toxic in the tissue of the shellfish that humans consume.

---

[1]Biomagnification is the process of a chemical getting concentrated as it moves up the food chain. This occurs because it is not completely eliminated from organisms and as such, increases in concentration, only to be passed on at this higher concentration to the next trophic level where the process is repeated.

Symbiodinium species are found as photosynthetic endosymbionts in tropical corals and molluscs, where they exist as a non-flagellated (**palmella**) stage of the dinoflagellate. Dinoflagellates are also probably the most common source of bioluminescence in the ocean (page 27, upper right).

Stramenopiles

Stramenopiles (Heterokontophyta) are soil, marine, and freshwater autotrophs and heterotrophs. They are characterized by having a so-called **tinsel flagellum** with "hairs" made of a basal attachment, a hollow shaft, and glycoprotein filaments split into three parts at the ends. A second smooth **whiplash flagellum** also is often present. There are three groups of autotrophic stramenopiles: diatoms, the golden algae (which are not well represented in marine environments), and the brown algae. Only diatoms are covered in this chapter; the brown algae are covered in Chapter 32. The fourth group, oomycetes or water molds, are colorless and heterotrophic.

Diatoms, or bacillariophytes, are photosynthetic unicellular eukaryotes. Cell shapes are either round (**centric**) or elongated (**pennate**)—see Figures 4-5A and 4-5B. Figure 4-6 shows the different appearance of a diatom depending on whether it is viewed from the side (**girdle view**) or from above or below (**valve view**). Notice the distinctive golden brown color from the pigment fucoxanthin located in the **chromoplasts**, which may be of variable shape. Chlorophylls *a* and *c*, and β-carotene are also present. **Oil droplets** (the storage material) are frequently visible.

The cell wall, or **frustule**, is made of silica embedded in an organic matrix and consists of two halves, with one half overlapping the other in the same way the lid of a box overlaps its base. The larger portion is the epitheca and the lower one the hypotheca. Where the valves overlap, two

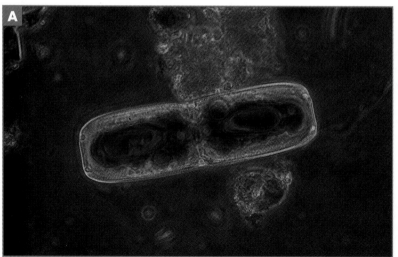
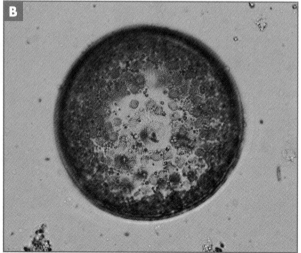

■ **4-5 Basic Diatom Shapes (Stramenopiles)** ≈ Diatoms present one of two basic shapes. **(A)** Pennate diatoms are elongated and may or may not be bilaterally symmetrical. This is a phase contrast micrograph of an unidentified pennate marine diatom. **(B)** Centric diatoms have radial symmetry. This is one of approximately 60 accepted species of *Coscinodiscus.*

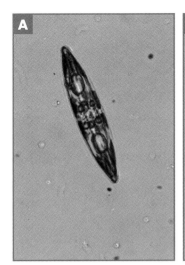

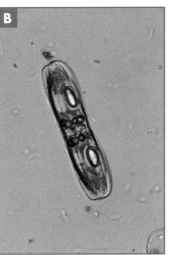

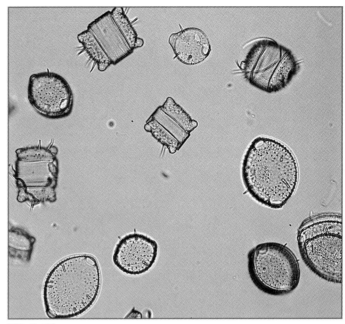

■ **4-6 Diatom Valve and Girdle Views** ≈ Each diatom frustule consists of an upper valve (epitheca) and a lower, smaller valve (hypotheca). This specimen is a species of *Navicula*. (**A**) *Navicula* is boat-shaped (*navicula*—little ship) when observed from the side, i.e., girdle view. (**B**) When observed from above or below, i.e., valve view, *Navicula* is rectangular, frequently with a slight constriction in the middle.

■ **4-7 Geologically Recent Marine Diatoms—Strew** ≈ Frequently in biology classes diatom diversity is studied using slides made from diatomaceous earth, which contains the empty frustules of deceased diatoms in great abundance. Shown is a little of that variety. Compare the appearance of these diatom relics with the living forms in Figure 4-8. The ornamentation on their frustules is much more apparent.

incomplete circular pieces wrap around them to form the **girdle**. Some pennate diatoms are motile and have a central, longitudinal line called a **raphe** (*raphe*—seam). Cell walls may be variously ornamented by grooves and holes. The frustule shape and its ornamentation are so distinctive that diatoms often can be identified from the frustules of deceased cells (Figure 4-7). Figure 4-8 shows a variety of living planktonic and sessile (*sess*—seated) diatoms.

The diatom life cycle is illustrated in Figure 4-9. Diatoms reproduce asexually by division in which each valve produces a new, smaller valve to form a new, complete frustule. After each division, the larger valve is the older valve and becomes the epitheca. This continues until the frustule reaches a critically small size, at which time the nucleus undergoes meiosis to produce gametes that are released. Fertilization produces a new cell and the cycle repeats.

Many pennate diatoms are motile by a gliding mechanism, which serves them well as they are most commonly found in sediments. Centric diatoms are nonmotile and are most frequently found in the plankton.

Haptophyta

Haptophytes are unicellular algae with two smooth flagella. They are distinguished by the presence of a **haptonema**

(*hapt*—to grasp, *nema*—thread) extending from the cytoplasm between the two flagella. It is composed of membranous layers surrounding seven microtubules, so is fundamentally different in structure from eukaryotic flagella, which have the 9+2 arrangement of microtubules within (nine pairs surrounding two single microtubules). The haptonema is a feeding structure that gathers food particles and delivers them to a **food vacuole** (*vacuus*—empty, *ole*—diminutive suffix) at the posterior of the cell.

Haptophytes are extremely abundant in marine waters and are important producers in marine food chains. They possess a number of photosynthetic pigments, including chlorophylls *a*, c_2, and a variant form of *a*, as well as fucoxanthin, β-carotene, and other accessory pigments.

Many haptophytes have calcium carbonate scales called **coccoliths** (*cocco*—berry or grain, *litho*—stone). These can associate with organic carbon and settle to deep-sea floor as one form of "marine snow." Such carbon deposits tie up atmospheric CO_2 for significant periods of time. Figure 4-10 is a micrograph of *Coccolithophora* grown in culture.

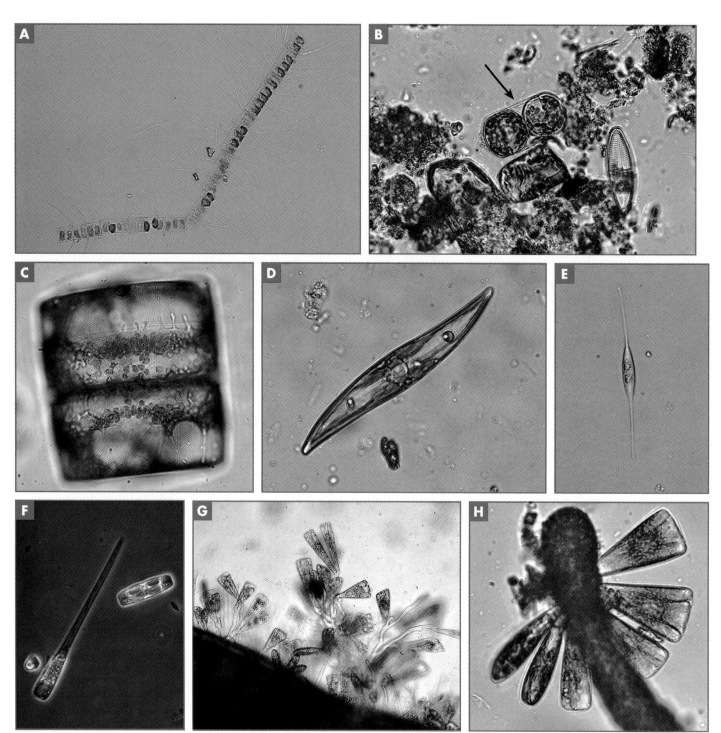

■ **4-8 A Gallery of Marine Diatoms (Stramenopiles)** ≈ **(A)** *Chaetoceros*, seen here in girdle view, is a centric diatom with over 200 validly recognized species. They are common and quite distinctive in the plankton, with their chains of radially symmetrical cells and hairs that emerge from the junctions between cells. One, two, or more belt-like chloroplasts occupy each cell. **(B)** *Melosira* (arrow) is a centric diatom that forms chains held together by mucilage secreted on valve surfaces and by spines along their edges. Plastids are numerous and located in the periphery of the cytoplasm. There are approximately 60 species in the genus. **(C)** This is a valve view of the same *Coscinodiscus* specimen shown in Figure 4-5B. From this view, it is clear that there are two attached cells. Note the delicate hexagonal holes in the cell wall and the numerous chloroplasts. **(D)** This specimen is either *Pleurosigma* or *Gyrosigma* in valve view. (Not enough detail in the cell wall sculpturing is shown to differentiate between the two.) It is a pennate diatom with two ribbon-like chromoplasts on either side. Note also the oil droplets. **(E)** Long, thin extensions projecting from an enlarged central region characterize the frustules of *Cylindrotheca*. Only two species are recognized. This is likely *C. fusiformis*. **(F)** On the left is a single cell of *Asterionella*. Typically, these cells form a circular arrangement where the dilated portions are connected and the narrower portions project outward like spokes on a wagon wheel. The other smaller diatom was not identifiable. **(G)** Wedge-shaped cells characterize *Licomorpha*. In this micrograph, a *Licomorpha* colony is growing as an epiphyte on a red alga. The branched stalks are made of a gelatinous material. **(H)** This *Licomorpha* is epiphytic on the green alga *Enteromorpha* and shows the cells in more detail than in **(G)**. The cells in the upper right are in valve view, whereas those in the lower left are in girdle view. *(continued)*

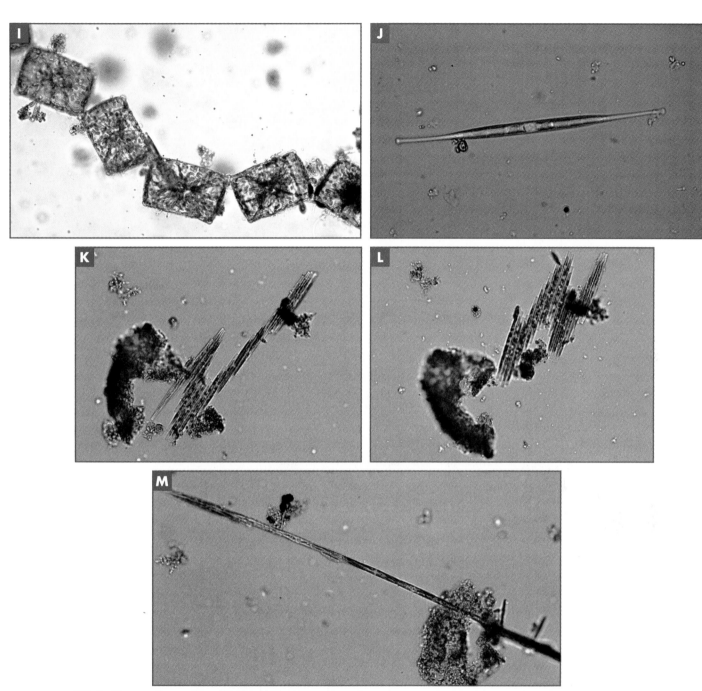

■ **4-8 A Gallery of Marine Diatoms (Stramenopiles)** ∼ *(continued)* (**I**) *Tabellaria*, shown here in valve view, is a centric diatom that forms distinctive zigzag colonies. (**J**) The pennate diatom *Fragilaria* frequently forms colonies with cells joined by their valve sides. This individual illustrates the general cellular structure, including the expanded ends. (**K** and **L**) *Bacillaria* forms colonies of cells joined along their valve surfaces. These remarkable diatoms glide across one another to move the entire colony. These two micrographs were taken a few seconds apart. Compare the relative positions of the individual cells. (**M**) The entire *Bacillaria* colony can extend so that cells remain attached by only the smallest overlap. This is the same colony as in (**K**) and (**L**).

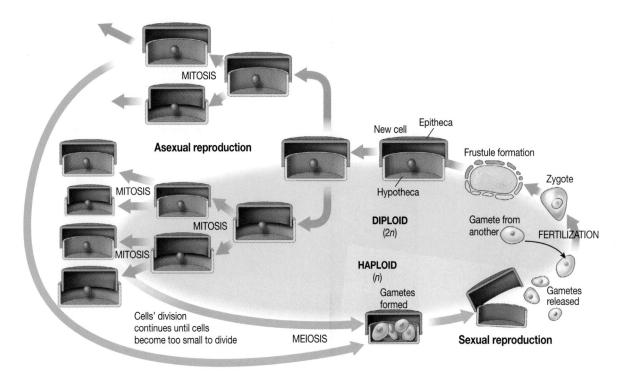

■ **4-9 Diatom Life Cycle** ≈ The majority of diatom reproduction is by division of the diploid cells. Mitosis and cell division (cytokinesis) of the protoplast is unremarkable, but it is the fate of the valves that is most interesting. In every division, each valve is passed on to a different daughter cell. The epitheca remains the epitheca of the daughter cell, and the daughter cell remains the same size as the original. However, the hypotheca of the original cell becomes the epitheca of the daughter cell, which necessarily is smaller than the original. This process continues until the cell reaches a critically small size, at which time it undergoes meiosis to produce gametes and sexual reproduction occurs.

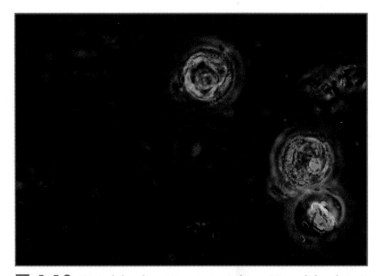

■ **4-10** *Coccolithophora* **Grown in Culture (Coccolithophora)**
≈ Note the two discoid golden chloroplasts, the two smooth flagella, and the scales on the cell's surface.

Ircinia

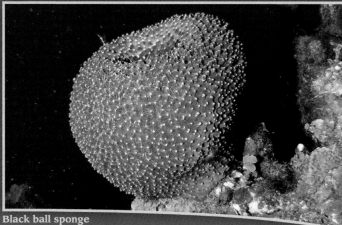

Black ball sponge

5 Porifera

Poriferan sponges (Table 5-1) are **sessile** (attached), encrusting benthic animals that feed by filtering the water and capturing particulate matter (Figures 5-1 through 5-2). Most species grow attached on hard substrata, though some can anchor in stable mud sediments. Sponges often are prominent components of epifaunal ("fouling") communities on hard substrata at all latitudes and can be especially important sessile components of coral reef systems. They are thought to be the oldest metazoans and the

Phylum Porifera presently comprises ~15,000 extant species (mostly marine), though their taxonomy is complex and species are hard to distinguish because of their simple basic structure and variability in form. They are considered to be the sister taxon to the Eumetazoans.

Sponges are considered to be colonial organisms by some researchers and the simplest of the multicellular animals by others. They often are brightly colored, but are otherwise rather featureless. They lack many of the

■ Table **5-1** ≈ Poriferan Classes

Class	General Description	Examples	Approximate Number of Species	Etymology
Hexactinellida (Figure 5-8)	"Glass sponges" with silicon spicules (mineralized components of skeleton) consisting of six rays	Venus' Flower Basket (*Euplectella*)	500	*hex*—six, *actin*—ray, *elli*—dim
Calcarea (Figure 5-9)	"Calcareous sponges" with calcium carbonate spicules (mineralized components of skeleton) needle-shaped or with three to four rays	*Leucosolenia* and *Sycon*	400	*calca*—lime
Demospongiae (Figure 5-10)	Silicon spicules, protein skeleton, or both; all have multiple oscula (point at which water exits the sponge)	*Spongia*, *Pseudoceratina*, and *Aplysina*	14,100	*demos*—people, *sponga*—sponge
Homoscleromorpha—disputed	Silicon spicules very small or absent; most are encrusting forms		>100	*homo*—same, *sclero*—hard, *morph*—form

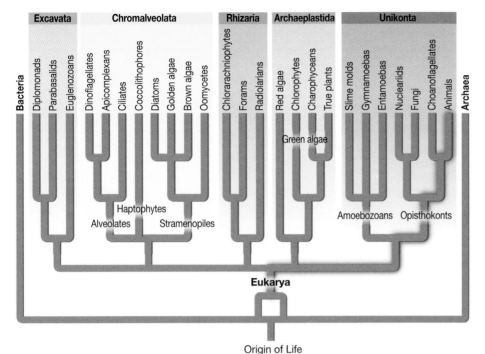

■ **5-1 Phylogeny of the Three Domains of Life** ≈ The traditional view of Poriferans (disputed by some) characterizes them as multicellular, heterotrophic organisms, that are motile in one or more life stages. Like all animals, they are Opisthokonts (*opisthios*—posterior, *codos*—tail), named for the single flagellum present in one or more life-cycle stages and located posteriorly. This presumes monophyly with the Fungi and others. The Poriferans are generally considered part of the Parazoa (*para*—near, *zoa*—animals) (Figure 5-2), although this is commonly considered a paraphyletic grouping. See Appendix A for definitions of terms, clades, and taxa in this figure.

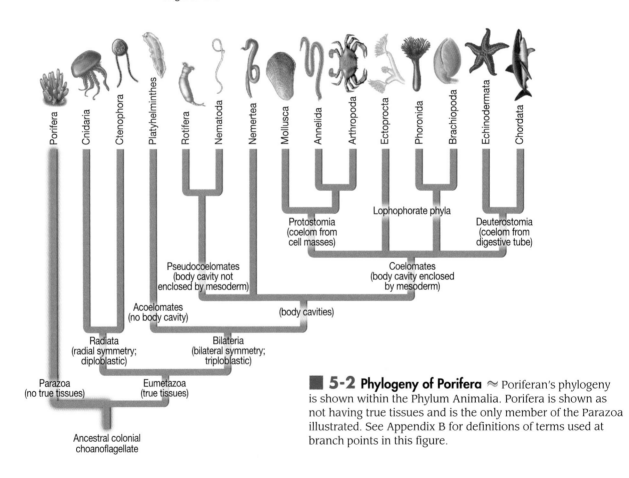

■ **5-2 Phylogeny of Porifera** ≈ Poriferan's phylogeny is shown within the Phylum Animalia. Porifera is shown as not having true tissues and is the only member of the Parazoa illustrated. See Appendix B for definitions of terms used at branch points in this figure.

structural and organizational characteristics common to most other animals and generally there is no recognizable body symmetry (though a few erect species are radial). Their simple morphology and lack of tissue germ layers—and thereby visibly obvious internal structure, such as a gut or digestive system—belies their complexity in other regards. For example, all sponge cells retain the capacity for amoeboid movement and are totipotent (capable of developing into all-body cell types). If the cells of a sponge colony are disaggregated, they can rapidly re-assort themselves and the sponge can repair and regain its organizational structure. Wounds or physical damage to the colony

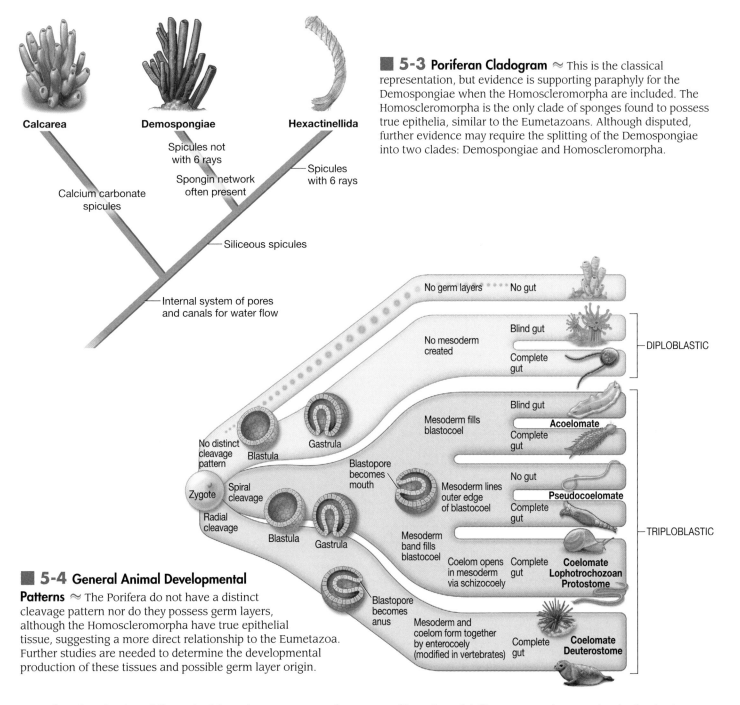

Calcarea

Demospongiae

Hexactinellida

Spicules not with 6 rays

Spongin network often present

Spicules with 6 rays

Calcium carbonate spicules

Siliceous spicules

Internal system of pores and canals for water flow

■ **5-3** Poriferan Cladogram ≈ This is the classical representation, but evidence is supporting paraphyly for the Demospongiae when the Homoscleromorpha are included. The Homoscleromorpha is the only clade of sponges found to possess true epithelia, similar to the Eumetazoans. Although disputed, further evidence may require the splitting of the Demospongiae into two clades: Demospongiae and Homoscleromorpha.

No germ layers · · · · No gut

No mesoderm created

Blind gut

Complete gut

DIPLOBLASTIC

Zygote

No distinct cleavage pattern

Blastula

Spiral cleavage

Radial cleavage

Gastrula

Blastula

Gastrula

Blastopore becomes mouth

Blastopore becomes anus

Mesoderm fills blastocoel

Blind gut

Acoelomate

Complete gut

Mesoderm lines outer edge of blastocoel

No gut

Pseudocoelomate

Complete gut

Mesoderm band fills blastocoel

Coelom opens in mesoderm via schizocoely

Complete gut

Coelomate Lophotrochozoan Protostome

Mesoderm and coelom form together by enterocoely (modified in vertebrates)

Complete gut

Coelomate Deuterostome

TRIPLOBLASTIC

■ **5-4** General Animal Developmental

Patterns ≈ The Porifera do not have a distinct cleavage pattern nor do they possess germ layers, although the Homoscleromorpha have true epithelial tissue, suggesting a more direct relationship to the Eumetazoa. Further studies are needed to determine the developmental production of these tissues and possible germ layer origin.

may therefore heal rapidly and, although sponges may be preyed upon by a variety of fish and invertebrates (e.g., molluscs and echinoderms), the cells of many species often are rich in complex organic macromolecules (e.g., terpenes), many of which are presumed to act as predator anti-feedants. Others are thought to act as antifoulants to prevent overgrowth by other sessile invertebrates. Sponges have therefore featured prominently in natural product molecular prospecting by the pharmaceutical industry.

Body Form

The general body form of sponges consists of layers of cells covering the proteinaceous (**spongin**) (Figure 5-5)

and/or mineral (siliceous or calcareous) **spicules** (*spic*—arrowhead, *ule*—diminutive suffix) (Figure 5-6) that constitute a supporting skeleton. The skeleton may be a disorganized and seemingly featureless network of supporting spicules or comprise an intricate and highly regular structure. Although they lack a digestive tract or gut, they do feed effectively on suspended particulate matter by filtering water that enters the body through external pores, or **ostia** (singular—ostium; *os*—mouth). Internally, the water channels can be complex and are lined by collar cells (also known as **choanocytes**; *choan*—funnel, *cyte*—cell), which drive water currents by ciliary action. Cellular capture of the particles leads to their intracellular digestion.

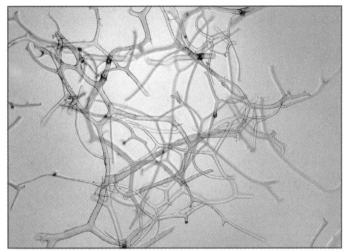

5-5 Micrograph of Protein Skeleton ≈ Spongin is an important skeletal element in many sponges. It is a protein, one of a variety of collagen types found within the Phylum Animalia.

1. Spicule

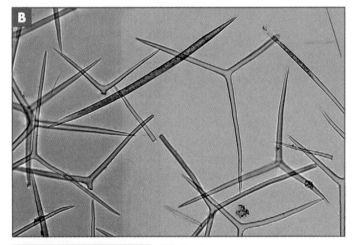

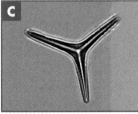

5-6 Spicules ≈ (A) Triradiate (three rays) spicules are visible on the surface of this sponge. (B) Various spicule shapes, including triradiate, are shown in this photomicrograph of *Grantia*. (C) Spicules are commonly visible in plankton tow samples as in this photomicrograph.

There are three main body morphologies among sponges (Figure 5-7): **asconoid** (*asco*—sac, *oid*—resembling), **leuconoid** (*leuco*—lacking color), and **syconoid** (*sycon*—fig). Each body plan limits the complexity of the internal water channels of the colony, and hence the filtering ability of the sponge and the maximum size that can be attained. Individual colonies range from only a few centimeters to many tens of centimeters in diameter.

Reproduction

As in many invertebrate groups, both sexual and asexual reproduction can occur in sponges. Some species form **gemmules**, or balls of cells, from which a new colony can arise asexually. Sexual reproduction and fertilization

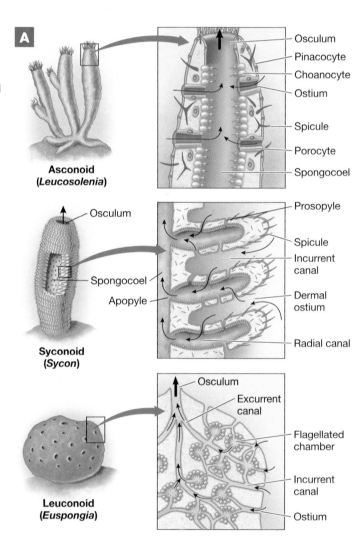

5-7 Syconid Sponge ≈ (A) Shown are the three primary sponge canal system arrangements. The simplest is with choanocytes in the **spongocoel** and is called the asconoid pattern. It is seen in *Leucosolenia* (Figures 5-9B and 5-9C). More complex is the arrangement of the syconoid type as seen in *Grantia* (*Scypha*) (Figures 5-7B and 5-7C). Here the choanocytes lie in radial canals outside the spongocoel. The most complex and common structure is where choanocytes lie within chambers (flagellated chamber) such as in *Aplysina* (Figures 5-10N through 5-10P). Each pattern has evolved multiple times in separate sponge clades. *(continued)*

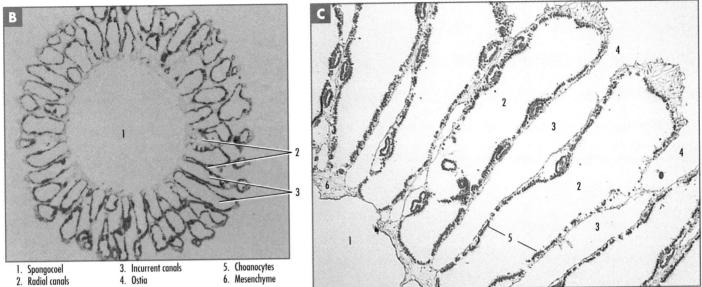

1. Spongocoel
2. Radial canals
3. Incurrent canals
4. Ostia
5. Choanocytes
6. Mesenchyme

■ **5-7** *Synconid* **Sponge** ≈ *(continued)* (**B** and **C**) These photomicrographs of *Grantia* (*Schypa*) shows the spongocoel, radial canals, incurrent canals, and ostia. This is the same *Grantia* specimen viewed at higher magnification. The spongocoel, **incurrent canal**, and **radial canal** with its collar cells (choanocytes) are visible. The flagella of the choanocytes are visible as a faint border along the edge of the radial canal.

leads to the embryo developing into a ciliated larva, which can swim and disperse in the plankton prior to settling to the substratum, attaching and growing into a new benthic colony.

Taxonomy

The evolutionary relationship between the four sponge clades is yet to be resolved but the Hexactinellida includes the glass (siliceous) sponges (Figure 5-8), the Calcarea (calcareous) sponges (Figure 5-9), and the Demospongiae, the demosponges (Figure 5-10). The recently recognized Homoscleromorpha is the only clade of sponges found to possess true epithelia, similar to the Eumetazoans. They have been viewed as a member of the Demospongiae clade, but relationships are in dispute. Figure 5-2 shows the placement of Porifera within Animalia and Figure 5-3 illustrates one hypothesis for the phylogeny of the Porifera, incorporating the three most commonly recognized clades.

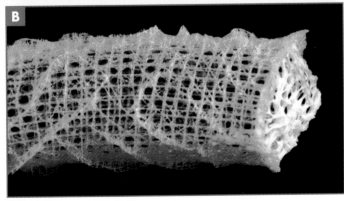

■ **5-8 Hexactinellida** ≈ (**A**) Entire *Euplectella aspergillum* skeleton approximately 21 cm in length. (**B**) Close up of *Euplectella aspergillum* siliceous skeleton (approximately 2.5 cm across).

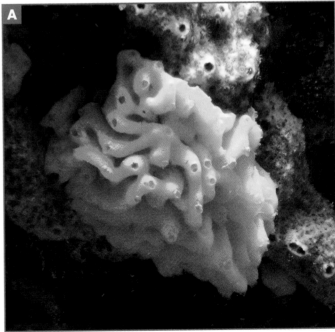

■ **5-9 Calcarea** ≈ (**A**) *Clathrina canariensis*, the yellow calcareous sponge, is found in the western temperate Atlantic on the lower side of overhangs and caves. *(continued)*

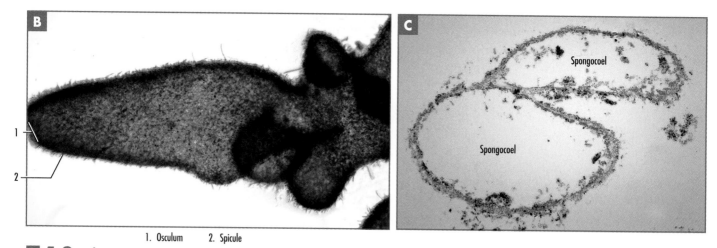

1. Osculum   2. Spicule

■ **5-9 Calcarea** ≈ *(continued)* (**B**) This micrograph of a whole mount of *Leucosolenia* shows spicules and an osculum. *Leucosolenia* is an asconoid sponge. (**C**) This micrograph of *Leucosolenia* cut in cross section shows the simple structure of the asconoid body plan with spongocoel of neighboring sponges indicated.

Orange ball sponge   Puffball sponge   Barrel sponge

Netted barrel sponge   Black ball sponge   Azure vase sponge

■ **5-10 Demospongiae** ≈ (**A**) Orange ball sponge, *Cinachyra* sp., is found under ledges and in caves along coral reefs in the tropical West Atlantic to 30 m. Note the pits (oscula) and algae growth. (**B**) Puffball sponge, *Tethya aurantia*, is a Northeastern Pacific species common in the kelp bed habitat (Chapter 33) where it occasionally washes ashore during storms. (**C**) Barrel sponge, *Xestospongia muta*, lives in the Caribbean. Specimens can be large enough for a diver to enter the "barrel." A large specimen may be more than 100 years old. This specimen is about 1 m tall. (**D**) Netted barrel sponge, *Verongula gigantea*, is also found in the Caribbean. This specimen is about 70 cm tall. (**E**) Black ball sponge, *Ircinia strobilina*, ranges from the Caribbean to northern South America. It is most common in brightly lit, shallow reef areas. Note the conical bumps covering the external surface. (**F**) Azure vase sponge, *Callyspongia plicifera*, inhabits the Caribbean. Note the sculpturing on the exterior of this coral reef wall inhabitant. *(continued)*

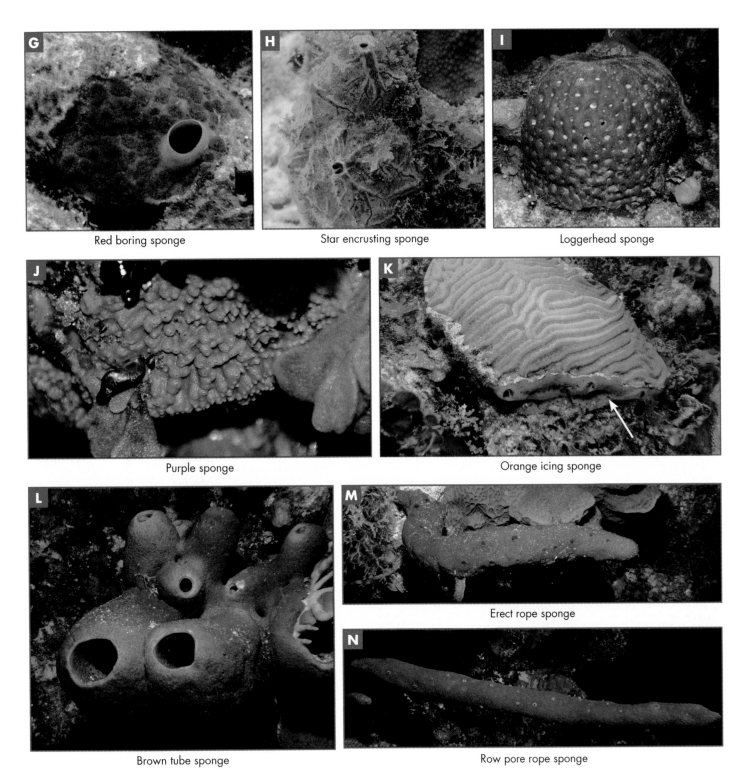

Red boring sponge

Star encrusting sponge

Loggerhead sponge

Purple sponge

Orange icing sponge

Brown tube sponge

Erect rope sponge

Row pore rope sponge

■ **5-10 Demospongiae** ≈ *(continued)* **(G)** Red boring sponge, *Cliona delitrix*, is a Western Central Atlantic species. This sponge bores into coral heads. Note the bumps covering the surface and the large osculum of this shallow reef inhabitant. Brittle stars (Chapter 18) often live in the oscula. **(H)** Star encrusting sponge, *Halisarca* sp., has a variable distribution depending on the species. Note the visible star patterns around the oscula. **(I)** Loggerhead sponge, *Spheciospongia vesparium*, is found in the Caribbean. At the top of this species, there is a central depression with numerous oscula, often with commensal shrimp. **(J)** *Haliclona permollis* is found throughout the Pacific with colonies usually growing to about 10 cm on rocks and on available surfaces as part of fouling communities (Chapter 33). Note the oscula at the end of the finger-like projections. **(K)** Orange icing sponge, *Mycale laevis* (arrow), is a Western Central Atlantic species. This sponge grows in association with a number of different hard coral species. Here it is growing on a brain coral (Chapter 6). **(L)** Brown tube sponge, *Agelas conifera*, is another Carribean species. Note the large oscula, commonly inhabited by commensal organisms. This species grows in a cluster of sponges all joined at the base. **(M)** Erect rope sponge, *Amphimedon compressa*, is also a Caribbean species. It inhabits coral reef tops and walls where the oscula can be seen scattered along the length of the organism's axis. **(N)** Row pore rope sponge, *Aplysina cauliformis*, is found in the Caribbean and northern South America. Notice the oscula of this species are surrounded by a raised ridge lighter in color than the other sponge parts. *(continued)*

Yellow tube sponge

Convoluted tube sponge

Branching tube sponge

Pink vase sponge

Pitted sponge

■ **5-10 Demospongiae** ≈ *(continued)* (**O**) Yellow tube sponge, *Aplysina fistularis*, is common in shallow reef areas of the Caribbean and coastal areas of South American, where cardinal fish often can be seen living within the osculum. (**P**) Convoluted barrel sponge, *Aplysina lacunosa*, are found in the Caribbean and northern South America. Note the deeply convoluted exterior surface. (**Q**) Branching tube sponge, *Pseudoceratina crassa*, is found in the Caribbean, as are (**R**) pink vase sponge, *Niphates digitalis*, and (**S**) pitted sponge, *Verongula rigida*. Note the yellow color along the edge and interior of the oscula of the pitted sponge.

Finger coral

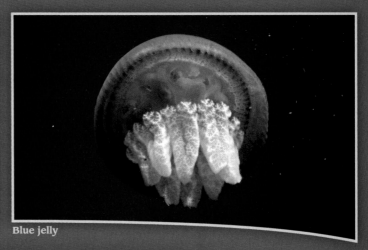
Blue jelly

6 Cnidaria

The predominantly marine Cnidaria (*cnide*—nettle [stinging plant], *aria*—plural suffix) (Table 6-1) consists of both pelagic and benthic animals found throughout the world's oceans. Pelagic examples include: jellyfish (Scyphozoa), siphonophores (Hydrozoa), and box jellies (Scyphozoa/Cubozoa). Benthic representatives include colorful corals and sea anemones (Anthozoa) and attached hydrozoans. The group is composed of radially symmetrical, diploblastic (possessing only endoderm and ectoderm), gelatinous animals (Figures 6-1, 6-2, 6-3, and 6-4). Many cnidarians are colonial (e.g., corals) and some (e.g., siphonophores) consist of colonies of both **polyps** and **medusae** (refers to the mythological creature, Medusa, who had snakes for hair). Cnidarians are predatory, and

■ Table **6-1** ≈ Cnidarian Classes

Class	General Description	Examples	Approximate Number of Species	Etymology
Anthozoa (Figures 6-8 through 6-13)	Polyp form only; both colonial and solitary	Sea anemones, corals, black corals, soft corals, sea pens, gorgonians	6,000+	*antho*—flower, *zoa*—animals
Scyphozoa (Figures 6-14 and 6-16)	Solitary medusae (polyp usually absent)	Jellyfish, including *Aurelia, Chrysaora,* and others	200	*skypho*—cup, *zoa*—animal
Cubozoa (Figure 6-15)	Cube or box-shaped medusa and true eyes	*Chironex fleckeri, Carukia barnesi,* and others	36+	*cubo*—cube shape, *zoa*—animal
Hydrozoa (Figures 6-17 through 6-22)	Solitary or colonial, medusae or polyp may be missing; both marine and freshwater	*Physalia physalis, Obelia, Tubularia,* and others	3,600+	*hydro*—water serpent, *zoa*—animal
Staurozoa	The stalked jellyfish; solitary; polyps only	*Halicystis* and *Lucernaria*	50	*stauros*—a cross, *zoa*—animal

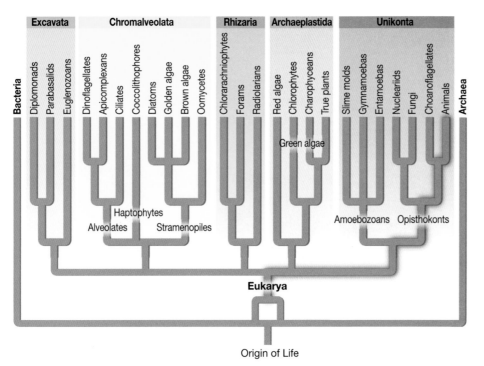

6-1 A Phylogeny of the Three Domains of Life ≈ This is a proposed phylogeny of life first presented as Figure 1-1. Note the position of the Animalia second from the right at top. See Appendix A for definitions of terms, clades, and taxa in this figure.

6-2 General Animal Developmental Patterns ≈
The Cnidarian developmental sequence is shown in the context of diploblastic and triploblastic animals. The path leading to the Cnidarians passes through: no distinct cleavage pattern, blastula, gastrula, no mesoderm formed, to blind gut.

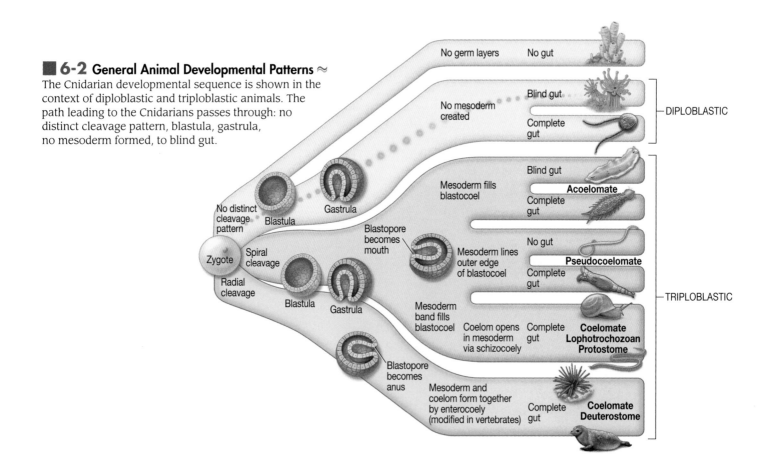

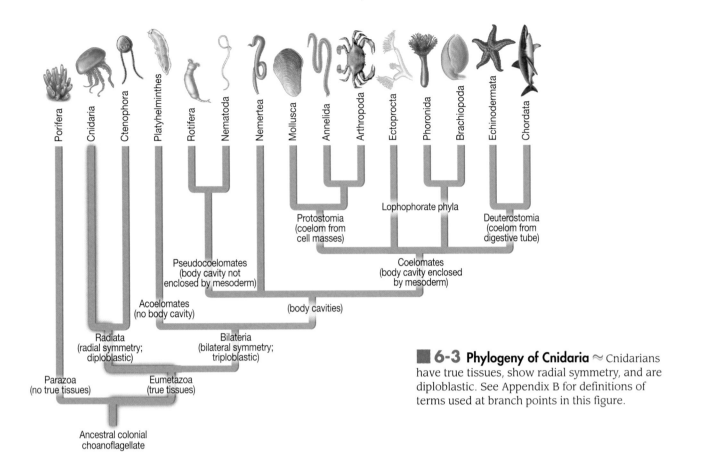

Porifera
Cnidaria
Ctenophora
Platyhelminthes
Rotifera
Nematoda
Nemertea
Mollusca
Annelida
Arthropoda
Ectoprocta
Phoronida
Brachiopoda
Echinodermata
Chordata

Protostomia
(coelom from
cell masses)

Lophophorate phyla

Deuterostomia
(coelom from
digestive tube)

Pseudocoelomates
(body cavity not
enclosed by mesoderm)

Coelomates
(body cavity enclosed
by mesoderm)

Acoelomates
(no body cavity)

(body cavities)

Radiata
(radial symmetry;
diploblastic)

Bilateria
(bilateral symmetry;
triploblastic)

Parazoa
(no true tissues)

Eumetazoa
(true tissues)

Ancestral colonial
choanoflagellate

6-3 Phylogeny of Cnidaria ~ Cnidarians have true tissues, show radial symmetry, and are diploblastic. See Appendix B for definitions of terms used at branch points in this figure.

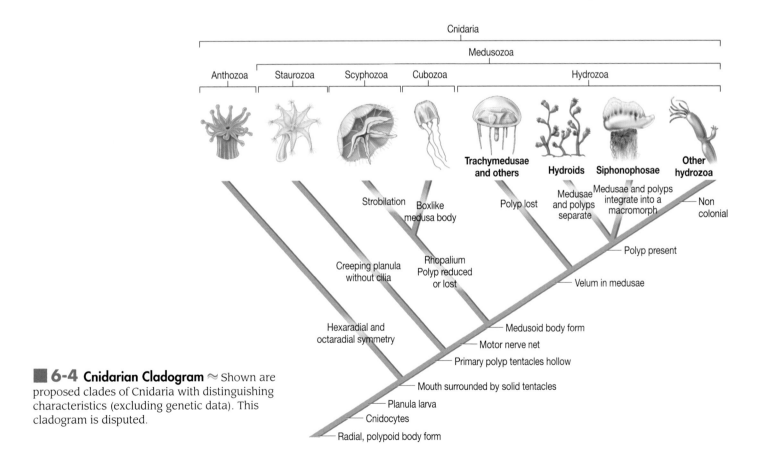

Cnidaria

Medusozoa

Anthozoa
Staurozoa
Scyphozoa
Cubozoa
Hydrozoa

Trachymedusae
and others
Hydroids
Siphonophosae
Other
hydrozoa

Strobilation

Boxlike
medusa body

Polyp lost

Medusae
and polyps
separate

Medusae and polyps
integrate into a
macromorph

Non
colonial

Creeping planula
without cilia

Rhopalium
Polyp reduced
or lost

Polyp present

Velum in medusae

Hexaradial and
octaradial symmetry

Medusoid body form

Motor nerve net

Primary polyp tentacles hollow

Mouth surrounded by solid tentacles

Planula larva

Cnidocytes

Radial, polypoid body form

6-4 Cnidarian Cladogram ~ Shown are proposed clades of Cnidaria with distinguishing characteristics (excluding genetic data). This cladogram is disputed.

though they have a simple nervous system, rely on **cnido-cytes** (*cnide*—nettle, *cyte*—a cell) and their **cnidae** (cell structures that are discharged from the cnidocytes), including the stinging cnidae called **nematocysts** (*nema*—thread, *cyst*—sac), to stun prey prior to engulfing it. Corals and some other cnidarians have symbiotic relationships with Dinoflagellates (zooxanthellae), which, in the case of reef-building corals, provide the majority of their nutrition (Figure 6-5). Cnidarians are most diverse on coral reefs, and stony corals are major contributors to the calcium carbonate structure of the reef itself.

Synapomorphies of the group include the presence of tentacles surrounding the mouth; cnidocytes (Figure 6-6)

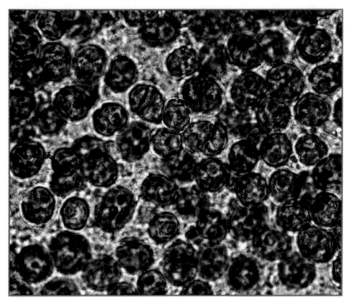

■ 6-5 Endosymbiotic Dinoflagellates ≈ These zooxanthellae are unstained and taken fresh from the tentacles of *Anthopleura xanthogrammica* (Figure 6-8A). Actual size is about 100 μm.

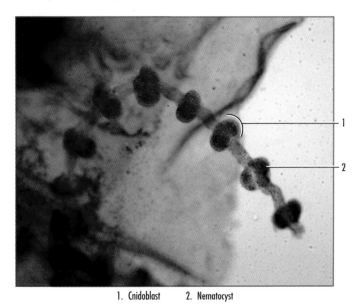

1. Cnidoblast   2. Nematocyst

■ 6-6 *Aurelia* (Whole Mount) ≈ The tentacles and edge of an *Aurelia* are shown with location of cnidocyte and enclosed nematocysts indicated.

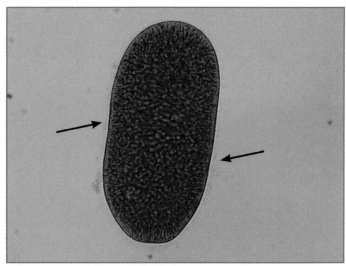

■ 6-7 *Aurelia* Planula Larva ≈ This ciliated planula larva of *Aurelia* is approximately 100 μm in length. Arrows indicate cilia.

(nematocysts and others); and a ciliated **planula larva** (Figure 6-7). They have a hydrostatic skeleton, and an incomplete (blind) digestive tract. Some species are highly motile (e.g., jellyfish), whereas others (e.g., corals) are sessile as adults.

Cnidarians have amazing regenerative abilities useful both for healing and reproduction. Colonial cnidarians, such as corals, typically reproduce asexually via cloning, fission, budding, and fragmentation. Most cnidarian species are **dioecious** (*di*—two, *oikos*—house; that is, separate sexes). The idealized cnidarian life cycle alternates between a sessile polyp and a planktonic medusa body form. **Broadcast spawning** is the norm, and fertilization is external. A ciliated planula larva then develops. The planula may be either **lecithotrophic** (*lecitho*—yolk of an egg, *trophic*—feeder), that feeds off of yolk from the egg or **planktotrophic** (*plankto*—to drift, *trophic*—feeder), generally feeding on phytoplankton and zooplankton. Much variation exists in the cnidarian life cycle, and examples are provided corresponding with the different taxa.

Both morphological and molecular data support the Anthozoa as the sister taxon to the Mesozoa clade composed of the other cnidarian taxa—Scyphozoa, Cubozoa, and Staurozoa. These latter three may be sister taxa to one another, though some phylogenies place the cubozoans and staurozoans within the Scyphozoa. One possible cladogram for the Cnidaria is presented in Figure 6-4.

Anthozoa

The Anthozoa (*anthos*—flower, *zoa*—animal) includes over 6,000 species and is the most diverse group of Cnidaria. The medusa stage has been lost and the flowery polyp form is usually large, conspicuous, and sessile. Sea anemones (Figure 6-8), sea pens (Figure 6-9), sea pansies (Figure 6-10), gorgonians (Figure 6-11), and stony and

Giant green anemone

Metridium algae free

Giant anemone

Corkscrew anemone

Strawberry anemone

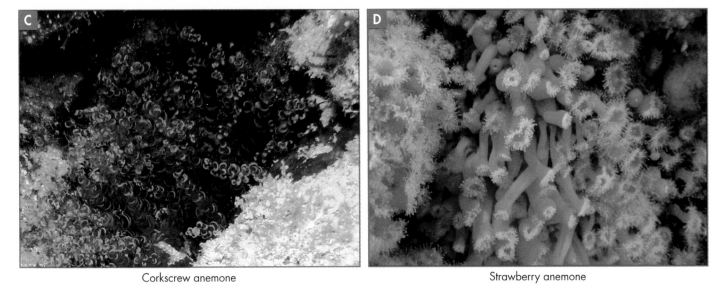

■ **6-8 Anemones (Anthozoa)** ≈ (A) The giant green anemone, *Anthopleura xanthogrammica*, is found in the Northeast Pacific. It may carry endosymbiotic zooxanthellae, as shown on the left, or not, as in the specimen on the right. These anemones measure 15 cm or more across the oral surface. (B) The giant anemone, *Condylactis gigantean,* is a Caribbean species that reaches sizes of about 20 cm across the oral surface. (C) Another, slightly smaller Caribbean species is the corkscrew anemone, *Bartholomea annulata*. It is about 14 cm in diameter. (D) The Northeastern Pacific strawberry anemone, *Corynactis californica*, achieves sizes of about 2 cm across the oral surface. *(continued)*

Brooding anemone

Painted anemone

Aggregate anemone

Orange plumose anemone

Plumose anemone, preserved specimen

Metridium, cross-section

1. Tentacles
2. Mouth (siphonoglyph)
3. Oral disc
4. Pedal disc
5. Pharynx
6. Septum
7. Gastrodermis
8. Epidermis
9. Mesoglea
10. Tertiary septum
11. Gastrovascular cavity
12. Complete septum
13. Retractor muscles

■ **6-8 Anemones (Anthozoa)** *(continued)* ≈ **(E)** The Northeastern Pacific is also home to another small (2 cm) species, the brooding anemone, *Epiactis prolifera*. **(F)** The painted anemone, *Urticina crassicornis,* measures about 9 cm across its oral surface. It is found in the Northeastern Pacific and extreme Northwestern Atlantic. **(G)** The aggregate anemone, *Anthopleura elegantissima,* shown at low tide. Note how this anemone forms large monoclonal colonies and attaches pieces of shells and sand to its outer surface. This material protects the organism at low tide from the drying effects of the sun. **(H)** The Orange plumose anemone, *Metridium farcimen,* grows to 1 m in height. Like many anemones, it can move along the rocky substrate to which it is usually attached. It is found in subtidal and intertidal areas and ranges from Alaska to Southern California. **(I)** (left) This is a preserved specimen of the Plumose anemone, *Metridium.* It is found in the Northern Pacific and Atlantic. This specimen is about 9 cm across its oral surface; (middle and right) Shown are *Metridium* cross section. *(continued)*

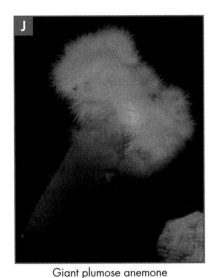

Giant plumose anemone

■ 6-8 Anemones (Anthozoa)

(continued) ≈ (J) The giant plumose anemone, *Metridium giganteum*, is found in the Northern Pacific and Atlantic. It is about 18 cm tall.

■ 6-9 Sea Pen (Anthozoa) ≈ This specimen of *Ptilosarcus gurneyi* is about 22 cm and is found in the Northeastern Pacific. Sea pens are widely distributed in temperate and tropical waters, and consist of multiple polyps, including the secondary polyps that form vanes.

1. Secondary polyps   2. Budding zone   3. Stalk (peduncle, primary polyp)

Kathryn Stephenson Craven, Ph.D., Armstrong Atlantic State University

1. Peduncle

■ 6-10 Sea Pansy (Anthozoa) ≈ *Renilla reniformis* is a resident of sandy habitats of Southern California south to Mexico. Sea pansies principally inhabit temperate to tropical waters and consist of multiple polyps.

other corals (Figure 6-12) are all anthozoans. Polyps typically rely on prey to swim over their tentacles in order to eat, though in most species, the majority of their energy actually comes from carbon-fixing endosymbiotic dinoflagellates (zooxanthellae) or green algae. Tropical corals are important as their skeleton is the calcium carbonate from which reefs are derived, however, corals and anemones and their relatives are found in a range of other habitats as well.

Anthozoa includes both **monoecious** (*mono*—one, *oeci*—house) and dioecious (*di*—two, *oeci*—house) species (sexes are separate). Asexual reproduction is common in coral colonies. Spawning is usually a once-a-year coordinated event, and fertilization is external. Planula larvae develop from the zygote and eventually settle out on hard substrate and metamorphose into a polyp. See Figure 6-13 for a representative coral life cycle.

A

B

Bipinnate sea plume

C

Encrusting gorgonian

D

Sea fans

Yellow gorgonian

■ **6-11 Gorgonians (Anthozoa)** ≈ (A) The sea fan, *Gorgonia ventalina*, occurs in the Caribbean and coastal Florida where specimens grow to 35 cm across. (B) The bipinnate sea plume, *Pseudopterogorgia bipinnata*, reaches about 60 cm in height in the Western Atlantic. (C) Encrusting gorgonians, *Erythropodium caribaeorum*, occur in the Western Atlantic where they reach about 45 cm in height. (D) Yellow gorgonians, *Diodogorgia nodulifera*, occur in the Western Atlantic. This specimen is about 25 cm. *(continued)*

Shelf-knob sea rod

California golden gorgonian

Black sea rod

Split-pore sea rod

Porous sea rod

Swiftia
1. Coral polyp   2. Tentacle

■ **6-11 Gorgonians (Anthozoa)** ≈ *(continued)* (E) Shelf-knob sea rod, *Eunicea succinea*, occurs in the Gulf of Mexico and the Caribbean. This specimen measures 100 cm plus. (F) The California golden gorgonian, *Muricea californica*, grows throughout the Northeastern Pacific. (G) Black sea rod, *Plexaura homomalla*, is a Caribbean species. This specimen is 100 cm. (H) Split-pore sea rod, *Plexaurella* spp., occurs in the Western Atlantic with specimens to 100 cm. (I) Porous sea rod, *Pseudoplexaura* spp., is another Caribbean species. This specimen is 1.2 m. (J) Note tentacles extended on this *Swiftia* sp.

Elkhorn coral

Mushroom coral

Pillar coral

Lettuce coral

Knobby brain coral

■ **6-12 Corals (Anthozoa)** ~ **(A)** Elkhorn coral, *Acropora palmatem*, is a Caribbean species that may grow to 3.7 meters across. This specimen is about 2.1 m. **(B)** Mushroom coral, *Actinodiscus*, occurs across the Indo-Pacific and South Pacific. A single disk of this species about 3.5 cm in diameter. **(C)** Pillar coral, *Dendrogyra cylindrus*, is another Caribbean species. The specimen to the left is about 1.5 m, the one in the middle 50 cm, and the one to the right is about 30 cm high. **(D)** Lettuce coral, *Agaricia*, occurs in the Western Central Atlantic. This specimen is 30 cm across. **(E)** Knobby brain coral, *Diploria clivosa*, occurs in the Caribbean. The specimen shown is 35 cm across. *(continued)*

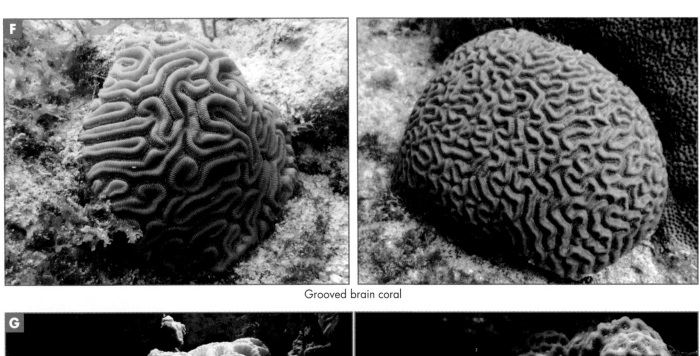

Grooved brain coral

Honeycomb coral

Disk or plate coral

Flower pot coral

■ **6-12 Corals (Anthozoa)** ≈ *(continued)* (**F**) Grooved brain coral, *Diploria labyrinthiformis*, is a Caribbean species. The specimen to the left is 30 cm and the specimen to the right is 60 cm across. (**G**) Honeycomb coral, *Favites abdita*, occurs in the Indo-Pacific. The specimen to the left is 14 cm and the specimen to the right is 50 cm across. (**H**) Disk or plate coral, *Fungia*, occurs in the Indo-Pacific. This specimen is 13 cm. (**I**) Flower pot coral, *Goniopora*, is a South Pacific species. The specimen shown is 14 cm. *(continued)*

Toadstool leather coral

Ten-ray star coral

Mazed brain coral

Great star coral

Button polyp

■ **6-12 Corals (Anthozoa)** ~ *(continued)* (J) Toadstool leather coral, *Sarcophyton*, lives in the Indo-Pacific. The specimen on the left is 35 cm and the specimen in the middle is 40 cm across. (K) Ten-ray star coral, *Madracis decactis*, is a Western Atlantic species. This specimen is 45 cm across. (L) Mazed brain coral, *Meandrina meandrites*, lives in the Caribbean. The specimen is 30 cm. (M) Great star coral, *Montastraea cavernosa*, principally occurs in the Western Atlantic. (N) Button polyp, *Palythoa*, is an Indo-Pacific species. This individual is about 3 cm in diameter. *(continued)*

Slipper coral

Clubtip finger coral

Stony coral

■ **6-12 Corals (Anthozoa)** ≈ *(continued)* (**O**) Slipper coral, *Polyphyllia talpina*, occurs in the Indo-Pacific and Western Pacific. (**P**) Clubtip finger coral, *Porites porites*, is a Caribbean species. This specimen is approximately 45 cm across. (**Q**) *Euphyllia* sp. are large polyped Indo-Pacific stony corals. They begin adult life as solitary polyps that grow into mound-like colonies. They are uncommon in the wild but are commonly collected for saltwater aquarists. Clownfish may be found in association with these corals.

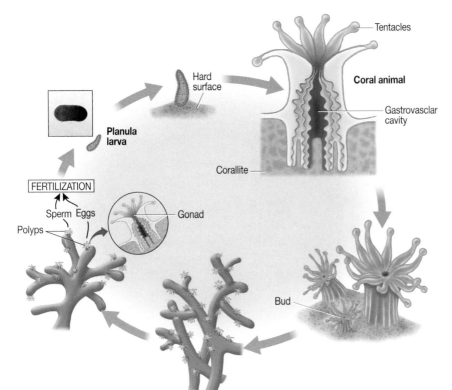

Tentacles

Hard surface

Planula larva

Coral animal

Gastrovasclar cavity

Corallite

FERTILIZATION

Sperm Eggs

Polyps

Gonad

Bud

■ **6-13 Generalized Coral Life Cycle** ≈ There is great variety in coral life cycles. The ability to reproduce both sexually and asexually is common. Different species may be monoecious or dioecious. In addition, many species release eggs and sperm into the water where fertilization occurs, leading to the planula larva. Others retain their eggs where they are fertilized from sperm released into the water. The planula larvae settle where they develop into a coral polyp. The polyp (corallite) forms the calcium carbonate skeleton. Asexual budding forms additional corallites, which merge to form the colonial shape. As the colony enlarges, some polyps form reproductive organs producing egg and/or sperm and the life cycle repeats.

Scyphozoa and Cubozoa

Cubozoa (*cubo*—a cube, *zoa*—animal) are included with the Scyphozoa (*scypho*—a cup) in this discussion. Together they include approximately 200 species. Scyphozoans (*skyphos*—cup-shaped, *zoa*—animal) include animals commonly called "jellyfish." They have reduced, tapering polyps, or lack a polyp stage altogether, and the medusa (jellyfish) is the dominant stage (Figure 6-14). Characteristic of scyphozoans are **rhopalia** (Figure 6-16)—sensory organs—located around the base of their bell's margin (umbrella-shaped portion of body). Rhopalia are capable of sensing vibrations, scent, light, and gravity.

The 20 species of box jellies (Figure 6-15) inhabit warm water, have a distinct square **velum** with a ring of tissue (**velarium**) constricting the opening, and possess highly poisonous nematocysts. The extremely venomous Australian Irukandji box jelly, *Carukia barnesi*, is tiny (12 to 20 mm) but mighty; it produces a sting strong enough to kill humans! Cubozoans also have relatively complex eyes with lenses, corneas, and retinas.

Medusae are typically responsible for the sexual portion of the life cycle, and polyps, called **scyphistomae**, produce juvenile medusae asexually during a process called strobilation. The medusae, freed from the differentiating scyphistomae are called **ephyrae**. The ephyra develops into an adult medusa, which is either male or female. Figure 6-16 shows the life cycle of *Aurelia* and representative species.

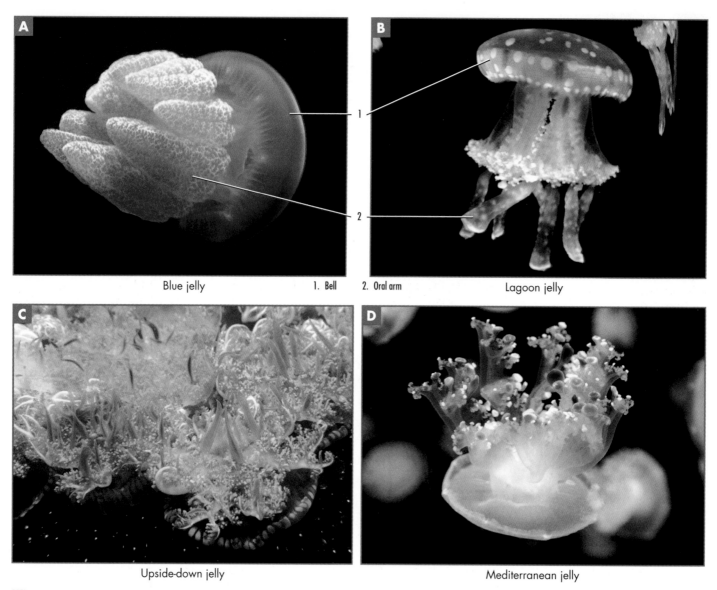

Blue jelly   1. Bell   2. Oral arm   Lagoon jelly

Upside-down jelly   Mediterranean jelly

■ **6-14 Sea Jellies (Scyphozoa)** ≈ (A) Blue jelly, *Catostylus mosaicus*, is an Indo-Pacific species. The specimen shown is about 30 cm. (B) Lagoon jelly, *Mastigias papua*, lives in the Central and Southern Pacific and Caribbean. (C) Upside-down jelly, *Cassiopea frondosa*, lives in the Caribbean and is abundant along the Florida coast. This specimen is about 12 cm. (D) The Mediterranean jelly, *Cotylorhiza tuberculata*, surprisingly lives in the Mediterranean and connected seas. This specimen is about 13 cm. *(continued)*

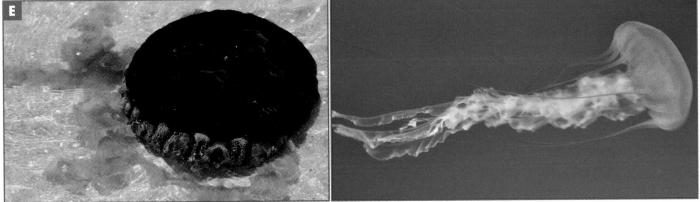

Black sea nettle

■ **6-14** **Sea Jellies (Scyphozoa)** ≈ *(continued)* (**E**) The black sea nettle, *Chrysaora achlyos*, occurs the Northeastern Pacific. The specimen on left is 60 cm across and is in excess of 2 m in length. The specimen on the right is about 60 cm in length.

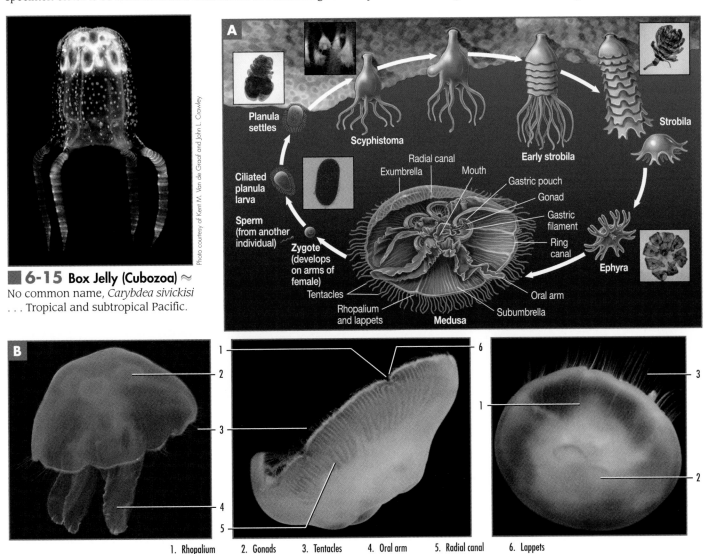

■ **6-15** **Box Jelly (Cubozoa)** ≈
No common name, *Carybdea sivickisi*
. . . Tropical and subtropical Pacific.

1. Rhopalium   2. Gonads   3. Tentacles   4. Oral arm   5. Radial canal   6. Lappets

■ **6-16** ***Aurelia* Life Cycle** ≈ (**A**) Moon jelly, *Aurelia* sp. . . . Throughout the world's oceans, but generally tropical and subtropical. Although this is a representative scyphozoan life cycle, there is a lot of variation between species. The *Aurelia* life cycle is well studied, indicating that sexes are separate with the zygote developing on the fleshy oral arms of the egg-producing individuals. Scyphistoma may reproduce asexually by budding, allowing for individuals to continue to produce new adult medusa forms for years. (**B**) Moon jelly, *Aurelia* sp. (left) The oral arms and tentacles can be seen hanging from the medusa of this individual. Gonads and radial canals can be seen through this translucent umbrella. Moon jelly, *Aurelia* sp. (middle) Tentacles and radial canals are visible in this individual. Note the rhopalium (seen as indentations around the umbrella) and lappets, the bumps of tissue around the rhopalium. These thickened ridges assist in the bell's contraction. Moon jelly, *Aurelia* sp. (right) Tentacles, radial canals, and gonads are visible in this individual.

Hydrozoa

Hydrozoa includes the only freshwater cnidarians, however almost all hydrozoans are marine. Examples of this diverse marine taxon include: hydroids (Figure 6-17), fire corals, and siphonophores such as the Portuguese Man-o-War, bell jelly (*Polyorchis penicillatus*, Figure 6-18A) and the by-the-wind-sailor (*Velella velella*, Figure 6-18B). There are approximately 3,500 extant hydrozoans. Hydrozoans are typically colonial, but differ from other cnidarians in that the colonies of some species are composed of both medusae and polyps (Figure 6-19A). Polyps (Figures 6-19 and 6-20) and medusae (Figure 6-21) are relatively small; most polyps are no larger than 1 mm and medusae are generally less than a few centimeters. Additionally, many species lack a medusa stage, while others lack a polyp stage. Life cycles vary, but characteristic of Hydrozoa, new medusae bud laterally from polyps or from a portion of the colony. The hydrozoan nematocysts (Figure 6-22) are the most diverse of the Cnidaria.

Clytia bakeri

1. Hydroid   2. Bean clam

Ostrich-plume hydroid

■ **6-17 Hydroids (Hydrozoa)** ≈ (**A**) *Clytia bakeri* has no common name. It occurs in the Northeastern Pacific in subtropical to temperate waters. This specimen is approximately 2 cm from attachment point to top of colony. (**B**) Ostrich-plume hydroid, *Aglaophenia struthionides*, occurs in the Eastern Pacific. This specimen is about 7 cm from base to apex.

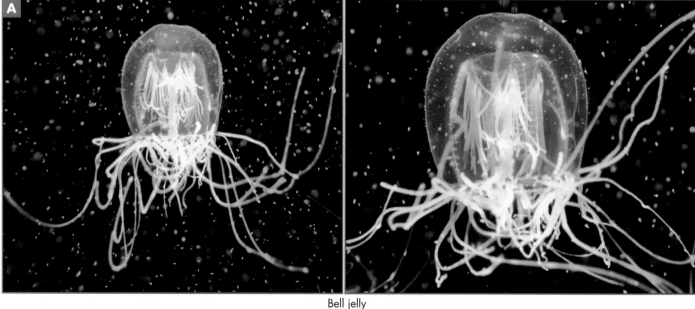

Bell jelly

■ **6-18 Siphonophores (Hydrozoa)** ≈ (**A**) Bell jelly, *Polyorchis penicillatus*, occurs in the Northeastern Pacific. This specimen is about 3 cm across. *(continued)*

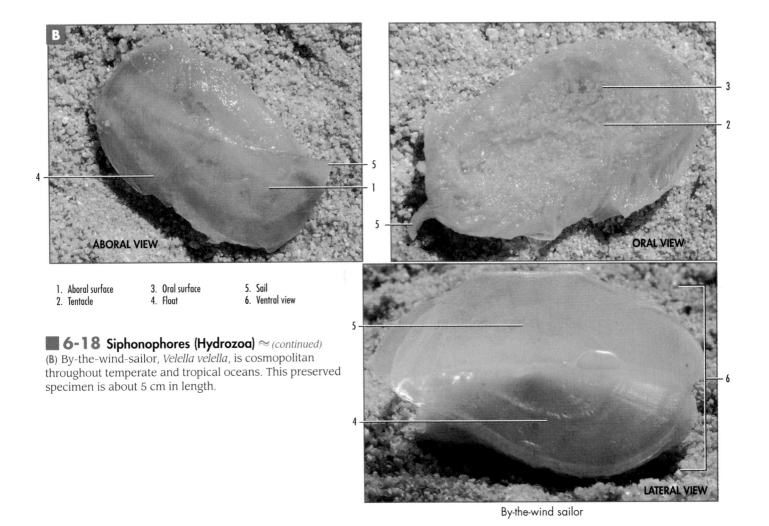

1. Aboral surface   3. Oral surface   5. Sail
2. Tentacle   4. Float   6. Ventral view

■ **6-18 Siphonophores (Hydrozoa)** ≈ *(continued)*
(B) By-the-wind-sailor, *Velella velella*, is cosmopolitan throughout temperate and tropical oceans. This preserved specimen is about 5 cm in length.

By-the-wind sailor

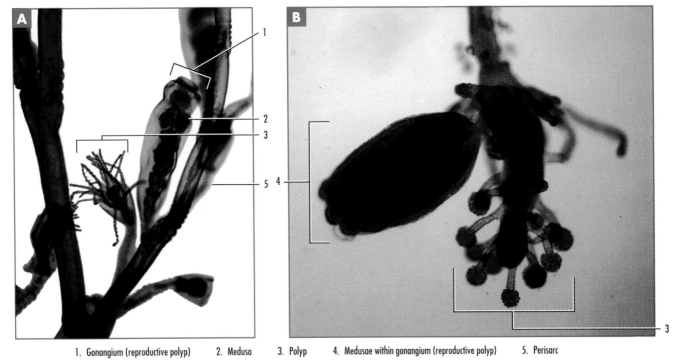

1. Gonangium (reproductive polyp)   2. Medusa   3. Polyp   4. Medusae within gonangium (reproductive polyp)   5. Perisarc

■ **6-19 Medusa and Polyp Forms (Hydrozoa)** ≈ Both of these micrographs are of whole mount specimens. **(A)** *Obelia*, is cosmopolitan throughout the world's coastal oceans. Both medusa and polyp forms are shown. Medusae are present as buds within an asexually reproducing gonangium. **(B)** *Pennaria*, is cosmopolitan throughout the world's coastal oceans.

1. Cnidoblast   2. Tentacle   3. Polyp

■ **6-20 Polyps (Hydrozoa)** ≈ Both of these are micrographs of whole mount specimens. **(A)** This is an *Obelia* polyp. **(B)** This is *Pennaria's* polyp form.

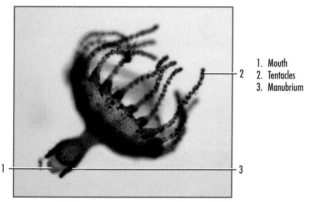

1. Mouth
2. Tentacles
3. Manubrium

■ **6-21 Medusa (Hydrozoa)** ≈ The *Obelia* medusa is shown. During preparation of this microscope slide, the medusa umbrella turns inside out, hence the tentacles do not surround the mouth in the photomicrograph.

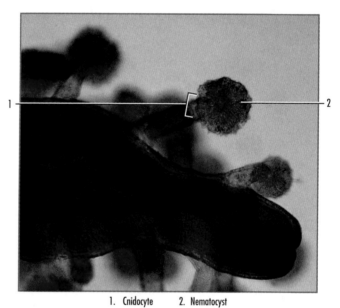

1. Cnidocyte   2. Nematocyst

■ **6-22 Nematocysts (Hydrozoa)** ≈ Nematocysts are visible within the cnidocyte of this *Pennaria*.

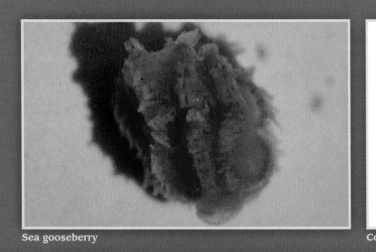
Sea gooseberry

Comb jelly

7 Ctenophora

Members of Ctenophora (*ktenos*—a comb *phoros*—bearing), the comb jellies are important marine predators (Table 7-1 and Figure 7-1). Most ctenophores are planktonic, and individuals have been found throughout the world's oceans. Some nearshore species bloom during spring and fall, following the increase of prey species. There are thought to be 100–150 species of comb jellies. Ctenophores display two planes of radial symmetry, each perpendicular longitudinally to one another. Most comb jellies, though nearly transparent, are bioluminescent. Many are very fragile, making it difficult to collect specimens for study. Since the 1980s, species of *Mnemiopsis* have been accidentally transported by shipping and become invasive in the Caspian, Black, Azov, Mediterranean, North, and Baltic Seas, and *Beroe ovata* has been found in the Caspian Sea.

The general body form for ctenophores varies greatly. However, the group is characterized by eight longitudinal bands of cilia in short rows, called **comb rows**, or **ctenes** (Figures 7-2, 7-3 and 7-4), that move synchronously and function in propulsion. Other planktonic species flap wing-like lobes to soar through the water and some benthic species rely instead on musculature to move their bodies in waves along the seafloor. Most ctenophores capture plankton with sticky **colloblast cells** (collocytes) (*kolla*—glue, *blastos*—bud; producer) situated on two long tentacles

■ Table **7-1** ≈ Ctenophoran Classes

Class	General Description	Examples	Approximate Number of Species	Etymology
Tentaculata (Figures 7-2, 7-3 and 7-4)	Highly variable between species, but all with long contractile tentacles of different length	*Pleurobrachia, Mnemiopsis, Cestum* and *Leucothea*	125	*tenere*—hold
Nuda	Similar in morphology to Tentaculata but without tentacles	*Beroe* and *Neis*	25	*nudus*—naked

located on the aboral (*ab*—away from, *os*—mouth) end, though others have adapted ctenes that function as a biting, tooth-like structure. The mouth is located at one end (oral) and two anal pores, opening to the exterior, are located at the aboral end. Ctenophores eat zooplankton: crustaceans, larvae, and other ctenophores. Most comb jellies range in size from a few millimeters to a few centimeters, though *Cestum* is as large at 1.5 m.

The majority of comb jellies are **holoplanktonic** (plankton for their entire life) and reproduce sexually, though asexual fragmentation is common to the benthic platyctenids (an order of comb jellies that are benthic, living on rocks, algae, or the body of other invertebrates). Fertilization is external, and the larva develops into either a

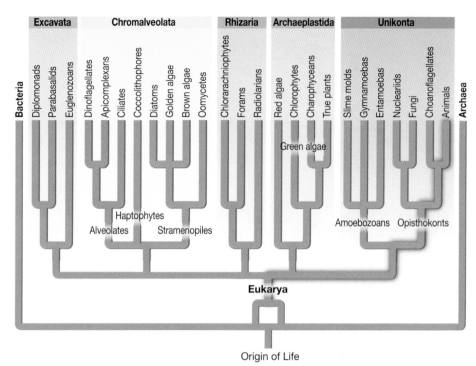

■ 7-1 Phylogeny of the Three Domains of Life ≈ This is a proposed phylogeny of life first presented as Figure 1-1. Note the position of the Animalia second from the right at top. See Appendix A for definitions of terms, clades, and taxa in this figure.

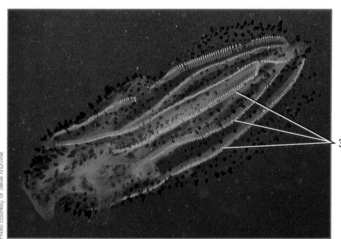

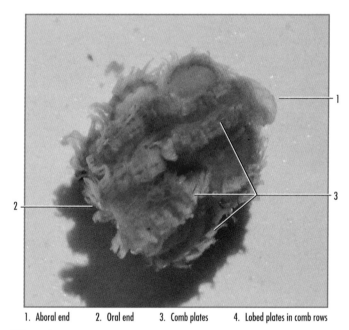

1. Aboral end   2. Oral end   3. Comb plates   4. Lobed plates in comb rows

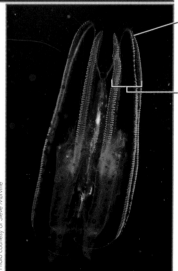

■ 7-2 Comb Jelly (Ctenophora) ≈ The comb rows (ctenes) are visible in *Leucothea pulchra*, a common ctenophoran in the Northeastern Pacific. This is a lobate ctenophore, meaning it is a member of the Order Lobata and has two muscular lobes. These can be seen in the photo to the right.

■ 7-3 *Pleurobrachia* spp. (Ctenophora) ≈ This preserved Cydippida ctenophore is widely used in biology classes and is a common predator in coastal areas of the Northeastern Pacific with 11 known species. Commonly called the sea gooseberry.

planktonic adult (most species), or settles to the seafloor if a benthic species. Most species are hermaphroditic, and *Mnemiopsis* has been shown to be able to self-fertilize.

At first ctenophores might seem to resemble the gelatinous Cnidaria, sharing some developmental traits with them. Historically, the two groups were classified together as Phylum Coelenterata. However, various lines of evidence, including molecular, indicate that they are actually quite different from one another. Unsurprisingly, the exact placement of Ctenophora within the animal phylogeny has not yet been resolved. Some researchers now suggest that the presence of anal pores and the apparent presence of a type of mesoderm may link Ctenophora as the sister taxon to the Bilateria (Figure 7-5), rather than in a diploblastic clade with Cnidaria (Figure 7-6).

■ **7-4 Living Sea Gooseberry** ∼ A living sea gooseberry, *Pleurobranchia brachei*, shows the tentacles typical of Tentaculata. Tentacles extend and contract as the individual moves about its environment. They have eight rows of combs and light is refracted from them giving the false appearance of bioluminescence. Sea gooseberries are found in surface waters near shore and in the open ocean to depth. They occur worldwide.

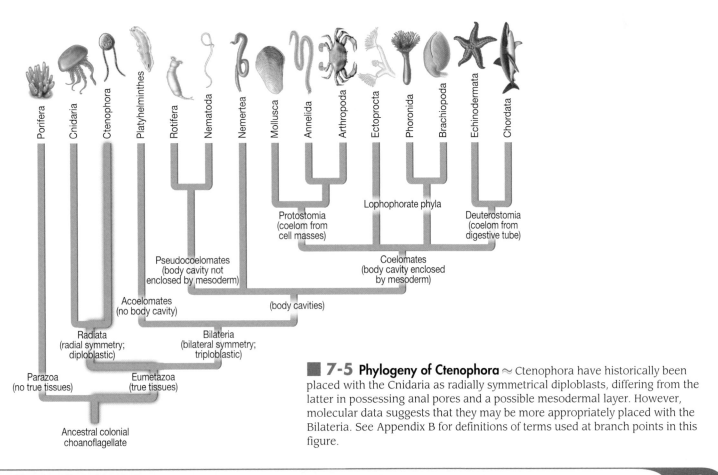

■ **7-5 Phylogeny of Ctenophora** ∼ Ctenophora have historically been placed with the Cnidaria as radially symmetrical diploblasts, differing from the latter in possessing anal pores and a possible mesodermal layer. However, molecular data suggests that they may be more appropriately placed with the Bilateria. See Appendix B for definitions of terms used at branch points in this figure.

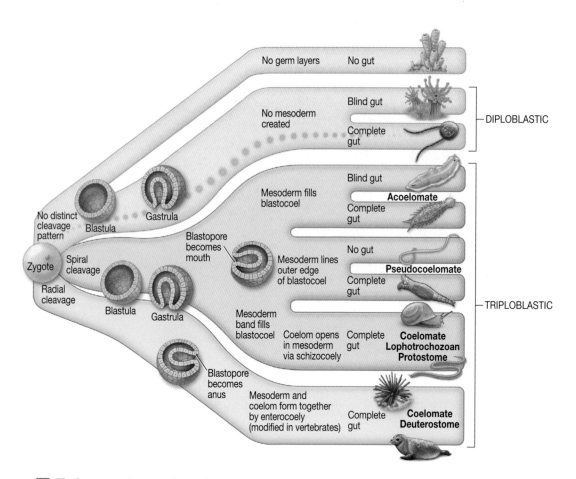

No germ layers   No gut

No mesoderm created   Blind gut   Complete gut

DIPLOBLASTIC

No distinct cleavage pattern

Blastula

Gastrula

Zygote

Spiral cleavage

Radial cleavage

Blastula   Gastrula

Blastopore becomes mouth

Mesoderm fills blastocoel   Blind gut   **Acoelomate**   Complete gut

Mesoderm lines outer edge of blastocoel   No gut   **Pseudocoelomate**   Complete gut

Mesoderm band fills blastocoel

Coelom opens in mesoderm via schizocoely   Complete gut   **Coelomate Lophotrochozoan Protostome**

Blastopore becomes anus

Mesoderm and coelom form together by enterocoely (modified in vertebrates)   Complete gut   **Coelomate Deuterostome**

TRIPLOBLASTIC

■ **7-6 General Animal Developmental Patterns** ∼ The Ctenophora show radial symmetry with no distinct cleavage pattern during development. They differ from the Cnidaria in having a complete digestive tract (i.e., both mouth and anus are present).

Echiridium (no common name)

Notoplana (no common name)

8 Platyhelminthes

Platyhelminths (*platy*—flat, *helminths*—worm) are unsegmented flatworms. There are approximately 25,000 species found in a myriad of habitats. The group is diverse, including the free-living, paraphyletic Turbellaria (*turbell*—stir, *aria*—like) (Figures 8-1, 8-2, 8-3, and 8-4), the mostly endoparasitic flukes (Trematoda), the primarily ectoparasitic monogenetic flukes (Monogenea), and the solely endoparasitic tapeworms (Cestoda) (Table 8-1). There is not a single synapomorphy that unites this group, and some researchers argue this phylum is not monophyletic. Because of this and other unresolved issues associated with the validity of this clade, and because the free-living flatworms are those most commonly encountered by the intertidal explorer and scuba diver, only the turbellarians are described in this chapter. However, all classes have marine members.

The flatworms are triploblastic, display cephalization (*cephal*—head), lack a circulatory system, and are bilaterally symmetrical. They are acoelomate and lack a circulatory system or hard outer covering (**cuticle**) (Figures 8-5 and 8-6). Turbellarians have an incomplete gut with a pharynx of variable location depending on the species. Most also have at least one flattened surface and a ciliated epidermis. Small worms use cilia for movement, but larger worms use muscles for crawling and swimming.

Flatworms can reproduce asexually by transverse or longitudinal fission, budding, or more rarely, self-fertilization. Almost all turbellarians are hermaphroditic and development is *direct* (no larval stage). However, some larger species have a feeding larval stage. Typically, turbellarians cross-fertilize one another.

The approximately 4,500 species of turbellarians are predominantly marine and most are tiny, typically only a few millimeters, but some can attain lengths of up to 50 cm. Most are meiofaunal (living between grains of sand) predators of other small invertebrates, or detritivores and are found abundantly within nearshore sediments or crevices on reefs and rocky shores. A few turbellarians are pelagic carnivores, some are symbiotic with other organisms (*Bdelloura candida* is a parasite on the horseshoe crab, *Limulus polyphemus*), and some possess zooxanthellae.

The phylogeny for the platyhelminths has not yet been resolved. Figure 8-5 illustrates a possible phylogeny and shows the placement of Platyhelminthes within Animalia.

■ 8-1 *Notoplana acticola* (Turbellaria) ≈ Also known as *Notocomplana acticola*, this turbellarian is fairly common in the rocky intertidal habitats of California. This specimen is about 3 cm. Note the two dark eyespots on the anterior end (arrow).

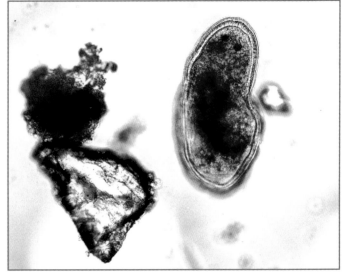

■ 8-2 *Enchiridium punctatum* (Turbellaria) ≈ This turbellarian has a ventral, posterior sucker. Although this individual is about 2 cm, members of this species have been reported up to 4 cm by 1 cm in size.

■ 8-3 Flatworm (Turbellaria) ≈ This photograph is of an unidentified turbellarian found in a littoral sample. The object in the lower left corner is a grain of sand.

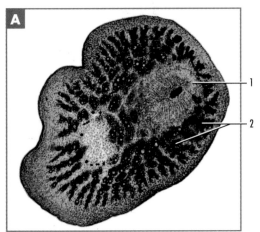

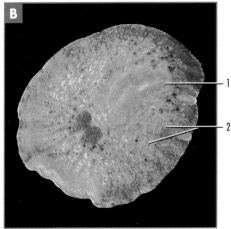

■ 8-4 Flatworm (Turbellaria) ≈ These micrographs are of an unidentified flatworm found living in a mixed sandy-rocky intertidal habitat. (**A**) In this light micrograph, the multiple branches of the gastro-vascular cavity are visible, as is the muscular pharynx. (**B**) This is a dark field micrograph of the same individual. It measured approximately 500 μm in length.

1. Muscular pharynx
2. Branches of gastrovascular cavity

Class	General Description	Examples	Approximate Number of Species	Etymology
Turbellaria (Figures 8-1 through 8-4)	Most free-living; ciliated external covering; ventral mouth; acoelomate	*Pseudobicerosi, Alloioplana,* and *Notoplana*	4,500	*turbell*—stir, *aria*—connected with
Trematoda	Most parasitic; no ciliated external covering; usually with suckers for attachment and feeding; cylindrical or leaf shaped	*Aspidogaster, Cotylogaster,* and *Lobatostoma*	18,000	*trema*—having holes, *toda*—form
Monogenea	All parasitic and most ectoparasites; no ciliated external covering; attachment organ with hooks	*Gyrodactylus, Dactylogyrus,* and *Neobenedenia*	1,000	*mono*—one, *gene*—origin
Cestoda	Tapeworms; anterior end with suckers and/or hooks; body usually in a series of segments	*Bothriocephalus* and *Diphyllobothrium*	1,000	*cest*—girdle, *toda*—form

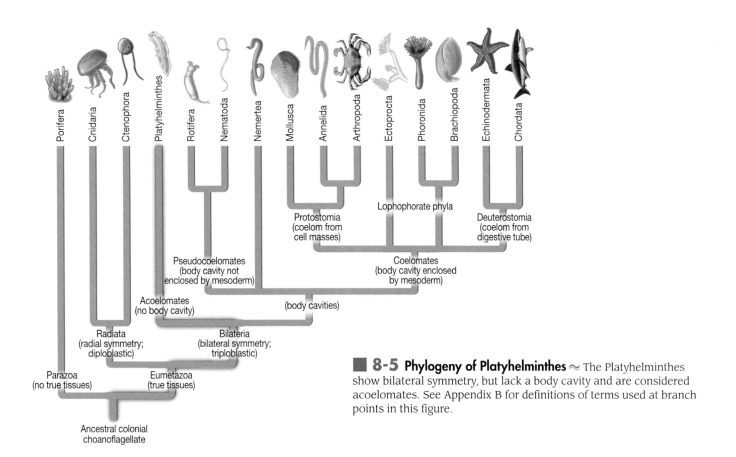

■ **8-5 Phylogeny of Platyhelminthes** ~ The Platyhelminthes show bilateral symmetry, but lack a body cavity and are considered acoelomates. See Appendix B for definitions of terms used at branch points in this figure.

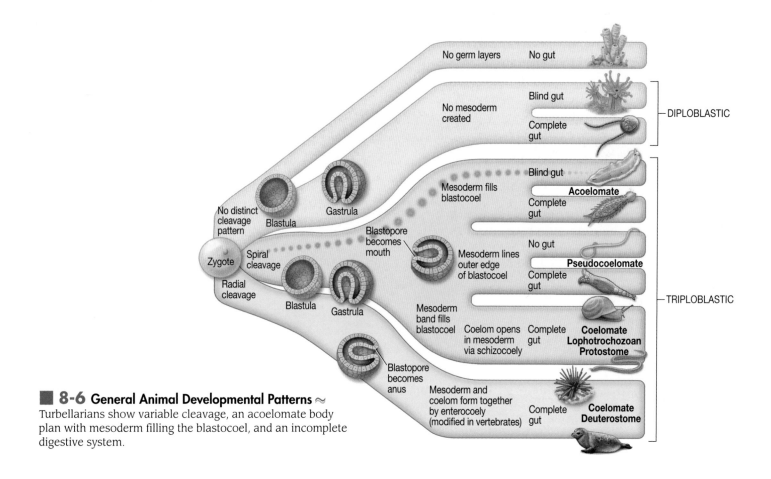

No germ layers — No gut

No mesoderm created — Blind gut / Complete gut — DIPLOBLASTIC

Zygote

No distinct cleavage pattern — Blastula — Gastrula

Spiral cleavage

Radial cleavage — Blastula — Gastrula

Blastopore becomes mouth

Mesoderm fills blastocoel — Blind gut / Complete gut — **Acoelomate**

Mesoderm lines outer edge of blastocoel — No gut / Complete gut — **Pseudocoelomate**

Mesoderm band fills blastocoel — Coelom opens in mesoderm via schizocoely — Complete gut — **Coelomate Lophotrochozoan Protostome**

Blastopore becomes anus

Mesoderm and coelom form together by enterocoely (modified in vertebrates) — Complete gut — **Coelomate Deuterostome**

TRIPLOBLASTIC

■ **8-6** General Animal Developmental Patterns ≈

Turbellarians show variable cleavage, an acoelomate body plan with mesoderm filling the blastocoel, and an incomplete digestive system.

Lacy Bryozoan

Lacy Bryozoan

9 Ectoprocta

Ectoprocts (*ecto*—outside, *proct*—anus) (Table 9-1), also called bryozoans (*bryo*—moss, *zoa*—animal) or moss animals, are small, colonial, encrusting animals. There are approximately 4,500 species of ectoprocts, the vast majority of which are found in marine, benthic environments; however, a few are found in freshwater. Extant species are typically low, inconspicuous, and encrusting on rocks, algae and other solid objects (Figure 9-1), or plant-like, and less commonly, lacy and upright (Figure 9-2). Coloration ranges from whitish or beige to bright hues such as orange and red. Ecologically, Ectoprocta (bryozoa) compete for space with other encrusting organisms and are preyed upon by urchins and grazing fish. They can, at times, be considered a fouling organism and become a nuisance, growing out of control on structures such as piers and boat hulls. Natural products chemistry researchers recently have become interested in ectoprocts. The compound Bryostatin 1, isolated from *Bugula neritina*, has been shown to inhibit cancer cell proliferation and is also being tested for its antidepressant qualities.

■ Table **9-1** ≈ Ectoproct Classes

Class	General Description	Examples	Approximate Number of Species	Etymology
Stenolaemata	Individuals are tubular in shape with calcified walls and no operculum; mineralized external skeleton	*Batostoma, Crisia, Diaperoforma*, and *Tubulipor*	500	*steno*—narrow, *laemo*—throat
Gymnolaemata (Figures 9-1 and 9-2)	Individuals are flattened or cylindrical in shape; operculum in some, not in others; mineralized or chitinous external skeleton; this class contains the majority of the bryozoans.	*Bugula neritina, Diaperoforma, Celleporella*, and *Membranipora*	4,000	*gymno*—naked, *laemo*—throat
Phylactolaemata (Figure 9-3)	Only freshwater species; all species have only one zooid form: the feeding form known as an autozooids	*Cristatella, Lophopodelia*, and *Lophopus*	20	*phylacto*—guard, *laemata*—depths of the sea

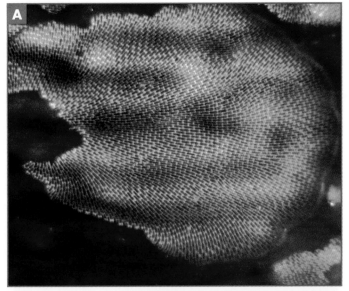

■ **9-1** *Membranipora membrancea (Ectoprocta)* ≈
(A) *Membranipora membrancea* is a bryozoan widely distributed throughout the Pacific and Atlantic Oceans. Typically, this species is found on kelp or other intertidal algae, but it may be found on rocks and other objects. (B) Shown are *Membranipora membrancea* zooecia encrusted on the stipe of *Macrocystis*.

■ **9-2** Bryozoans as Part of a Fouling Community
(Ectoprocta) ≈ (A) A variety of bryozoans, worms, sponges, and other invertebrates are fouling this pier piling. Note the lobate, unidentified bryozoan. (B) A closer view of the same bryozoan shown in (A). The openings into the zoecium of individual zooids are visible. The lophophore is extended for feeding through these openings.

Adult ectoproct colonies are generally sessile (*sessil*—to sit), though a few species are motile. Each **zooid** (individual organism in the colony) uses a **lophophore**—ciliated tentacles surrounding the mouth (Figure 9-3)—to capture microplankton via suspension feeding. The lophophore (*loph*–a crest or ridge, *phor*–to bear) is capable of being retracted into the trunk and in some species is covered with an **operculum** (*oper*—lid, *ulum*—diminutive suffix) when retracted. Ectoprocta means "anus outside"; in this group the anus of the U-shaped digestive tract opens up just below the mouth and under the base of the lophophore (Figure 9-3). The zooid epidermis secretes an organic or mineral exoskeleton called the **zooecium**. Similar to colonial

corals, zooids are connected by tissue but live independently. However, in some species, zooids are polymorphic, and are specialized for different functions within the colony. Zooids are approximately half a millimeter in length and colonies can range from a few millimeters to several centimeters.

Most ectoprocts are hermaphroditic, though maturity of male and female reproductive organs is usually not simultaneous, thus minimizing the possibility of self-fertilization. Reproduction also occurs asexually by budding. Most species are brooders (retaining eggs within the coelom or within a specialized brood chamber), though some are broadcast spawners (releasing a large number of gametes

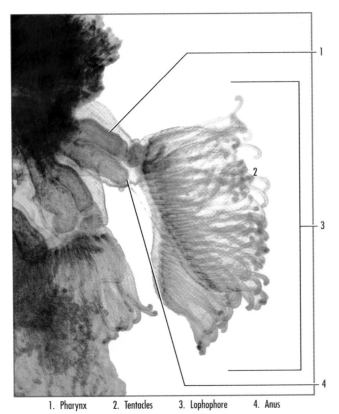

1. Pharynx   2. Tentacles   3. Lophophore   4. Anus

■ **9-3 Lophophore** ≈ The tentacles of this *Cristatella* are visible in this whole mount photomicrograph of a lophophore in feeding position. The lophophore, pharynx, and anus are all visible.

into the water). Larval forms are quite diverse in the ectoprocts in terms of morphology but all possess a ciliated corona (*corona*—crown) that aids in locomotion. Some are planktotrophic (feed on plankton) and some are lecithotrophic (feed on yolk). Larvae eventually settle on substrate or sediment, develop into a zooid (individual), and begin growth of a new colony.

As lophophorates, ectoprocts are grouped together in a clade with Phoronids, Brachiopods, and other Lophotrochozoans, though the exact relationships between taxa have not been resolved. See Figure 9-4 for one possible phylogeny depicting the relationship of Lophotrochozoa within Animalia and Figure 9-5 for its developmental pattern. Table 9-1 lists the three main groups of Ectoprocta found in marine habitats: Phylactolaemata, Stenolaemata (with calcified zooid walls), and Gymnolaemata (with flattened and cylindrical zooids). A cladogram showing proposed relationships within the Lophotrochozoa is shown in Figure 9-6.

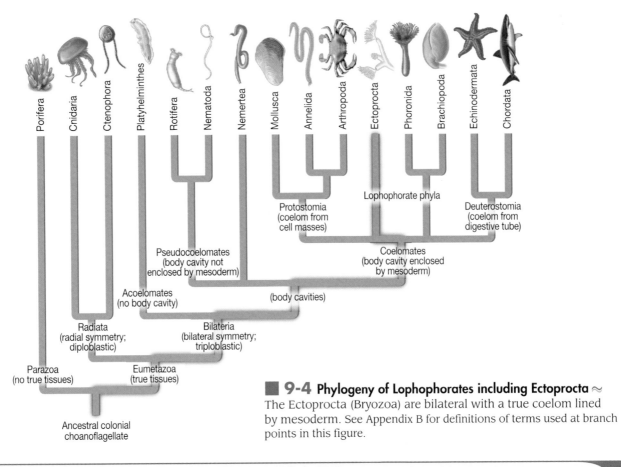

■ **9-4 Phylogeny of Lophophorates including Ectoprocta** ≈ The Ectoprocta (Bryozoa) are bilateral with a true coelom lined by mesoderm. See Appendix B for definitions of terms used at branch points in this figure.

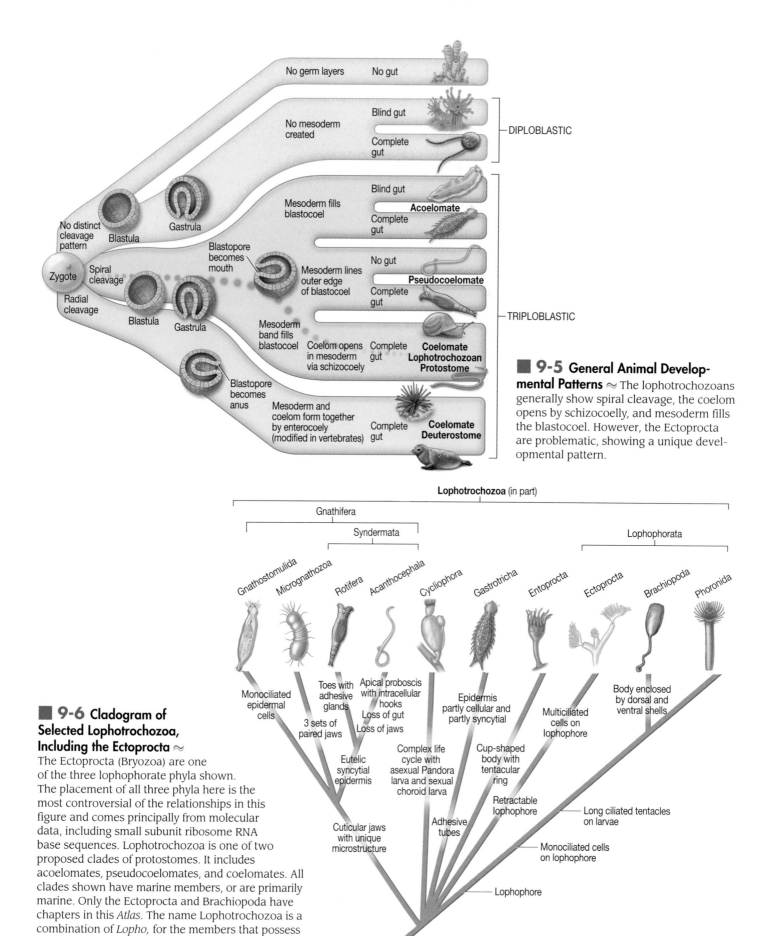

No germ layers   No gut

No mesoderm created

Blind gut

Complete gut

DIPLOBLASTIC

No distinct cleavage pattern

Zygote

Blastula

Gastrula

Spiral cleavage

Radial cleavage

Blastula

Gastrula

Blastopore becomes mouth

Mesoderm fills blastocoel

Blind gut

Complete gut

Acoelomate

Mesoderm lines outer edge of blastocoel

No gut

Complete gut

Pseudocoelomate

TRIPLOBLASTIC

Mesoderm band fills blastocoel

Coelom opens in mesoderm via schizocoely

Complete gut

Coelomate Lophotrochozoan Protostome

Blastopore becomes anus

Mesoderm and coelom form together by enterocoely (modified in vertebrates)

Complete gut

Coelomate Deuterostome

■ **9-5 General Animal Developmental Patterns** ≈ The lophotrochozoans generally show spiral cleavage, the coelom opens by schizocoelly, and mesoderm fills the blastocoel. However, the Ectoprocta are problematic, showing a unique developmental pattern.

Lophotrochozoa (in part)

Gnathifera

Syndermata

Lophophorata

Gnathostomulida

Micrognathozoa

Rotifera

Acanthocephala

Cycliophora

Gastrotricha

Entoprocta

Ectoprocta

Brachiopoda

Phoronida

Monociliated epidermal cells

3 sets of paired jaws

Toes with adhesive glands

Apical proboscis with intracellular hooks

Loss of gut

Loss of jaws

Epidermis partly cellular and partly syncytial

Multiciliated cells on lophophore

Body enclosed by dorsal and ventral shells

Eutelic syncytial epidermis

Complex life cycle with asexual Pandora larva and sexual choroid larva

Cup-shaped body with tentacular ring

Retractable lophophore

Long ciliated tentacles on larvae

Cuticular jaws with unique microstructure

Adhesive tubes

Adhesive tubes

Monociliated cells on lophophore

Lophophore

■ **9-6 Cladogram of Selected Lophotrochozoa, Including the Ectoprocta** ≈

The Ectoprocta (Bryozoa) are one of the three lophophorate phyla shown. The placement of all three phyla here is the most controversial of the relationships in this figure and comes principally from molecular data, including small subunit ribosome RNA base sequences. Lophotrochozoa is one of two proposed clades of protostomes. It includes acoelomates, pseudocoelomates, and coelomates. All clades shown have marine members, or are primarily marine. Only the Ectoprocta and Brachiopoda have chapters in this *Atlas*. The name Lophotrochozoa is a combination of *Lopho,* for the members that possess a lophophore, and *trochozoa,* for the trochophore larva (Figure 11-3) possessed by others.

Lamp shells

Lingula

10 Brachiopoda

Brachiopods (*brachi*—arm, *poda*—foot), also known as lamp shells, superficially resemble bivalve molluscs (Table 10-1 and Figure 10-1), with their two calcareous hinged shells. However the two groups are not closely related. Unlike molluscs, brachiopods have two unequally sized valves (shells), that are oriented horizontally rather than vertically, and possess an aperture (hole in valve) and **pedicle** (stalk—see next paragraph) on the dorsal side of the ventral valve. Similar to bivalves, lamp shells are solitary suspension feeders found in benthic habitats. Species are either attached to the substratum or burrow in the sediment. All brachiopods are marine and today most are found along the continental shelf at higher latitudes. The Brachiopoda have a rich fossil record dating from the Cambrian,

however there are only 350 extant species; most species went extinct during the great Permian extinction event. The Terebratulida (articulated brachiopods) are the most common living lamp shells. The Hawaiian inarticulated brachiopod, *Lingula reevii*, has been listed as a National Oceanic and Atmospheric Administration (NOAA) Species of Concern since 2004, due to habitat destruction, historical overexploitation, and the continued need to provide live specimens for Waikiki Aquarium.

Historically, Brachiopoda was separated into two groups: the Articulata and the Inarticulata, based upon articulation of the valve hinge and its muscles, among other characteristics. Recent evidence, however, suggests that the articulation of the valve hinge may not be a

■ Table **10-1** ≈ Brachiopod Classes

Class	General Description	Examples	Approximate Number of Species	Etymology
Inarticulata (Figure 10-1A)	Do not have a connecting hinge between the valves, but rather are held together by muscles; have a long pedicle	*Lingula* and *Glottidia*	45	*in*—not, *articulat*—a joint
Articulata (Figure 10-1B, C, & D)	Have a connecting hinge between the valves and a short fleshy stalk called a pedicle	*Terebratella* and *Terebratalia*	290+	*articulat*—a joint

1. Valves   2. Pedicle   3. Body mass   4. Lophophore

■ **10-1 Brachiopoda** ≈ (**A**) *Lingula* is an inarticulate brachiopod. The pedicle, ventral, and dorsal valves are visible. *Lingula* occupies a burrow into which it will withdraw if disturbed. Eleven species are recognized and are all considered "living fossils." This specimen is approximately 5 cm along the length of its valves. Brachipods are widely distributed and abundant enough in some areas to support limited commercial harvesting. They are principally in cold, deepwater, benthic environments. (**B**) *Terebratalia* is a genus of articulate brachiopods. Here the valves are separated and the body mass can be seen, including the lophophore. (**C** and **D**) Brachiopods are very abundant in the fossil record and have been found in 500-million-year-old strata.

phylogenetically useful character. Brachiopods have a mantle and mantle cavity similar to that in molluscs (see Chapter 11). Inside the mantle cavity is a lophophore (Figure 10-1B), a hollow crown of tentacles, used in feeding and respiration. Suspension feeding occurs as water containing detritus and small plankton flows over the lophophore. The majority of lamp shells have a long pedicle (Figure 10-1A), a fleshy stalk extending from the articulating end of the two valves—and the object source of the group's

name, which enables the animal to attach to sediment or bury itself. Pedicles vary between the two groups: Inarticulata, such as *Lingula*, have long and muscular pedicles, while the Articulata have either short, inflexible pedicles lacking musculature or bendable muscular stalks. A few brachiopod species do not have a pedicle. Brachiopods average approximately 5 cm in length.

Most brachiopods are dioecious. Fertilization typically occurs externally, although some species are brooders.

Inarticulates have direct development with no larvae. Miniature juvenile brachiopods feed on plankton and swim using their lophophore. Eventually, they settle to the bottom as their shell continues to grow and get heavier. Articulates display indirect development, forming a larva, which feeds on its yolk (lecithotrophic). It spends a relatively short period of time in the plankton before metamorphosing into an adult.

Possessing a lophophore, lamp shells are thought to be most closely related to other lophophorates, such as phoronids and ectoprocts (bryozoans) (Figure 10-2).

Lophophorates and Trochozoa are placed together as the Lophotrochozoa, though there is evidence that suggests lophophorates may actually be deuterostomes, not protostomes as previously thought. Recent studies also suggest that articulation may not be a good character for dividing species into the Articulata and Inarticulata. Other work supports the hypothesis that the group is polyphyletic, i.e., various brachiopod groups evolved separately from ancestors of the phoronid. See Figure 10-3 for placement of the Lophotrochozoa in the animal phylogeny.

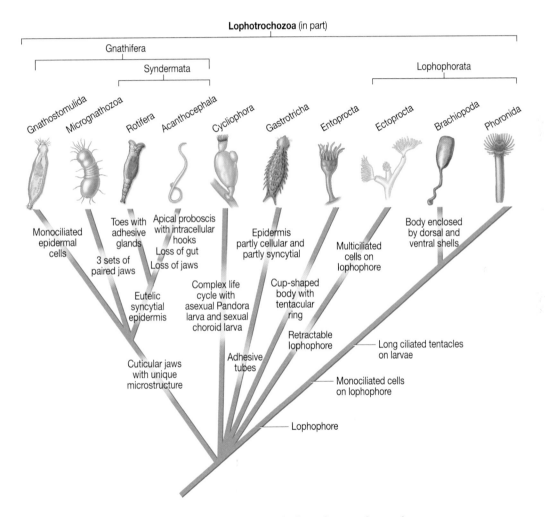

■ 10-2 Cladogram of Selected Lophotrochozoa, Including the Brachiopoda ≈ This cladogram shows a number of proposed sister clades for a portion of the Lophotrochozoa. Chapter 9 discusses the Ectoprocta. The other clades are presented here for perspective on the morphological diversity of the Lophotrochozoa. The brachiopods, lophophorates (Lophophorata), and lophotrochozoans are all controversial groups. Even their placement in protostome versus deuterostome clades is disputed, largely because they show characters of both groups. Molecular data support the Lophotrochozoa grouping, but has done little to help determine relationships between presumed sister clades. Molecular data do support sister clade status for the Brachiopoda and Phoronida. The name Lophotrochozoa is a combination of *Lopho*, for the members that possess a lophophore, and *trochozoa*, for the trochophore larva (Figure 11-3) possessed by others.

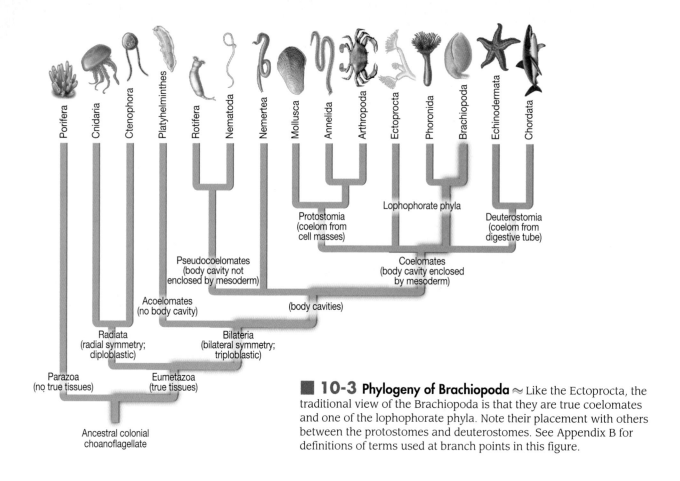

Porifera
Cnidaria
Ctenophora
Platyhelminthes
Rotifera
Nematoda
Nemertea
Mollusca
Annelida
Arthropoda
Ectoprocta
Phoronida
Brachiopoda
Echinodermata
Chordata

Protostomia
(coelom from
cell masses)

Lophophorate phyla

Deuterostomia
(coelom from
digestive tube)

Pseudocoelomates
(body cavity not
enclosed by mesoderm)

Coelomates
(body cavity enclosed
by mesoderm)

Acoelomates
(no body cavity)

(body cavities)

Radiata
(radial symmetry;
diploblastic)

Bilateria
(bilateral symmetry;
triploblastic)

Parazoa
(no true tissues)

Eumetazoa
(true tissues)

Ancestral colonial
choanoflagellate

■ **10-3 Phylogeny of Brachiopoda** ~ Like the Ectoprocta, the traditional view of the Brachiopoda is that they are true coelomates and one of the lophophorate phyla. Note their placement with others between the protostomes and deuterostomes. See Appendix B for definitions of terms used at branch points in this figure.

Clam gills (cross section)

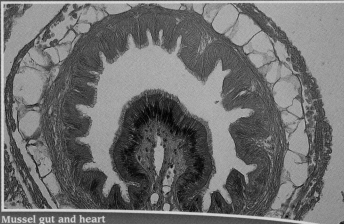

Mussel gut and heart
(cross section)

11 Mollusca

Among the animals, Mollusca (Table 11-1) is second only to Arthropoda in diversity. There are almost 100,000 described species of extant molluscs. Molluscs are ubiquitous in terrestrial and aquatic habitats, but most are marine. They are found throughout the world's oceans, ranging from predatory pelagic squid to herbivorous benthic snails. Some molluscs are cultivated or harvested for food in many countries, and are an important source of income and nutrition. Coastal filter-feeding molluscs are particularly useful as indicator organisms; tissue samples can provide data on pollution levels.

In spite of their physical diversity, molluscan morphology is based on modifications of a basic body plan. This body plan includes **cephalization** (the concentration of sensory receptors and some appendages on the head) and a soft, unsegmented body (visceral mass) with a **muscular**

■ Table **11-1** ≈ Molluscan Classes

Class	General Description	Examples	Approximate Number of Species	Etymology
Polyplacophora (Figure 11-7)	Seven or eight articulating plates with a dorsoventrally flattened body and a distinct muscular foot	*Cryptochiton* and *Mopalia*	1,000	*poly*—many, *placo*—flat, *phora*—movement or carry
Cephalopoda (Figure 11-8)	Highly modified foot and shell; mantle forms a posterior body mass; arms and tentacles pronounced with a well-developed eye; shell often reduced or absent	*Nautilus*, squid, cuttlefish, and octopus	800	*cephalo*—head, *podous*—foot
Bivalvia (Figure 11-9)	Enclosed in a two-part shell (two valves); head much reduced; labial palps around mouth; and no radula	*Venus*, *Tridacna*, *Donax*, and *Mytilus*	9,200	*bi*—two, *valva*—folding door
Scaphopoda (Figure 11-10)	A one–piece tubular shell encloses the body, which is open at both ends; radula present; mantle is the primary respiratory organ	*Dentalium*	900	*skaphe*—boat or trough, *podous* —foot
Gastropoda (Figure 11-11)	Snail appearance with body in a coiled shell; radula present; enlarged muscular foot and mantle	*Haliotis*, *Norrisia* and *Strombus*	80,000	*gaster*—stomach, *podous* —foot

foot (Figure 11-1). The visceral mass includes a **mantle**, which secretes an external calcareous shell. Most molluscs possess a rasp-like **radula** (*radul*—scraper) used for scraping algae off rocks (Figure 11-2), though this structure has been variously modified for other uses and lost in bivalves. The muscular foot is used for creeping along and adhering to rocks and other surfaces.

In general, molluscs are dioecious (separate sexes) with external fertilization, though many monoecious species exist (where one individual produces both egg and sperm), as does internal fertilization. A **trochophore** larva (*trocho*—wheel, *phoros*—to bear) precedes a **planktotrophic veliger** (*velum*—covering, *ger*—bearing) larval stage in ancestral taxa (Figure 11-3). In some taxa, the veliger is the only larval form. Some species have direct development and no larval stage. A bivalve life cycle is used as a representative of the molluscs (Figure 11-3).

A molluscan phylogeny is presented in Figure 11-4. The developmental pattern and a cladogram is shown in Figure 11-6. Only the four most common taxa will be discussed here. Evidence of shelled molluscs first appeared in the Cambrian. Molluscs are generally thought to share an ancestor with the other Lophotrochozoa (Figure 12-3), including annelids and sipunculids. Mollusc systematists currently disagree as to whether Lophotrochozoa originated from a segmented ancestor, or not.

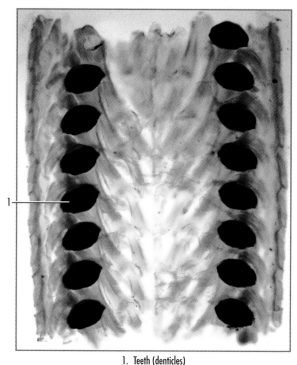

1. Teeth (denticles)

■ **11-2 Mollusca Radula** ≈ A chitinous radula with thickened "teeth" are visible in this photomicrograph. It is a structure unique to the Mollusca and is present in all but the bivalves.

| 1. Tentacle | 2. Radula | 3. Muscular foot | 4. Mantle | 5. Shell |

■ **11-1 Mollusca Morphological Characteristics** ≈ This limpet, resting on a bed of California mussels, *Mytilus californianus*, shows cephalization (note the tentacles containing sensory receptors), the muscular foot, mouth with chitinous radula, and the mantle typical of Mollusca.

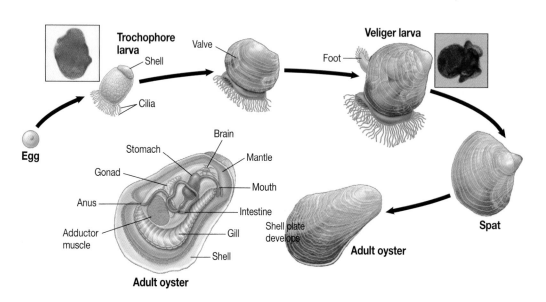

■ **11-3 Typical Mollusca Life Cycle** ≈ The oyster life cycle is shown as a representative bivalve life cycle. Note the trochophore and veliger larval stages.

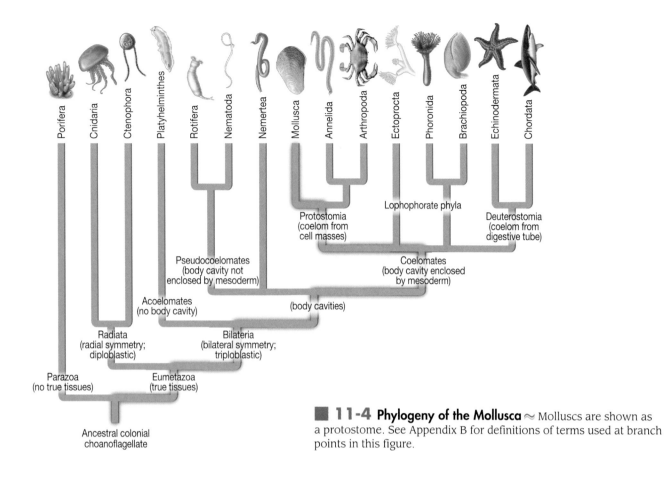

11-4 Phylogeny of the Mollusca ≈ Molluscs are shown as a protostome. See Appendix B for definitions of terms used at branch points in this figure.

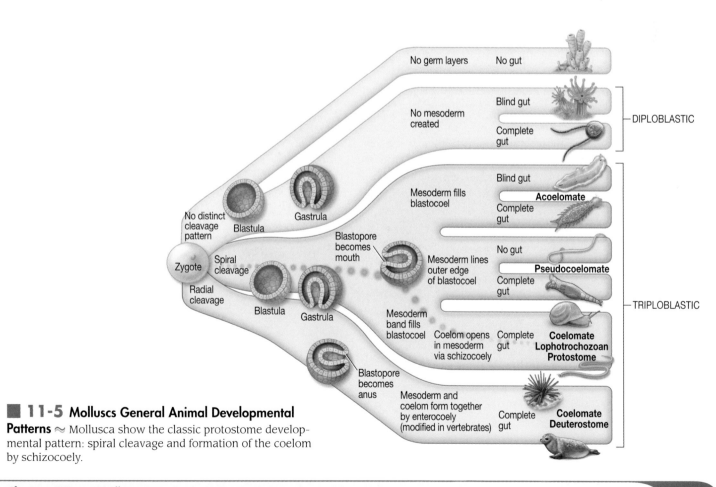

11-5 Molluscs General Animal Developmental Patterns ≈ Mollusca show the classic protostome developmental pattern: spiral cleavage and formation of the coelom by schizocoely.

Mollusca

Conchifera

Caudofoveata Solengastres Polyplacophora Monoplacophora Gastropoda Cephalopoda Bivalvia Scaphopoda

Torsion
Further concentration
of visceral mass
Open
circulatory system
Loss of radula
Bivalve shell
Lateral compression
of body

Loss of gills
Foot groove
Copulatory spicules
at posterior

Univalve, caplike shell
Serial repetition of soft parts

Beaklike jaws
Arms/tentacles and siphon
Closed circulatory system
Shell coiling
Well-developed head
Viscera concentrated dorsally
Dorsoventrally
elongated body

Loss of gills
Tusk-shaped,
open-ended shell

Unique shell with 7-8 plates
Mantle cavity extended
along sides of foot
Multiple gills

Nervous system decentralized
Head reduced
Spatulate foot
Expansion of mantle cavity to surround body

Calcareous spicules
form scales

Single, well-defined shell gland
Periostracum, prismatic, and nacreous layers to shell
Shell univalve
Multiple foot retractor muscles
Preoral tentacles
Large, muscular foot
Concentration of shell gland to produce solid shells
Posterior mantle cavity with one or more pair of gills
Radula
Chambered heart with atria and ventricle
Muscular foot (or foot precursor)
Calcareous spicules produced by mantle shell gland
Mantle
Reduction of coelom and development of hemocoel

■ 11-6 Molluscan Cladogram ~ This cladogram is limited to the Mollusca. No other lophotrochozoans are shown.

Polyplacophora

Polyplacophora (Figure 11-7) are solely marine and consist of a group of molluscs known as chitons. There are approximately 800 known extant species, most of which are between 3 to 12 cm in length. The chiton's mantle covers all (*Cryptochiton*) or part of the dorsal surface (in most species). The foot pulls the chiton along its path slowly via muscular undulations. The foot is also well adapted for clinging to rocks of wave-swept shores. Their shell is modified into eight imbricated (overlapping) and adjustable dorsal plates (shell valves) that allow the animal to wedge itself tightly into small crevices. During high tide, most chitons will venture out from their homing spot and use their radula to feed on algae and other small organisms. Herbivory of **macroalgae** (Chapter 28) is known in some species. Less commonly, a few species scavenge for detritis, and, in at least one instance, prey on invertebrates (*Placiphorella*).

Almost all chitons are dioecious and fertilization is external. The larva is a lecithotrophic trochophore, and metamorphosis occurs after this larva. Approximately 30 species are brooders with direct development of fertilized eggs.

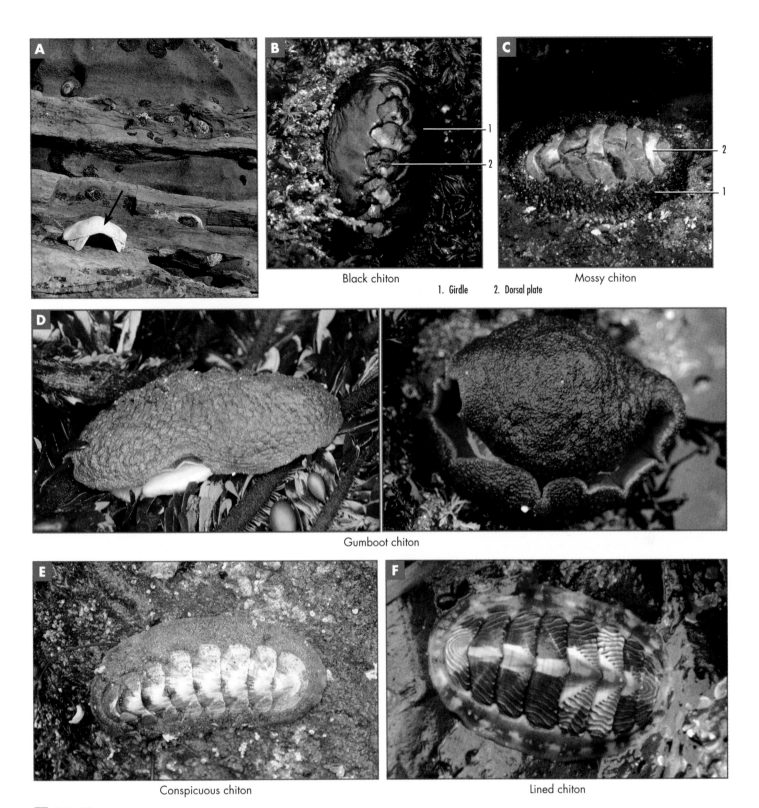

Black chiton

1. Girdle   2. Dorsal plate

Mossy chiton

Gumboot chiton

Conspicuous chiton

Lined chiton

■ **11-7 Chiton (Polyplacophora)** ≈ **(A)** High in the intertidal zone, a series of sandstone layers show molluscs attached on the vertical cliff and a single dorsal plate left from an expired chiton (arrow). **(B)** The black chiton, *Katharina tunicata*, shows a thick, black girdle that covers all but the mid-dorsal portion of the plates characterizing chitons. This species is very common in the low and middle rocky littoral habitat from Alaska to Santa Barbara, California. It grows to a length of 12 cm. **(C)** The mossy chiton, *Mopalia muscosa*, occurs along the Northeastern Pacific in low and middle rocky and estuarine littoral habitats. It grows to 9 cm. **(D)** The gumboot chiton (left), *Cryptochiton stelleri*, reportedly the largest of the chitons, can reach 33 cm. It inhabits rocky habitats from low tide to approximately 20 m. Like most chitons, the gumboot can curl up into a "pill-bug" type shape when disturbed (right). It ranges across the Northern Pacific from east to west in temperate and polar habitats. **(E)** *Stenoplax conspicua*, the conspicuous chiton, has a very limited range (low to middle rocky littoral) in the Northeastern Pacific, where it is Southern and Baja California's largest chiton, reaching 10 cm. Its white and green valves distinguish this from other chitons. **(F)** The lined chiton, *Tonicella lineata*, ranges across the Northern Pacific. It grows to 5 cm in the low rocky littoral to sublittoral habitats.

Cephalopoda

The cephalopods (Figure 11-8) differ from most other molluscs in that they are all adapted for swimming and most lead a pelagic life. Two extant groups exist: the Coleoida (squid, octopus, cuttlefish) and the Nautiloidea (with the nautilus being the only extant representative). Cephalopoda is entirely marine and includes approximately 700 extant species, but has an extensive fossil record, with approximately 10,000 extinct species. Cephalopods are known among invertebrates for their well-developed sensory and nervous systems, their speed, and intelligence. They are all predators. Octopods and squid are fished for bait and food in many countries.

The body plan is modified from that of most molluscs in that cephalopods have their head and foot on the same side of the body (dorsoventral elongation). They have multiple circumoral (surrounding the mouth) arms, a funnel, a chitinous beak, a shell in most, and eyes capable of forming images. The octopi are shell-less (Figures 11-8A and 11-8B), while the nautilus has an external shell (Figure 11-8F), and squid (Figures 11-8C and D) and cuttlefish (Figure 11-8E) have a reduced internal shell. Most cephalopods range between 6 to 7 cm. Many also have pigmented

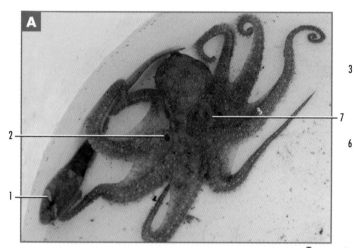

Two-spotted octopus

North Pacific giant octopus

1. California clingfish
2. Eyespot
3. Opening into the mantle cavity
4. Mantle
5. Suckers
6. Arm
7. Eye

■ **11-8 Octopi (Cephalopoda)** ≈ **(A)** The two-spotted octopus (left), *Octopus bimaculoides*, is a common inhabitant of the middle littoral to sublittoral (down to 20 m plus) habitats of the Northeastern Pacific. The "eyespots" and actual eyes can be seen in this specimen. It is approximately 18 cm across, although this species may reach 60 cm across the arms with a 20 cm, shell-less body. A California clingfish, *Gobiesox rhessodon*, (Chapter 24) is also in the container. A larger individual (right) is shown after having "inked" two of the authors. Contrast the color of these two specimens. When disturbed, this species, as with Cephalopods in general, can significantly change coloration and body color pattern. The eyes, mantle, opening into the mantle cavity, arms, and double rows of suckers on the arms are visible. **(B)** The North Pacific giant octopus, *Enteroctopus (Octopus) dofleini*, inhabits the coastal North Pacific, and is one of the largest octopi. Adults are up to 4.5 m across the arms, although accounts of much larger individuals have been reported. *(continued)*

■ **11-8 Squid (Cephalopoda)** ~ *(continued)* **(C)** The Caribbean reef squid, *Sepioteuthis sepioidea*, ranges throughout the Caribbean and coastal Florida. At various life-cycle stages, they inhabit shallow water of reefs or turtle grass (Chapters 32 and 33) near the surface in a school of a few individuals to several dozen. **(D)** The Humboldt squid (top), *Dosidicus gigas,* is an Eastern Pacific, usually deepwater species (200 to 800 m), which sometimes ventures into shallow water with reports of encounters with startled divers as this large squid "flies" by in large numbers. A meter stick is shown at the top of the photo. The arms, tentacles, eyes, fin, and mantle are shown. The funnel (middle, left), beak (middle, right), chitinous teeth of an arm tentacle sucker (bottom, left), and view into the mantle cavity (bottom, right) of a Humboldt squid (20 cm across opening) are shown. *(continued)*

Caribbean reef squid

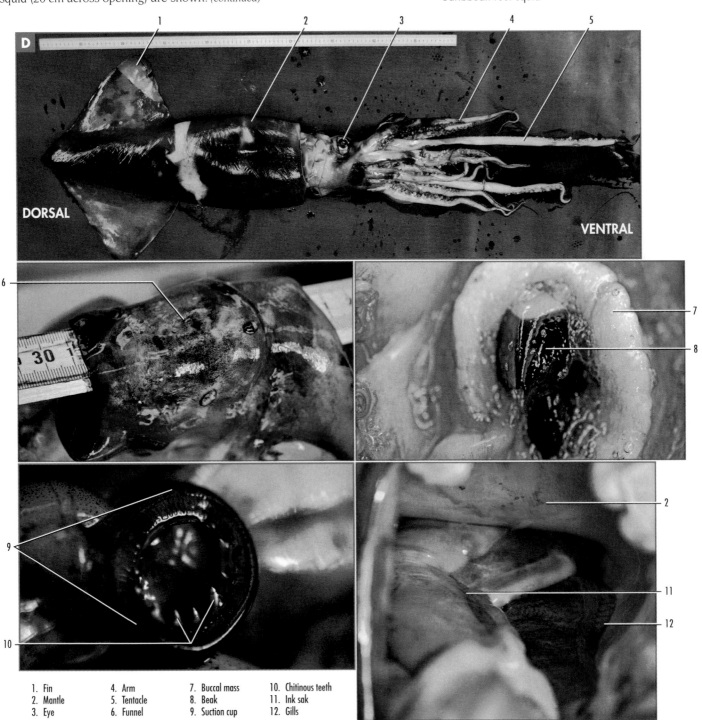

1. Fin	4. Arm	7. Buccal mass	10. Chitinous teeth	
2. Mantle	5. Tentacle	8. Beak	11. Ink sak	
3. Eye	6. Funnel	9. Suction cup	12. Gills	

■ 11-8 Cuttlefish and Nautilus (Cephalopoda)

~ *(continued)* **(E)** The European cuttlefis, *Sepia officinalis*, lives in the Eastern Atlantic Ocean and Mediterranean Sea. This specimen is approximately 20 cm, but individuals have been reported to 45 cm. **(F)** The nautilus (left), *Nautilus belauensis*, shown is approximately 20 cm across. They inhabit the Indo-Pacific Ocean in tropical and subtropical regions. longitudinal section (right) of the nautilus shell shows uninhabited chambers of the shell used in maintaining **buoyancy**. The chamber on the upper center and right is the chamber inhabited by the living organism.

European cuttlefish

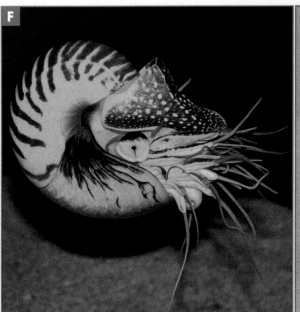

Nautilus

chromatophores and amazing abilities to camouflage against their surroundings (Figure 11-8A).

Cephalopoda are dioecious and fertilization occurs externally or internally. In both cases, courtship and sperm transfer from male to female occurs with cephalopod reproduction. Development of fertilized eggs is direct. Newly hatched cephalopods are planktonic.

Bivalvia

Bivalves (Figure 11-9) have been selected for an infaunal (burrowing) lifestyle. As discussed in Chapter 10, bivalves superficially resemble brachiopods, however their body is laterally compressed whereas brachiopods are dorso-ventrally compressed. Familiar bivalves include clams, oysters, mussels, and scallops. Most are attached to the substrate (e.g., mussels), and a few are motile (e.g., scallops) as adults. Some symbiotic species also exist. There are

approximately 15,000 species of extant bivalves, most of which are marine. Many bivalve species support important commercial fisheries. Oysters are the source of natural and cultured pearls. The highly derived shipworms (Teredinidae) are important ecologically for their ability to decompose wood in the ocean, but become a nuisance to humans for the same reason. They have been known to destroy engineered wooden structures such as docks and piers.

The protein and calcareous bivalve shell is composed of two similar hinged valves, with a dorsal attachment for the hinge. Bivalves lack a radula and have only a vestigial head. They are generally grouped by their feeding style and gill adaptations. Most bivalves have large, **ciliated gills** (page 83, left) used during suspension feeding; food particles are caught while water flows over the gills during respiration. Some species are scavengers, and others are carnivorous. Giant **clams** (Figure 11-9G), among others, harbor endosymbiotic **zooxanthellae** (Figure 6-5), which provide a major portion of the clams' energy needs. The bivalve foot, typically used for burrowing, is reduced and compressed compared to the foot of most molluscs. The foot of many bivalves has glands that produce **byssus threads** (Figure 11-9E), protein filaments used to attach the animal to substrate, (e.g., mussels on rock). Bivalves range in size from 2 mm to the tropical giant clam (*Tridacna gigas*), which can attain lengths of approximately 1 m.

Bivalves reproduce sexually and most individuals are either male or female, though some groups are either **protandric** (male early in life and female later in life . . .

pro—before, *andric*—man) or simultaneous **hermaphrodites** (producing sperm and egg at the same time). Interestingly, the edible oyster (*Ostrea edulis*) changes back and forth between male and female from year to year. Fertilization in bivalves is typically external with gametes sent out from the excurrent siphon, but it can occur inside the mantle cavity where eggs are brooded. Some bivalves have lecithotrophic veligers or planktotrophic veligers, while others retain the developing embryos until they develop into veligers, a **larviparous** (not laying eggs, but releasing larvae instead) strategy. See Figure 11-3 for the oyster life cycle.

American jackknife clam

1

1—Siphon

■ 11-9 Clams (Bivalvia) ≈ (A) The
American jackknife clam (top), *Ensis directus*, is found in coastal (littoral and sublittoral) oceans of the North and Southeastern Pacific and North and Southwestern Atlantic. This species is benthic and temperate in occurrence. Note the two valves (middle) typical of the Bivalvia. The maximum size of this species is 26 cm. When in feeding position, their siphons extend above the mud (right), moving water across their filter-feeding gills, as shown in this model. (B) *Spisula solidissima*, the surf clam, occurs along the Northwestern Atlantic where it can reach 12.5 cm in width. *(continued)*

Surf clam

Pismo clam

Bean clam   1. Siphons   2. Muscular foot

■ **11-9 Clams (Bivalvia)** ≈ *(continued)* (**C**) *Tivela stultorum*, the Pismo clam, is shown in a series of photographs burying itself in the sand. The entire process from surface to only siphons showing takes less than a minute. This commercially important clam grows to 20 cm or more, but it takes more than 26 years to do so. (**D**) The bean clam (left), *Donax gouldii*, is abundant along sandy beaches at some times of the year (as shown in this approximately 1 m² area) and nearly absent at others. Both siphons and the muscular foot are seen on the right. Most individuals are about 2 cm across their valves. *(continued)*

California mussel

1. Byssal threads

Bay mussel

■ **11-9 Mussels (Bivalvia)** ≈ *(continued)* (**E**) The California mussel (top, left), *Mytilus californianus*, grows to approximately 20 cm while inhabiting the surf-swept, rocky littoral environment of the Northeastern Pacific. They may form extensive mussel beds (top, right), competing for space within the littoral zone with other California mussels and a host of other species. Even their surfaces are used as home by other species (bottom, left) such as these buckshot barnacles, genus *Chthamalus* or *Balanus*. Strong byssal threads attach the mussels to their substrate (bottom, right). The threads are formed by a gland in the mussel's foot and are composed of proteins. (**F**) The blue or bay mussel, *Mytilus edulis*, predominantly occupies the quiet water of bays, estuaries, and sheltered areas of the open coast. However, they do occur with *Mytilus californianus*. Today, they are present throughout the Northern Hemisphere coastal waters, probably spread attached to the hulls of ships. *(continued)*

1. Mantle　　　　　　　Giant clam

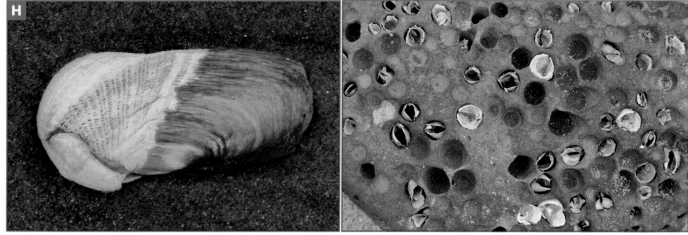

Piddock

■ **11-9** **Clams (Bivalvia)** ≈ *(continued)* **(G)** The giant clam (left), *Tridacna* spp., inhabits coral reefs in the shallow water of the Indo-Pacific. They have a brightly colored mantle with symbiotic zooxanthellae (Figure 6-5) living in the tissues. Most of their nutrients come from their symbiotic, dinoflagellate inhabitants. The largest species reaches a size of 1.2 m (*Tridacna gigas*) across their valves and up to 227 kg in weight. Once they settle and begin development into the adult form, the clams remain permanently attached to their point of settlement. The species shown is likely *Tridacna derasa* (right). **(H)** Boring bivalves include the piddocks, such as *Penitella penita* (left). Note the rough, rasping end of this bivalve. They bore into mud, clay, shale, and soft rock like this 80-million-year-old siltstone (right) along the San Diego coast. They range along the Northeastern Pacific from the mid-littoral to 20 m.

Scaphopoda

Scaphopoda (Figure 11-10), known as tusk shells, are a group of highly derived marine molluscs with a one-piece, elongated, tusk-shaped (curved) shell. The shell is unique among molluscs in being open at both ends. There are estimated to be 750–1,200 extant species of scaphopods. These molluscs are eyeless burrowers without gills that live with their anterior end buried in marine sediments. They are found in depths ranging from approximately 6 to 7,000 m. Historically, tusk shells of *Dentalium* were used as a type of wampum currency by Native Americans of the Pacific Northwest.

The posterior (smaller end of the shell) is oriented upward at an angle. The reduced head and foot are located beside one another at the larger, anterior end of the open shell. The upside-down head is inconspicuous and surrounded by tiny ciliated tentacles (captacula). The captacula search for food and transfer it to the mouth. Scaphopods are mainly predators of foraminiferans and tiny invertebrates, though some are detritivores.

Scaphopods are dioecious and fertilization is external. The zygote develops into both a lecithotrophic trochophore and then a shelled veliger larva before settling and metamorphosing into its adult form.

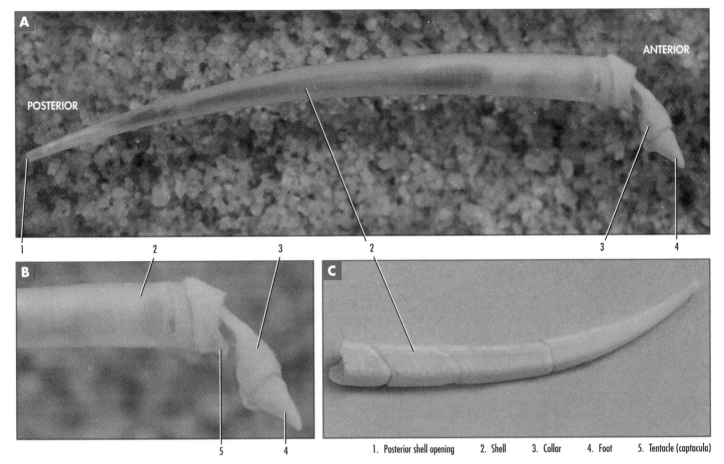

11-10 Tusk Shells (Scaphopoda) ~ (A) A typical scaphopodan. The entire organism is in, showing the unusual anatomy of a shell with two open ends. (B) This closeup of the anterior end shows this specimen's muscular foot and shell. (C) Shown is the shell of an expired scaphopodan.

1. Posterior shell opening 2. Shell 3. Collar 4. Foot 5. Tentacle (captacula)

Gastropoda

Gastropoda (Figure 11-11) is the most diverse molluscan group, with more than 80,000 described extant species found in marine, freshwater, and terrestrial habitats. Most are oceanic and include benthic (e.g., snails, nudibranchs, and sea hares) and planktonic representatives with light-weight or no shells (e.g., heteropods, bubble shells, and sea butterflies). The shell in most gastropods is external, but is absent in groups such as nudibranchs, and internal in some (*Aplysia*). Most gastropods are grazers, using their radula to scrape algae off rocks. However, some are filter feeders (e.g., *Crepidula*), others are scavengers (e.g., *Nassarius*), and some are deposit feeders (e.g., *Strombus*). Still other species are effective predators, often prying open, sucking up, or drilling into bivalves and other invertebrates. The cone snails (*Conidae*) have a modified radula coated in toxin that functions as a harpoon. Unsuspecting passers-by (worms and fish) are stabbed and paralyzed while the snail devours them; six species of cone snails (e.g., *Conus geographus*) produce neurotoxins that can kill humans as well. These toxins are being studied for their effects on the human nervous system in hopes of further understanding neuromuscular degenerative diseases.

Gastropods vary significantly between groups; the only synapomorphy shared by all taxa is larval **torsion**—180° counterclockwise twisting of the mantle cavity, visceral mass, and shell so that they are oriented over the head. In addition to the characteristic one-piece shell, the mantle of many snails also secretes a trap door-like **operculum** (*oper*—lid, *culum*—diminutive suffix), which closes protectively over the aperture (Figure 11-11D), allowing a snail to pull its head and foot inside. The foot, typically large and flat-tened, is used for movements such as crawling and swimming. Gastropods range in size from a few millimeters to more than 1 m.

Depending on the group, gastropods are either dioecious or monoecious. Dioecious species are broadcast spawners and fertilization is external, while hermaphrodites have internal fertilization. The fertilized egg of spawners develops into a trochophore, or in more derived taxa directly into a shelled veliger larva (both planktotrophic and lecithotrophic). Torsion occurs during the veliger stage. Hermaphroditic species typically lay eggs, depositing them onto the substrate.

Abalone

Angular unicorn

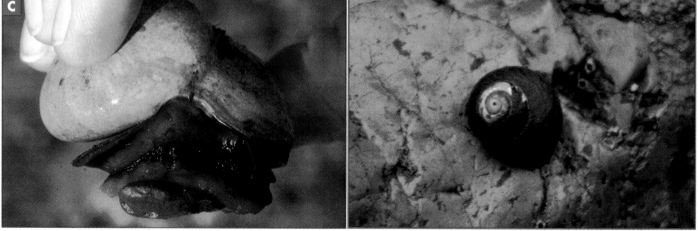

Norris' top snail

Black tegula

■ **11-11 Snails (Gastropoda)** ≈ **(A)** All abalones species are threatened throughout their worldwide range (except for the Eastern Atlantic). As many as 100 species have been reported, all of which are coastal. They are predominantly coldwater species that are prized for their muscular foot as a food source and for their iridescent, nacre-lined shells (left) as a decorative piece. Nacre (*nacr*—mother-of-pearl) is a material formed by the blending of organic and inorganic materials in the molluscs' mantle. Abalones have been over-harvested for decades. The green abalone, *Haliotis fulgens* (middle), is shown. Characteristic of this class is a large muscular foot (right), their primary mode of transportation. **(B)** The angular unicorn, *Acanthina spirata*, like many gastropods, is a predatory species. It lives in the rocky littoral habitat where it preys on a variety of organisms, including the gooseneck barnacle under attack in this photograph. *Acanthina spirata* is a Northeastern Pacific species. This specimen is about 4.5 cm. **(C)** The top snails include the Norris' top snail, *Norrisia norris* (left), and the black tegula (right), *Tegula funebralis*. Norris' top snail is found in the Southern, Northeastern Pacific in the lower littoral zone. The black tegula is found in the Northeastern Pacific, where it is a benthic inhabitant of the littoral zone. *(continued)*

Atlantic slipper shell

1. Operculum   3. Shell   5. Mantle
2. Mouth and operculum   4. Muscular foot

■ **11-11 Snails (Gastropoda)** ~ *(continued)* **(D)** The California horn snail, *Cerithidea californica* (top, left), is abundant in mudflats of salt marsh estuaries (middle, left). Part of a population is shown in an area of approximately 1.5 m^2. As they crawl, they feed on benthic diatoms (Chapter 4) growing on the mud and green algae. They have a distinct operculum (bottom, left) that closes during low tide and protects them from desiccation. **(E)** The muscular foot, tentacles, and mouth of this Atlantic slipper shell, *Crepidula fornicata* (top, right), can be seen on the ventral surface. Adults grow to 5 cm in length and inhabit the littoral to sublittoral, down to 70 m where they filter-feed. Frequently, these snails are found in stacks (bottom, right). When in larval form, individuals settle to begin the change into juvenile snails, which begin life as males. If they are alone, or another snail settles on top of them, they change into a female. If an individual settles upon an adult, it remains a male, only changing to female if it becomes the bottom-most member of the snail stack. *(continued)*

California horn snail

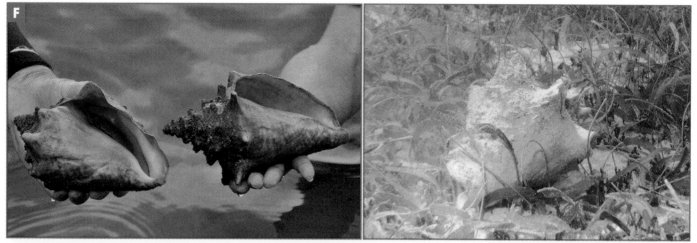

Queen conch

Lightning whelk

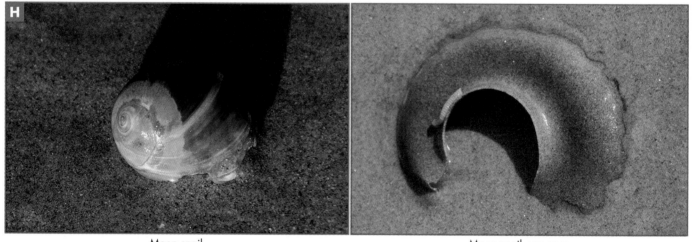

Moon snail   Moon snail egg case

■ **11-11** **Snails (Gastropoda)** ≈ *(continued)* (**F**) The queen conch (left), *Strombus gigas*, is one of the largest gastropods in the North-western Atlantic. It grows to 35 cm and is widely used as food. Some areas, such as the islands of Bermuda and the Caribbean, have large middens of queen conch shells. It typically inhabits green grass beds (right). (**G**, left) The lightning whelk, *Busycon contrarium*, occurs in the Northwestern Atlantic from New Jersey to Texas. It is a large, predatory snail, consuming a variety of bivalve mollusks. It lives in the sandy or muddy substrate of shallow, protected areas. (right) These are *Busycon* egg cases. (**H**) The moon snail, *Neverita reclusiana* (left), ranges in the Northeastern Pacific from tropical to northern temperate. It occurs in sand flats where it is a predatory snail, drilling holes in clams, mussels, or other molluscs with its radula. It lays a distinctive egg case (right). *(continued)*

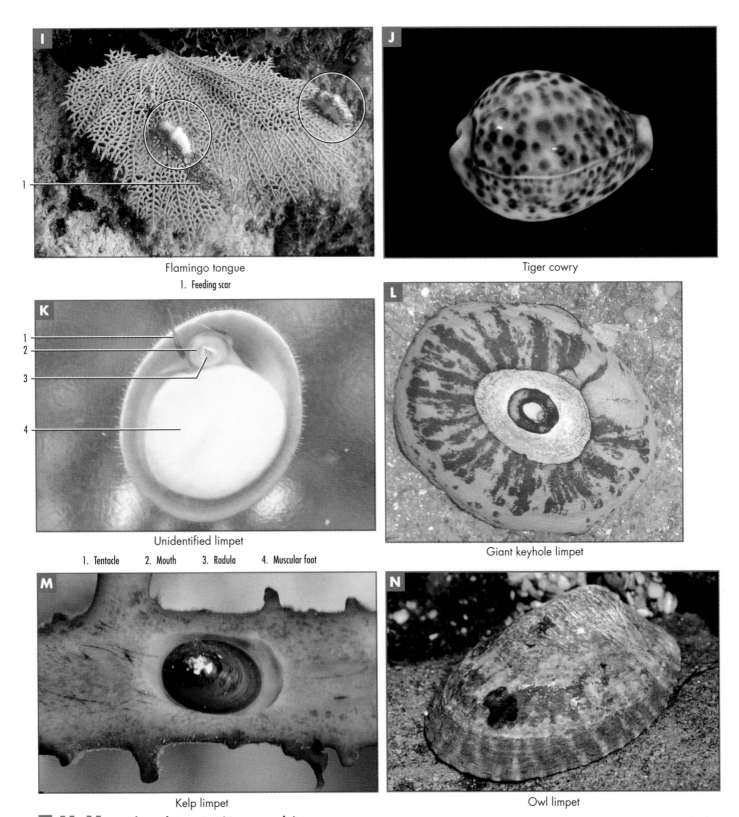

Flamingo tongue
1. Feeding scar

Tiger cowry

Unidentified limpet

1. Tentacle   2. Mouth   3. Radula   4. Muscular foot

Giant keyhole limpet

Kelp limpet

Owl limpet

■ **11-11 Snails and Cowries (Gastropoda)** ≈ *(continued)* (I) The flamingo tongue, *Cyphoma gibbosum*, is found in the tropical waters of the Western Atlantic from the surface to 30 m. Here it can be seen feeding on a gorgonian (Chapter 5). A dark feeding scar can be seen tailing the posterior end of the individual on the left. (J) The tiger cowry, *Cypraea tigris,* occurs in the Indian Ocean and Western Pacific on coral reefs and sandy bottom in the shallow subtidal habitat. (K) This limpet shows major features of the ventral surface: mouth with radula as this limpet feeds on algae coating a glass plate; muscular foot, and tentacles. (L) The giant keyhole limpet, *Megathura crenulata*, inhabits the Western Pacific, where they may grow to 13 cm or more in length. Their mantle surrounds their shell and is so large that it cannot be withdrawn into the shell. (M) The kelp limpet, *Notoacmea insessa*, is shown feeding on a feather-boa kelp stipe (*Ergregia menziesii*). Their highly specialized diet and littoral location make them easy to identify. They grow to 2 cm. (N) Owl limpets, *Lottia gigantea*, occur in the littoral zone along the Northeastern Pacific. They are the largest of the true limpets in the Northeastern Pacific, ranging up to 10 cm. Many individuals return to a "home" position on the rocks with the retreat of the tides and/or daylight. *(continued)*

California sea hare

Dorid

Violet fan nudibranch

Hopkin's rose

1. Cerata

Lion nudibranch

1. Gills

Brown-ringed nudibranch

1. Gills

■ **11-11 Sea Hare and Nudibranchs (Gastropoda)** ≈ *(continued)* (**O**) *Aplysia californica*, the California sea hare, occasionally grows to 30 cm and occurs in a variety of habitats from mudflats to exposed rocky shores and although most abundant in the littoral zone, does occur in the shallow sublittoral. This species is widely used for research because of its comparatively simple nervous system and very large nerve cells. (**P**) The dorid, *Archidoris montereyensis*, is a nudibranch with centralized gills in a retractable cluster. This specimen is not immersed in water and its gills are not visible. The nudibranchs (*nudus*—naked, *brankhia*—gills) are a large clade of nearly 3,000 species, many vibrantly colored, of sea slugs. (**Q**) The violet fan nudibranch, *Flabellina iodinea*, ranges across the Eastern Pacific from the Galapagos Islands north. Large specimens are 7 cm and are found from the littoral to 40 m. (**R**) Hopkin's rose, *Hopkinsia rosacea*, occurs in the Northeastern Pacific where it grows to 3 cm while displaying the long, fleshy filaments covering its ventral surface. It occurs in the littoral and sublittoral habitats down to 6 m. (**S**) The lion nudibranch, *Melibe leonine*, grows to 10 cm. It occurs from the littoral and sublittoral habitat down to 37 m where it inhabits eel grass beds. Its appearance is unique among the nudibranchs. This species feeds on plankton using the large oral hood on the right. Note the flat respiratory extensions from its body (arrow). (**T**) The brown-ringed nudibranch, *Diaulua sandiegensis*, grows to 10 cm, and occurs along the Northeastern Pacific where it feeds on sponges. The centralized gills are visible.

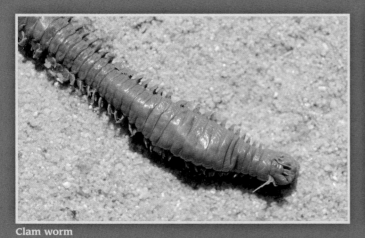
Clam worm

Christmas tree worm

12 Annelida

Annelids are coelomate segmented worms (Figures 12-1 and 12-2) found throughout the world in terrestrial, aquatic, and marine habitats. Annelids belong to Lophotrochozoa (along with flatworms, ecto-procts, brachiopods, and molluscs), and traditionally includes three groups (Figure 12-3): oligochaetes, marine polychaetes, and leeches (Hirudinea). These worms are extremely diverse, not only in terms of habitat, but also in their multitude of feeding mechanisms and life histories. Examples of such worms include benthic and pelagic predators; sedentary, tube-dwelling, suspension feeders; active deposit feeders; and burrowers in coral and sediment; as well as many others. We will focus on the polychaetes, which are summarized in Table 12-1.

Polychaetes

Polychaetes are predominantly free-living and benthic. However, the few species that are planktonic are typically well represented in terms of abundance. There are approx-imately 9,000 species of polychaete worms, and they are important components of many ecosystems. For instance, burrowing and deposit-feeding species help play a role in the **bioturbation** (turning and mixing) of sediment. Pogonophorans (beard worms) serve as the host for

chemosynthetic bacteria that are the base of hydrothermal vent food webs (see Figure 2-26). Recent studies show that Christmas tree worms, *Spirobranchus giganteus* (Figure 12-4), may exist in a mutualistic relationship with the reef-building corals in which they are embedded.

All annelids display similar segmentation (Figure 12-5). Segments are separated from one another by septa—each containing a coelom—and are similar in terms of most internal organs (Figure 12-6). Each segment possesses thin, flattened appendages (**parapodia**) that are used both for movement and diffusion of respiratory gases. The parapods have bristle-like protrusions of **chaetae** (setae and acicula) that vary depending on the species.

Life cycles differ, but most polychaetes have separate sexes and a trochophore larval stage (Figure 12-7). Some species reproduce asexually from budding (Figure 12-8A) or via **epitoky** (a segment is produced asexually, then breaks free of the worm and swims to the surface to release gametes for sexual reproduction, or in some worms, the entire worms transforms into a different form, which swims to the surface to release gametes) (Figure 12-8B).

Annelid systematics is still a work in progress. Evidence suggests that the oligochaetes and leeches should be placed together as either Clitellata or Oligochaeta. Within the polychaete clade itself, relationships are still being resolved.

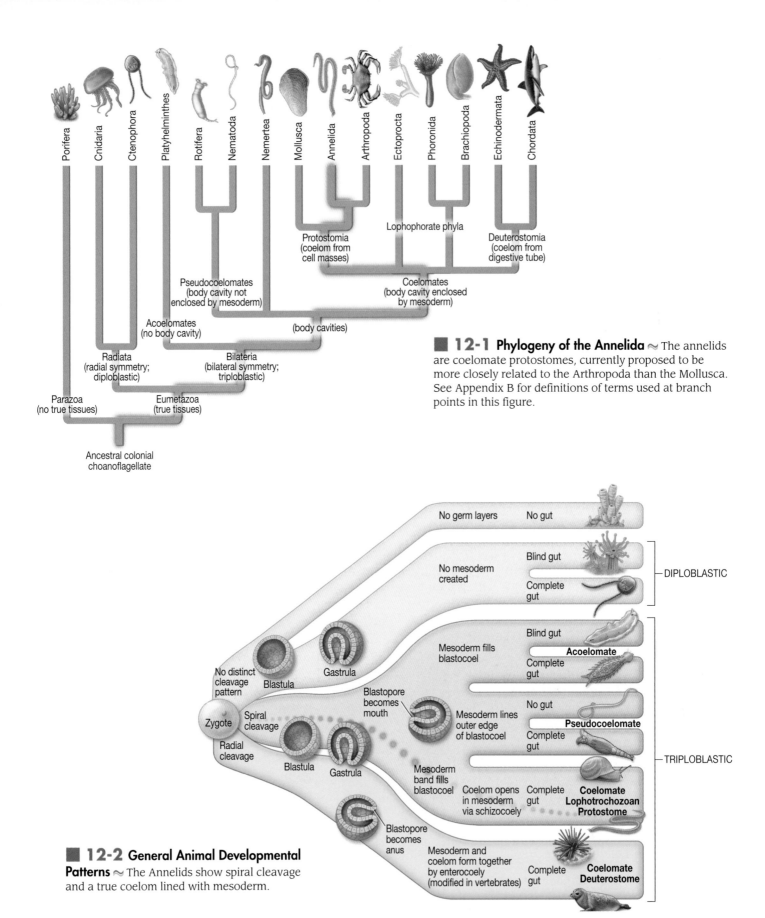

Porifera · Cnidaria · Ctenophora · Platyhelminthes · Rotifera · Nematoda · Nemertea · Mollusca · Annelida · Arthropoda · Ectoprocta · Phoronida · Brachiopoda · Echinodermata · Chordata

Protostomia
(coelom from
cell masses)

Lophophorate phyla

Deuterostomia
(coelom from
digestive tube)

Pseudocoelomates
(body cavity not
enclosed by mesoderm)

Coelomates
(body cavity enclosed
by mesoderm)

Acoelomates
(no body cavity)

(body cavities)

Radiata
(radial symmetry;
diploblastic)

Bilateria
(bilateral symmetry;
triploblastic)

Parazoa
(no true tissues)

Eumetazoa
(true tissues)

Ancestral colonial
choanoflagellate

■ 12-1 Phylogeny of the Annelida ~ The annelids
are coelomate protostomes, currently proposed to be
more closely related to the Arthropoda than the Mollusca.
See Appendix B for definitions of terms used at branch
points in this figure.

No germ layers · No gut

No mesoderm
created

Blind gut

Complete
gut

DIPLOBLASTIC

Mesoderm fills
blastocoel

Blind gut

Complete
gut

Acoelomate

No distinct
cleavage
pattern · Blastula · Gastrula

Blastopore
becomes
mouth

Mesoderm lines
outer edge
of blastocoel

No gut

Complete
gut

Pseudocoelomate

Zygote · Spiral
cleavage

Radial
cleavage · Blastula · Gastrula

Mesoderm
band fills
blastocoel

Coelom opens
in mesoderm
via schizocoely

Complete
gut

**Coelomate
Lophotrochozoan
Protostome**

Blastopore
becomes
anus

Mesoderm and
coelom form together
by enterocoely
(modified in vertebrates)

Complete
gut

**Coelomate
Deuterostome**

TRIPLOBLASTIC

**■ 12-2 General Animal Developmental
Patterns** ~ The Annelids show spiral cleavage
and a true coelom lined with mesoderm.

12-3 Annelid Cladogram

Lophotrochozoa (in part)

Annelida

Clitellata

Polychaeta (in part) | Oligochaeta (in part) | Hirudinida

Sabellidae Siboglinidae Nereidae Tubificidae Acanthobdellida Branchiobdellida* Hirudinea Echiura Sipuncula

15 segments

27 segments — 34 segments

Loss of setae
Anterior body sucker

No posterior body sucker

Proboscis in front of mouth — Anterior retractable introvert

Ciliary feathery arms — No mouth — Parapodia prominent

Posterior body sucker
Reduced septal walls
Reduced number of setae
Distinct, fixed reproductive system
Clitellum
Direct development
Hermaphroditism
Loss of parapodia

No setae

Lack parapodia

Annelid head

Parapodia

Metameric body

* No marine species

Paired epidermal setae

Coelom by schizocoely

12-3 Annelid Cladogram ≈ This cladogram shows synapomorphies of some Lophotrochozoa. Annelida includes the marine polychaetes and other clades.

Table 12-1 ≈ Polychaete Class

Class	General Description	Examples	Approximate Number of Species	Etymology
Polychaeta (Figures 12-4 through 12-15)	Well-developed head; paired appendages; no clitellum; many setae; very well-defined body segments	*Nereis, Eunice, Amphitrite, Sabella,* and *Chaetopterus*	10,000	*poly*—many, *chaet*—a bristle

Current molecular research suggests that Echiurans, also known as spoon worms, and the Siboglinidae, or beard worms, belong within the Annelida (rather than each in a Phylum of its own), though the exact placement of the groups has not yet been resolved. One possible cladogram is presented in Figure 12-3.

12-4 Christmas Tree Worm ≈ The Christmas tree worm, *Spirobranchus giganteus* is shown on its symbiont, star coral. Its morphology is representative of most tube-building polychaetes and, like most tube builders, it is restricted to its tube. The "Christmas tree" structure is the worm's respiratory organ. They range throughout the tropical ocean where they are filter feeders.

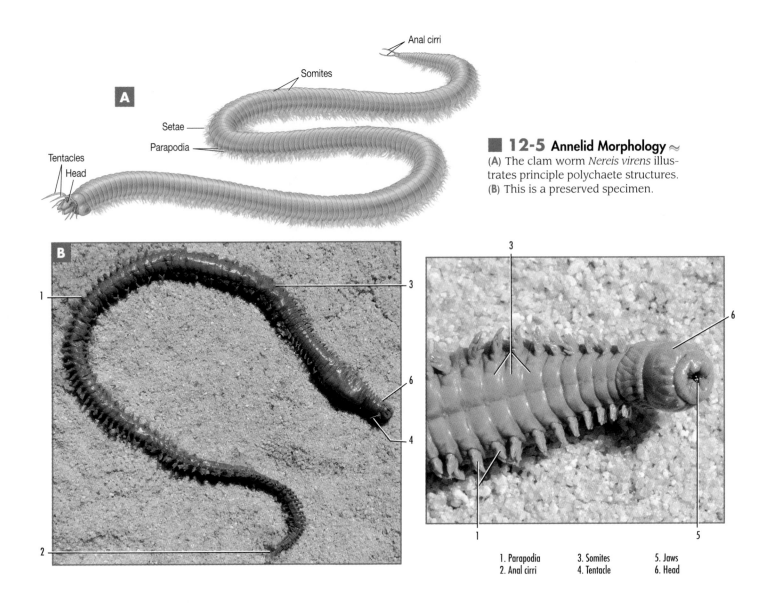

■ 12-5 Annelid Morphology ≈
(**A**) The clam worm *Nereis virens* illustrates principle polychaete structures.
(**B**) This is a preserved specimen.

1. Parapodia   3. Somites   5. Jaws
2. Anal cirri   4. Tentacle   6. Head

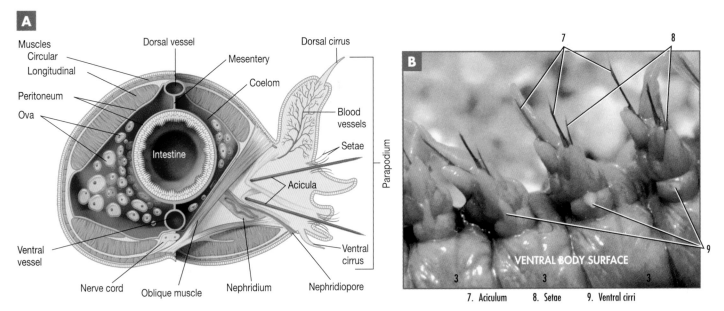

■ 12-6 Annelid Anatomy ≈ (**A**) The muscular arrangement in this clam worm is typical of the annelids, as are the ventral nerve cord, location of the blood vessels, and membranes between body segments (peritoneum). (**B**) Taken from a ventral view, this photograph shows some of the structures of parapodia and the chaetae of a clam worm.

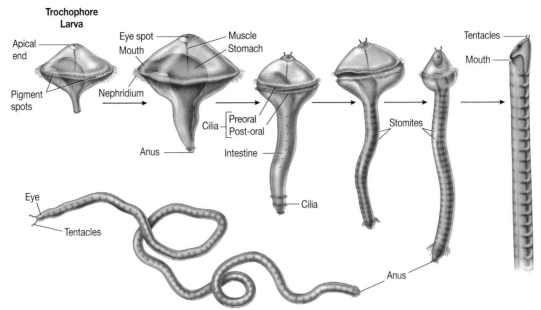

■ 12-7 Annelid Sexual Reproduction and Development ≈ Annelids typically show a protostome developmental pattern and some species have a planktonic trochophore larva, while others have **direct development** (no larval form). The polychaete *Polygordius* shows the former pattern. Following fertilization, a trochophore larva develops. As the trochophore matures, the body lengthens by adding segments and the head develops. As it continues to grow, it gradually acquires the features of the adult worm.

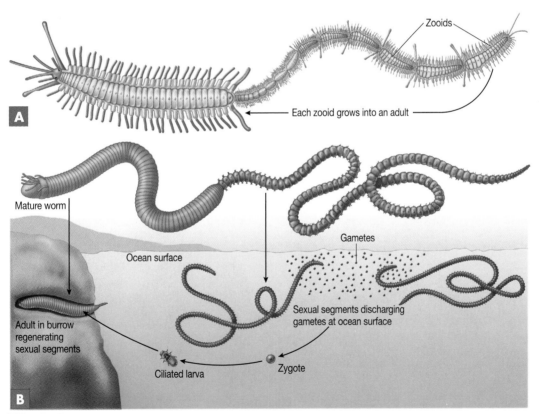

■ 12-8 Alternative Annelid Reproductive Patterns ≈ Annelids are capable of other methods of reproduction than that described in Figure 12-7, including asexual and epitoky. (**A**) One type of asexual reproduction is the formation of zooids, as in the species *Autolytus oyrpureomaculatus*. Each zooid develops into a new individual. (**B**) Other species reproduce sexually and asexually as part of a process known as epitoky. The palolo worm, *Eunice viridis*, develops new sexual segments (**epitokes**) by asexual reproduction. The epitokes break from the parent worms and swim to the ocean surface, discharging sperm and eggs. Fertilization takes place and the zygote develops into a larva, and then into a new adult worm. The reproduction of *Eunice viridis* takes place once a year, synchronously.

■ 12-9 Christmas Tree Worm ≈

The color of these worms' spiral crowns of radioles is highly variable. Most common colors are white, brown, orange, and maroon. Each radiole is ciliated and serves as a filter-feeding and respiratory organ. Their tube is not easily visible. These filter feeders are circumtropical.

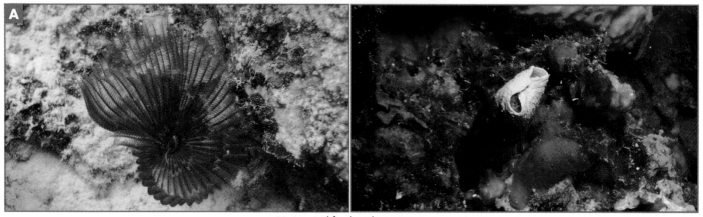

Variegated feather duster worm

Magnificent feather duster worm

Northern feather duster worm

■ 12-10 Feather Duster Worm ≈

(A) The variegated feather duster, *Bispira variegata*, (left) occurs throughout the Caribbean where it inhabits a parchment-like tube (right). It can be found on reefs and surrounding sandy areas from 6 m to 25 m. (B) The magnificent feather duster, *Sabellastarte magnifica*, is cosmopolitan and circumtropical. It may be up to 10 cm across the radioles of the crown. (C) The northern feather duster worm, *Eudistylia vancouveri*, occurs from low tide to 20 m in the Northeastern Pacific. As is generally true of sabellid worms, it lives in a secreted parchment-like tube.

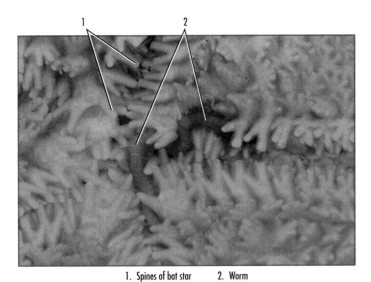

1. Spines of bat star   2. Worm

■ **12-11 Bat Star Worm** ≈ The bat star worm, *Ophiodromus pugettensis*, lives on the oral surface of bat stars in the ambulacral grooves (Figure 18-7B) near the mouth. As many as 20 worms have been reported on a single sea star.

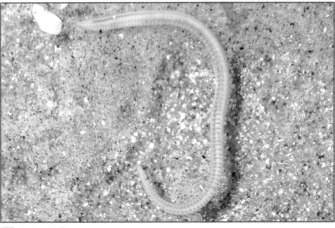

■ **12-12 Red-lined Worm** ≈ *Nephtys* is a genus of segmented worms, most of which live just below the surface of the sand hunting molluscs, other polychaetes (see Figure 12-13 for polychaete prey), and crustaceans. There are approximately 12 species that occur along sandy beaches of the Northeastern Pacific. They are normally found from the sand's surface to a depth of 20 cm.

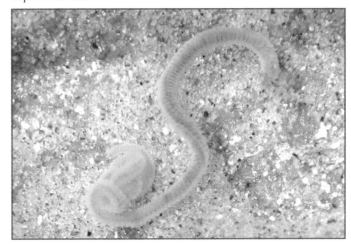

■ **12-13 Blood Worms** ≈ Worms in the genus *Euzonus* inhabit open to sheltered beaches. (left) This specimen was exposed by digging into substrate of an estuarine mudflat. *Euzonus* spp. live in tubes within the substrate, and range along the shores of the Northeastern Pacific. They may reach 3 cm in length and occupy the mid-littoral habitat, where they may be extremely abundant (2,500 to 3,000 per 30 square cm). They feed on organic matter coating sand grains (right). This specimen was uncovered on a sandy beach littoral environment.

■ **12-14 Sand-Castle Worm** ≈ *Phragmatophoma californica*, lives in a "condominium-style" castle. Each fan-shaped opening is for a single, 5-cm long individual. Inhabiting the rocky littoral habitat along exposed beaches, this worm establishes colonies under overhangs of rocks, competing for space with mussels. Their tubes are made from sand grains glued together with a protein bioadhesive secreted by the worm. By extending their tentacles from their tube's opening, they are capable of filter feeding.

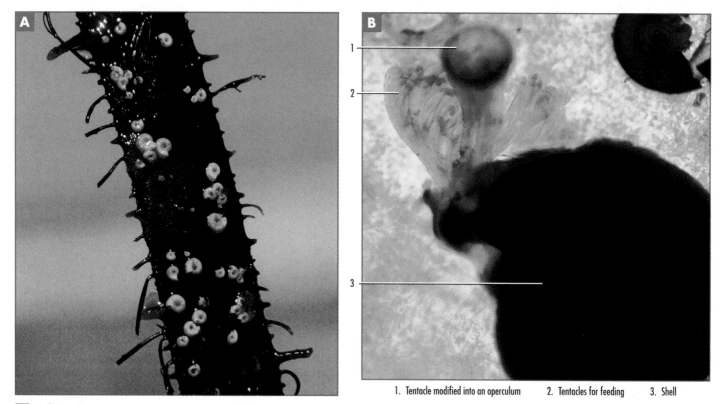

1. Tentacle modified into an operculum   2. Tentacles for feeding   3. Shell

■ **12-15** *Spirorbis* ≈ **(A)** This small annelid worm forms a spiral-shaped calcareous shell. Here they are attached to a blade of *Egregia* (Chapter 31). **(B)** *Spirorbis* belongs to the same family as the Christmas tree worm and like them, are filter feeders with a specialized operculum that closes the entrance to their shell when they are retracted.

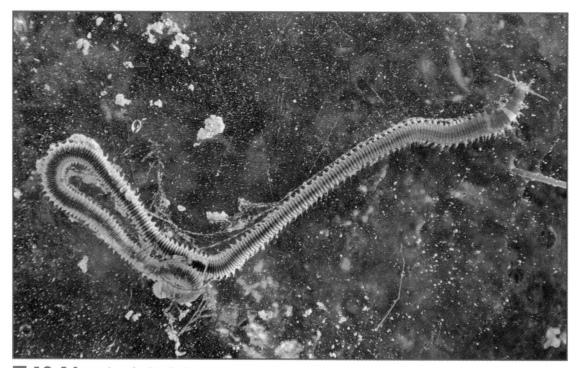

■ **12-16** **Unidentified Polychaete** ≈ This worm lives in a tube constructed of sand grains. It was living in the rocky intertidal area off Southern California.

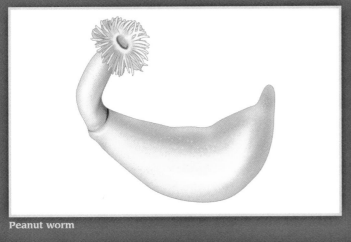
Peanut worm

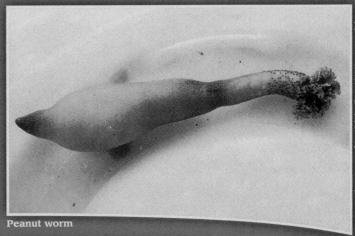
Peanut worm

13 Sipuncula

Sipunculids (*sipuncul*—a little siphon) are often called peanut worms. They are members of the Lophotrochozoa clade (Figure 13-1), which includes acoelomate and pseudocoelomate organisms, and as in the case of Sipuncula, protostomic coelomates. These worms have proven particularly problematic in establishing ancestral relationships. Molecular data support the cladogram in Figure 13-1 and their phylogenetic association with annelids (Figure 13-2), though they lack the segmentation and setae (bristles on the body composed of the protein chitin) that are hallmark characteristics of the Annelida.

The exact number of sipunculids is not known, but 250 species have currently been described. They are relatively abundant in the marine habitat, occurring from the intertidal to depths of 5,000 m. Some species inhabit mud, others the empty shells of deceased organisms, and still others bore into rock like the piddock bivalves (Figure 11-9H, bottom). They have muscular body walls and an anterior crown of 18–24 ciliated tentacles (above, right), which may be withdrawn and everted as part of a structure called the **introvert** (*intro*—inward, *vert*—to turn) (Figure 13-3).

Some species are detritivores and others are suspension feeders, but little is known about feeding styles of the group as a whole. Gases appear to be exchanged across the tentacles and introvert.

Both sexual and asexual reproduction occurs, although asexual reproduction is uncommon.

Table 13-1 provides specific information about sipunculid classes.

■ Table **13-1** ≈ Sipunculid Classes

Class	General Description	Examples	Approximate Number of Species	Etymology
Sipunculidea (Figures 13-3 through 13-5)	Tentacles at the end of the introvert and surrounding the mouth	*Golfingia, Sipunculus,* and *Themiste*	Estimate not available	*sipunculus*—a little siphon
Phascolosomatidea	Tentacles arranged in an arc at the tip of the introvert	*Aspidosiphon* and *Phascolosoma*	Estimate not available	*phascolo*—a leather bag, *somato*—a body

109

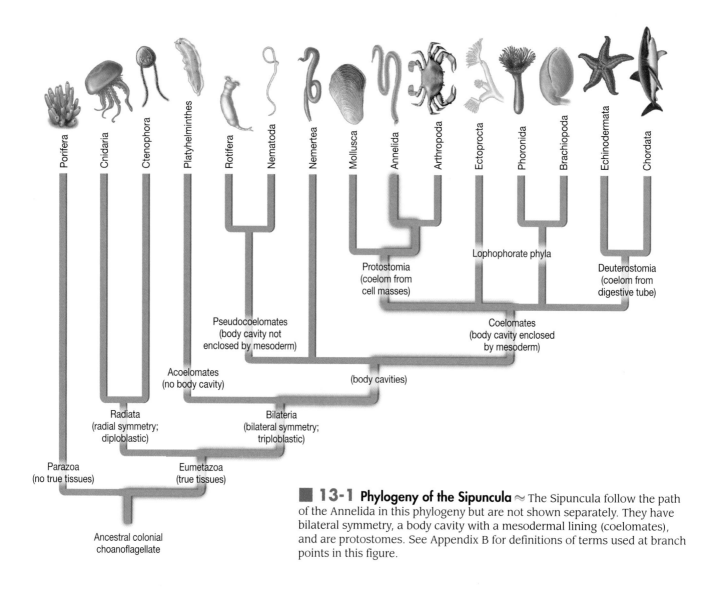

Porifera
Cnidaria
Ctenophora
Platyhelminthes
Rotifera
Nematoda
Nemertea
Mollusca
Annelida
Arthropoda
Ectoprocta
Phoronida
Brachiopoda
Echinodermata
Chordata

Protostomia
(coelom from
cell masses)

Lophophorate phyla

Deuterostomia
(coelom from
digestive tube)

Pseudocoelomates
(body cavity not
enclosed by mesoderm)

Coelomates
(body cavity enclosed
by mesoderm)

Acoelomates
(no body cavity)

(body cavities)

Radiata
(radial symmetry;
diploblastic)

Bilateria
(bilateral symmetry;
triploblastic)

Parazoa
(no true tissues)

Eumetazoa
(true tissues)

Ancestral colonial
choanoflagellate

13-1 Phylogeny of the Sipuncula ≈ The Sipuncula follow the path
of the Annelida in this phylogeny but are not shown separately. They have
bilateral symmetry, a body cavity with a mesodermal lining (coelomates),
and are protostomes. See Appendix B for definitions of terms used at branch
points in this figure.

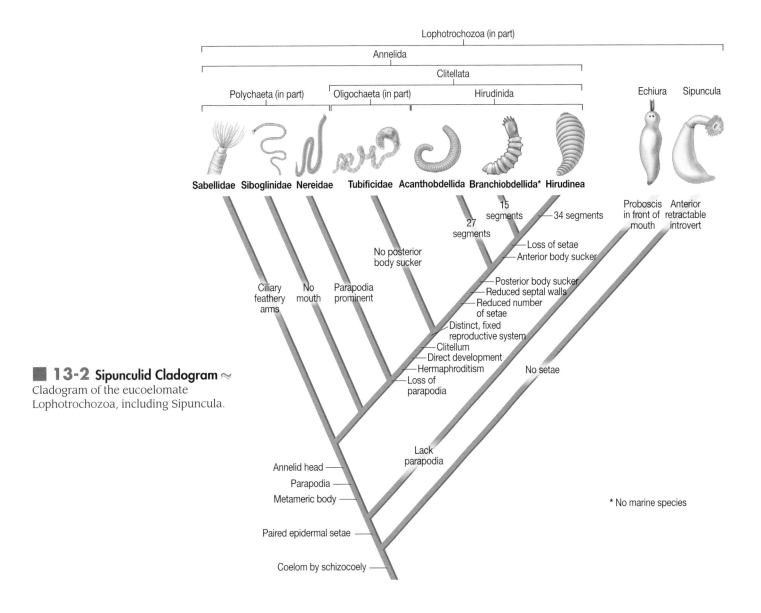

13-2 Sipunculid Cladogram ≈
Cladogram of the eucoelomate Lophotrochozoa, including Sipuncula.

Lophotrochozoa (in part)
Annelida
Clitellata
Polychaeta (in part)   Oligochaeta (in part)   Hirudinida
Echiura   Sipuncula

Sabellidae Siboglinidae Nereidae Tubificidae Acanthobdellida Branchiobdellida* Hirudinea

Proboscis in front of mouth   Anterior retractable introvert

15 segments — — 34 segments

27 segments

Loss of setae
Anterior body sucker

No posterior body sucker

Posterior body sucker
Reduced septal walls
Reduced number of setae

Ciliary feathery arms   No mouth   Parapodia prominent

Distinct, fixed reproductive system
Clitellum
Direct development
Hermaphroditism
Loss of parapodia

No setae

Lack parapodia

Annelid head
Parapodia
Metameric body

* No marine species

Paired epidermal setae

Coelom by schizocoely

1. Mouth   2. Introvert   3. Trunk   4. Papillae (bumps)

13-3 **Peanut worm** ≈ On this specimen (*Sipunculus*), note the gourd-shaped body with introvert. Tentacles are not visible. (**A**), (**B**), and (**E**) show the introvert extended; *(continued)*

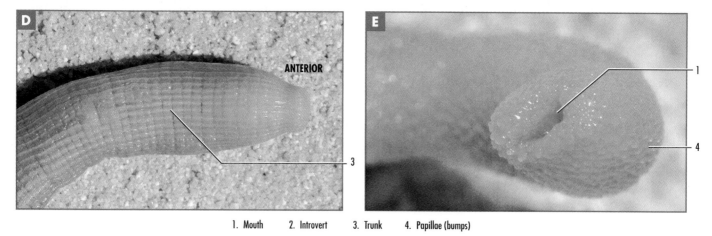

1. Mouth   2. Introvert   3. Trunk   4. Papillae (bumps)

■ **13-3 Peanut worm** ≈ *(continued)* (C) and (D) show the introvert retracted. The integument has deep longitudinal and transverse grooves that superficially resemble segmentation (and the surface of a peanut). However, the sipunculans are unsegmented worms.

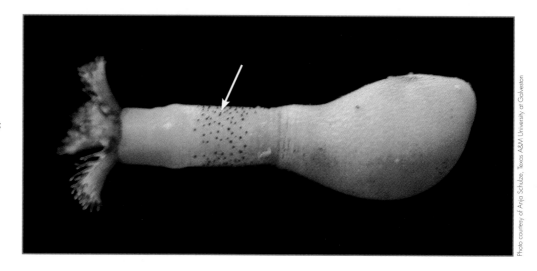

■ **13-4 Peanut worm** ≈
Themiste alutacea has scattered dark hooks along its introvert (arrow). Note the extended tentacles in contrast to *Sipunculus* (see Figure 13-3). *T. alutacea* occurs in the Western Atlantic.

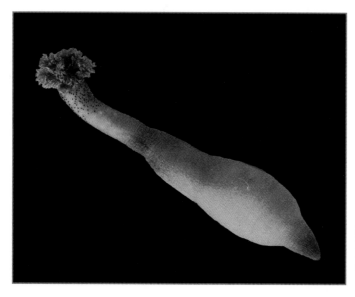

■ **13-5 Peanut worm** ≈ *Themiste pyrodies* occurs in the Eastern and Western Pacific. Note the extended tentacles and lack of segmentation characteristic of the sipunculids.

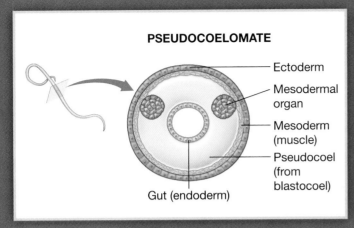

PSEUDOCOELOMATE

- Ectoderm
- Mesodermal organ
- Mesoderm (muscle)
- Pseudocoel (from blastocoel)
- Gut (endoderm)

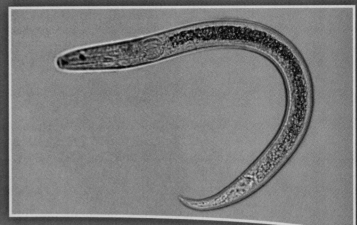

14 Nematoda

The nematodes (*nema*–thread) are an extremely important group of pseudocoelomates, both ecologically and in terms of the sheer number of individuals. There are species adapted to virtually all habitats, including the marine environment. Like all ecdysozoans, the roundworms are covered with a cuticle that must be molted as they grow.

Nematodes have bilateral symmetry, with a cylindrical body tapered at both ends, a complete digestive system, and a body wall with longitudinal muscles only. There are no respiratory or circulatory organs and the excretory organs are simple, if present. They show the protostome, pseudocoelomate pattern of development (Figures 14-1 and 14-2).

Nematodes generally have separate sexes and the males are smaller than females. Fertilization is internal and their eggs are microscopic with an environmentally resistant chitinous shell covering each egg.

Nematodes (Figure 14-3) are found throughout the world's oceans from pole to pole and from the surface to the depths of oceanic trenches. When sampling is done, the number of nematodes in marine sediments can be in the thousands per square meter of surface! Free-living forms range from the microscopic to a few centimeters. Species range from detritivores, carnivores, herbivores, and omnivores to parasites.

More than 25,000 nematodes species have been documented, but an understanding of their systematics has lagged, a situation made worse by the fact that experts estimate there are actually 500,000 to 1 million species. If accurate, this group would rival the insects in terms of total number of species. However, even the number of classes is disputed, in part because species are difficult to distinguish. Making things worse, their inclusion in the Ecdysozoa (Figure 14-4) is not even strongly supported by the available evidence. However, the evidence is compelling that they are a sister clade with the Nematomorpha (Figure 14-4). Although a considerable mountain of evidence exists to suggest that the two traditional nematode classes are inadequate, replacement taxonomies are disputed. Until monophylies are satisfactorily established, we present the traditional classes (Table 14-1) even though it is extremely likely that at least the Adenophorea is paraphyletic.

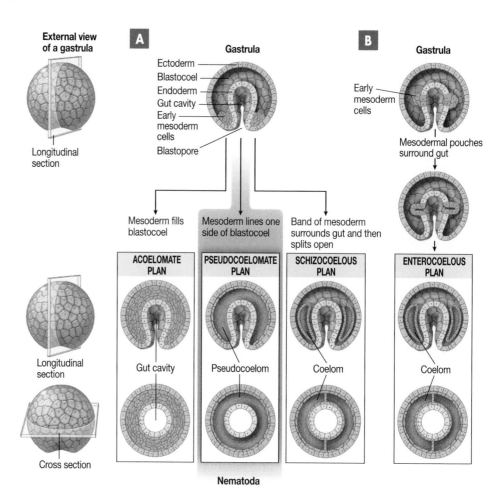

External view
of a gastrula

Longitudinal
section

A

Gastrula

Ectoderm
Blastocoel
Endoderm
Gut cavity
Early
mesoderm
cells
Blastopore

B

Gastrula

Early
mesoderm
cells

Mesodermal pouches
surround gut

Mesoderm fills
blastocoel

Mesoderm lines one
side of blastocoel

Band of mesoderm
surrounds gut and then
splits open

**ACOELOMATE
PLAN**

**PSEUDOCOELOMATE
PLAN**

**SCHIZOCOELOUS
PLAN**

**ENTEROCOELOUS
PLAN**

Gut cavity

Pseudocoelom

Coelom

Coelom

Longitudinal
section

Cross section

Nematoda

■ **14-1 Pseudocoelomate
Developmental Pattern** ≈
The generalized developmental
pattern of the protostomes is
shown in (**A**). The generalized
developmental pattern of the
deuterostomes is shown in (**B**).
Nematoda demonstrate the
pseudocoelomate plan.

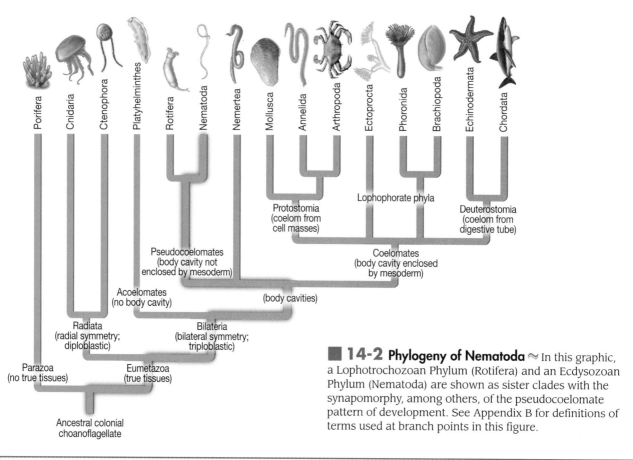

Porifera

Cnidaria

Ctenophora

Platyhelminthes

Rotifera

Nematoda

Nemertea

Mollusca

Annelida

Arthropoda

Ectoprocta

Phoronida

Brachiopoda

Echinodermata

Chordata

Protostomia
(coelom from
cell masses)

Lophophorate phyla

Deuterostomia
(coelom from
digestive tube)

Pseudocoelomates
(body cavity not
enclosed by mesoderm)

Coelomates
(body cavity enclosed
by mesoderm)

Acoelomates
(no body cavity)

(body cavities)

Radiata
(radial symmetry;
diploblastic)

Bilateria
(bilateral symmetry;
triploblastic)

Parazoa
(no true tissues)

Eumetazoa
(true tissues)

Ancestral colonial
choanoflagellate

■ **14-2 Phylogeny of Nematoda** ≈ In this graphic,
a Lophotrochozoan Phylum (Rotifera) and an Ecdysozoan
Phylum (Nematoda) are shown as sister clades with the
synapomorphy, among others, of the pseudocoelomate
pattern of development. See Appendix B for definitions of
terms used at branch points in this figure.

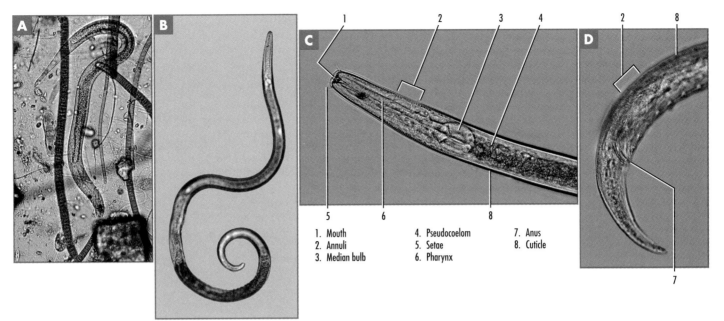

1. Mouth
2. Annuli
3. Median bulb
4. Pseudocoelom
5. Setae
6. Pharynx
7. Anus
8. Cuticle

■ **14-3 Littoral Nematode** ~ (**A**) This micrograph shows a Nematode taken from the high littoral zone of a rocky habitat along the Eastern Pacific. (**B**) Morphological and anatomical features in this free-living nematode are visible. Look closely. (**C**) and (**D**) show the complex outer covering called the cuticle with its surface rings called annuli. At first glance the worm appears segmented, but annuli are superficial.

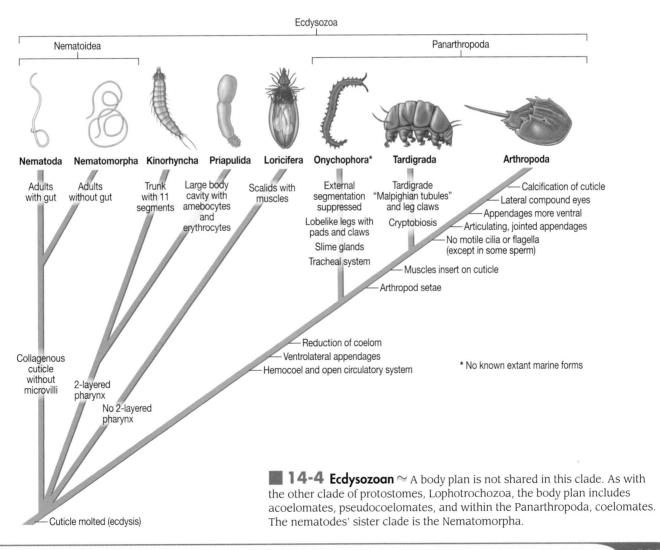

■ **14-4 Ecdysozoan** ~ A body plan is not shared in this clade. As with the other clade of protostomes, Lophotrochozoa, the body plan includes acoelomates, pseudocoelomates, and within the Panarthropoda, coelomates. The nematodes' sister clade is the Nematomorpha.

Class	General Description	Examples	Approximate Number of Species	Etymology
Adenophorea	Mostly free-living; lacking tail sensory organs; anterior sensory organs large	*Monhstera* and *Plectus*	Marine number not known	*adeno*—a gland, *phore*—carry
Secernentea (Figures 14-3 and 14-4)	Tail sensory organs present; paired excretory organs	*Metastongylus*	Marine number not known	*Se*—apart, *cerne*—to separate

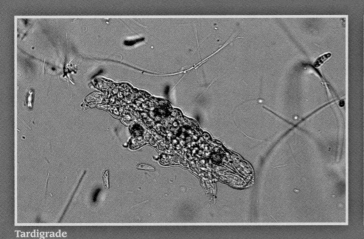

Tardigrade

Tardigrade

15 Tardigrada

Tardigrada, or water bears (Figure 15-1), are found predominantly in freshwater or damp terrestrial ecosystems. They are tiny (typically 0.5 mm or less), yet complex animals. Of approximately 930 species, about 160 are marine. Water bears are extremely abundant meiofauna (borderline microscopic animals), however due to their small size, we know little about their ecological niche in interstitial communities.

The tardigrade body has a chitinous, segmented exoskeleton, and four pairs of legs with claws; three pairs function in forward motion, and the rear-facing posterior pair is used for reversing. Modified mouthparts (**buccal**

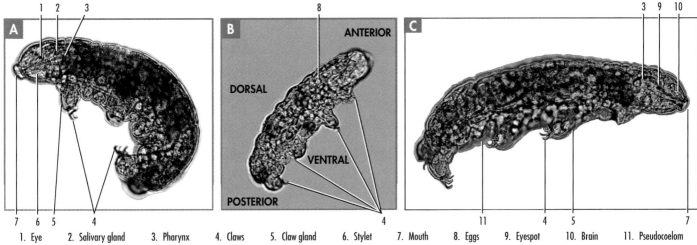

1. Eye   2. Salivary gland   3. Pharynx   4. Claws   5. Claw gland   6. Stylet   7. Mouth   8. Eggs   9. Eyespot   10. Brain   11. Pseudocoelom

■ **15-1 Tardigrade** ≈ This live specimen shows the characteristic morphology of this clade. They have no apparent body segments and a ventral nerve cord. Note the claws and what appear to be "stubby" legs (actually claw glands). In (**A**) the eyespot, surrounding salivary gland, stylet (used to pierce plant cells and eat the cell contents), and mouth are indicated. In (**B**), all four "legs" can be seen. (**C**) Indicates the claws on each "leg," an eyespot, stylets, mouth, and brain (anterior portion of the ventral nerve cord). These specimens are approximately 200 to 250 μm.

stylets) are used for puncturing and sucking prey, typically nematodes and other meiofauna. One unique tardigrade characteristic is their ability to survive extreme conditions, such as desiccation, pressure, and radiation, by entering a near-death state of suspended metabolism called **crypto-biosis** (*crypto*–hidden, *bios*–life). Physically, they become dried out and rolled up to form a **tun** (*tun*–a cask), which can survive for up to ten years! Aided by intermittent cryptobiosis, tardigrades can live for over a hundred years. Due to their extreme hardiness, two tardigrade species were subjected to, and survived, exposure to UV light in outer space for ten days in 2008.

Most water bears are dioecious, though many asexual species reproduce via **parthenogenesis** (*partheno*—with fertilization, *genesis*—origin). In sexual reproduction, sperm is typically deposited in the female through a **gono-pore** (*gono*—seed, *pore*—a passage), either before or during molting. Development is direct, with no larval stage.

Tardigrade phylogeny has not been resolved. Recent evidence suggests that they may be closely related to arthropods and Onychophora (velvet worms) in the clade Pan-arthropoda. One phylogeny for the Ecdysozoa, animals that shed their exoskeleton, is proposed in Figure 15-2. Characteristics of tardigrade classes are provided in Table 15-1.

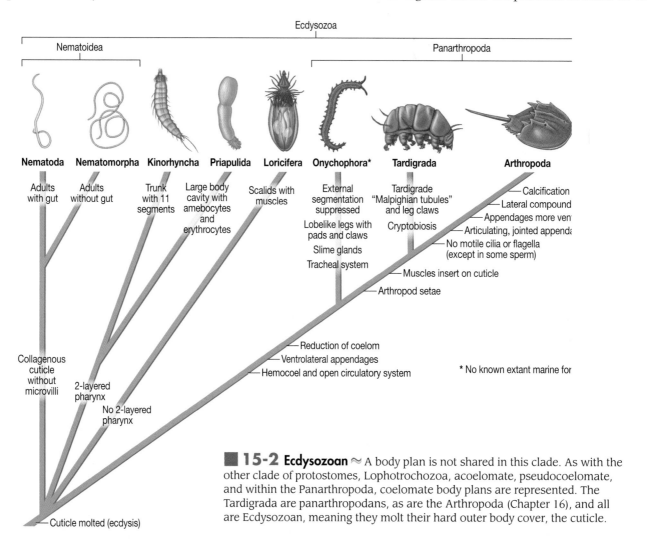

■ **15-2 Ecdysozoan** ≈ A body plan is not shared in this clade. As with the other clade of protostomes, Lophotrochozoa, acoelomate, pseudocoelomate, and within the Panarthropoda, coelomate body plans are represented. The Tardigrada are panarthropodans, as are the Arthropoda (Chapter 16), and all are Ecdysozoan, meaning they molt their hard outer body cover, the cuticle.

■ **Table 15-1** ≈ Tardigrade Classes

Class	General Description	Examples	Approximate Number of Species	Etymology
Eutardigrada	Without lateral appendages	*Halobiotus*	≈3	*eu*—true, *tardi*—slow, *grada*—steps
Heterotardigrada (Figure 15-1)	Appendages with four similar claws	*Archechiniscidea* and *Batillipedidae*	Marine number not clear	*hetero*—different, *tardi*—slow, *grada*—steps
Mesotardigrada	Six claws of equal length at each foot	*Thermozodium esakii*	1	*meso*—middle, *tardi*—slow, *grada*—steps

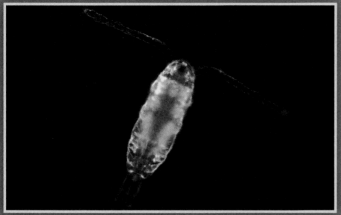
Calanoid copepod

Unidentified shrimp

16 Arthropoda

Arthropods are the most diverse and successful invertebrate group on the planet with over 1.5 million recognized species, although it is widely presumed there may be as many as 30 million waiting to be described (Table 16-1). Marine arthropods include sessile (e.g., barnacles) and mobile individuals, as well as planktonic and benthic representatives. In general, arthropods have a chitinous jointed exoskeleton, and display specialized segmentation. They have compound eyes and one or two pair of antennae.

One possible cladogram explaining the relationship within the Arthropoda is depicted in Figure 16-1. The Myriapoda are terrestrial, and the Hexapoda (mostly insects) are almost entirely terrestrial and freshwater. The Chelicerata (*cheli*—claw, *cer*—horn, *ata*—group suffix) and Crustacea (*crusta*—shell, *acea*—group suffix), both with abundant marine representatives, are discussed below. Figures 16-2 and 16-3 show the relationship of Arthropoda to other Animalia.

Chelicerata

Chelicerata is an ancient group. Among the approximately 70,000 extant species few are marine, with only four species of horseshoe crabs (Merostomata) and approximately

1,000 species of Pycnogonida (sea spiders). Pycnogonids (Figure 16-4) and horseshoe crabs (Figure 16-5) are both benthic. Morphologically, chelicerates are characterized by a loss of antennae, and having a prehensile first pair of appendages (**chelicerae**) and two segments: a cephalothorax and an abdomen.

Horseshoe crabs have a heavily armored **carapace** (*carapace*—tortoise shell), possess specialized book gills, and a long tail spine (**telson**). They are omnivorous, eating mostly algae, worms, and molluscs. The only horseshoe crab in the United States, *Limulus polyphemus*, is found along nearshore, sandy habitats on the East Coast (Western Atlantic).

Horseshoe crabs are dioecious and their reproduction is external. The male releases sperm onto the eggs that the female deposits in the sand. A 1 cm trilobite larva develops from the zygote. As it develops and molts the telson grows and adult characteristics develop.

Pycnogonids are small, usually drab but sometimes brightly colored, animals that are often inconspicuous due to their size (averaging 1 to 10 mm). They are found throughout the ocean, ranging from nearshore to deep sea, and poles to tropics. Most species are benthic, though some can swim. Pycnogonids are predators of small, soft-bodied invertebrates. They have 4–6 pairs of legs, a pair of modified **ovigerous** legs for carrying eggs (in males and

Subphylum Class Subclass/Order	General Description	Examples	Approximate Number of Species	Etymology
Chelicerata (Figure 16-6)	With two body segments; the cephalothorax and abdomen with six pairs of cephalothoracic appendages, including a pair of mouthparts called the chelicerae and four pairs of walking legs; no antennae	Horseshoe crabs and sea spiders	1,000	*cheli*—claw, *cer*—horn, *ata*—group suffix
Pycnogonida (Figure 16-4)	Body mostly cephalothorax; mouth on a long proboscis; no respiratory system	*Nymphon* and *Pycnogonum*	1,000	*pycno*—compact, *goni*—knee
Merostomata (Figure 16-5)	Appendages with gills; compound lateral eyes	Horseshoe crabs, including *Limulus polyphemus* and *Tachypleus gigas*	4	*meros*—thigh, *stoma*—mouth
Crustacea (Figure 16-7)	Gills; head appendages, including two pairs of antennae; nauplius larval stage	*Squilla, Panulirus, Balanus, Cancer, Uca,* and *Lepas*	67,000	*crusta*—shell, *acea*—group suffix
Ostracoda (Figure 16-8)	Bivalve carapace; unsegmented body	*Cypridina* and *Gigantocyrpis*	6,000	*ostraco*—having a shell
Maxillopoda	Highly variable in number of segments for head, thorax, and abdomen; telson present	*Caridea, Dendrobanchiata,* and *Acetes*	10,000	*maxilla*—jawbone, *poda*—foot
Copepoda (Figure 16-9)	Four to five pairs of swimming legs; no carapace	*Calanus, Caligus,* and *Anomalocera*	13,000	*cope*—oar, *poda*—foot
Cirripedia (Figures 16-10 and 16-11)	Sessile with a reduced head and abdomen; carapace secretes plates composed of calcium carbonate; antennules become organs of attachment	*Balanus, Chthamalus, Tetraclita, Pollicipes,* and *Megabalanus*	1,200	*cirrus*—curl of hair, *pedis*—foot
Malacostraca	All segments with appendages; carapace covering part or all of thorax and head; head fused to one or more thoracic somites	*Idotea, Ligea, Gammarus, Squilla, Euphausia,* and *Cancer*	29,000	*malacos*—soft, *ostraco*—shell
Isopoda (Figure 16-12)	Body generally dorsoventrally flattened; no carapace	*Idotea* and *Ligea*	4,500 marine	*iso*—equal, *poda*—foot
Amphipoda (Figure 16-13)	No carapace; body generally compressed laterally	*Gammarus* and *Cyamus*	7,000	*amphi*—on both sides, *poda*—foot
Stomatopoda (Figure 16-14)	Small thorax and head with a large abdomen; a preying mantis look from enlarged, second thoracic appendages	*Lysiosquilla, Pullosquilla,* and *Nannosquilla*	400	*stomato*—mouth, *poda*—foot
Euphausiacea (Figure 16-15)	Carapace fused to all thorax segments	*Euphausia*	90	*eu*—well, *phausi*—bright, *acea*—pertaining to
Decapoda (Figures 16-16 and 16-17)	Carapace fused with and covering thoracic segments; eyes on stalks; five pairs of walking legs	*Cancer* and *Pagurus*	18,000	*deca*—ten, *poda*—foot

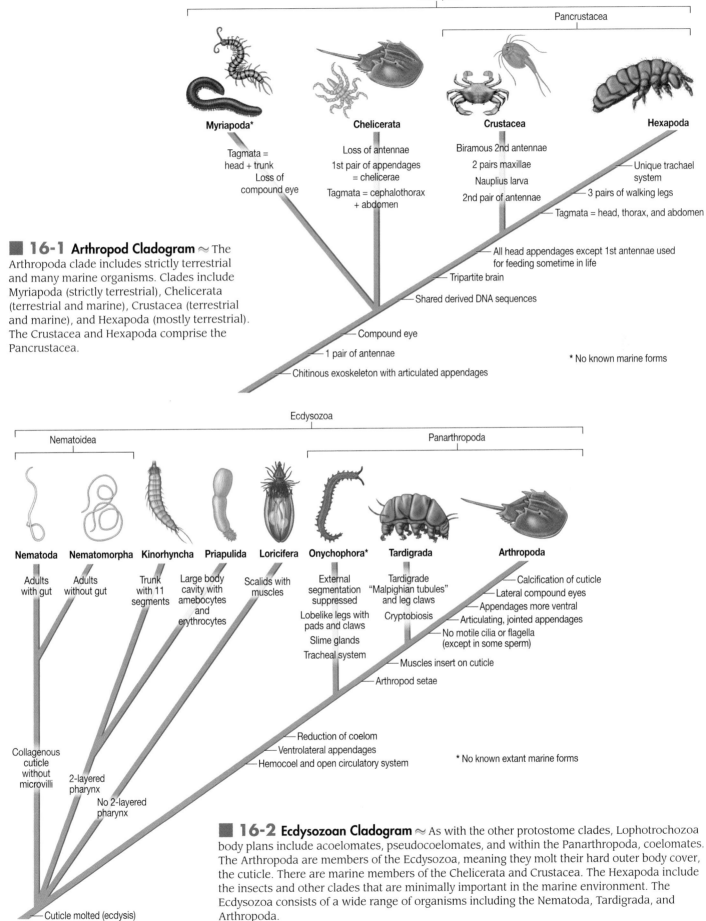

Arthropoda

Pancrustacea

Myriapoda*

Tagmata =
head + trunk
Loss of
compound eye

Chelicerata

Loss of antennae
1st pair of appendages
= chelicerae
Tagmata = cephalothorax
+ abdomen

Crustacea

Biramous 2nd antennae
2 pairs maxillae
Nauplius larva
2nd pair of antennae

Hexapoda

Unique trachael
system
3 pairs of walking legs
Tagmata = head, thorax, and abdomen

All head appendages except 1st antennae used
for feeding sometime in life
Tripartite brain
Shared derived DNA sequences

Compound eye
1 pair of antennae
Chitinous exoskeleton with articulated appendages

* No known marine forms

■ **16-1 Arthropod Cladogram** ≈ The
Arthropoda clade includes strictly terrestrial
and many marine organisms. Clades include
Myriapoda (strictly terrestrial), Chelicerata
(terrestrial and marine), Crustacea (terrestrial
and marine), and Hexapoda (mostly terrestrial).
The Crustacea and Hexapoda comprise the
Pancrustacea.

Ecdysozoa

Nematoidea

Panarthropoda

Nematoda

Adults
with gut

Nematomorpha

Adults
without gut

Kinorhyncha

Trunk
with 11
segments

Priapulida

Large body
cavity with
amebocytes
and
erythrocytes

Loricifera

Scalids with
muscles

Onychophora*

External
segmentation
suppressed
Lobelike legs with
pads and claws
Slime glands
Tracheal system

Tardigrada

Tardigrade
"Malpighian tubules"
and leg claws
Cryptobiosis

Arthropoda

Calcification of cuticle
Lateral compound eyes
Appendages more ventral
Articulating, jointed appendages
No motile cilia or flagella
(except in some sperm)
Muscles insert on cuticle
Arthropod setae

Reduction of coelom
Ventrolateral appendages
Hemocoel and open circulatory system

* No known extant marine forms

Collagenous
cuticle
without
microvilli

2-layered
pharynx

No 2-layered
pharynx

Cuticle molted (ecdysis)

■ **16-2 Ecdysozoan Cladogram** ≈ As with the other protostome clades, Lophotrochozoa
body plans include acoelomates, pseudocoelomates, and within the Panarthropoda, coelomates.
The Arthropoda are members of the Ecdysozoa, meaning they molt their hard outer body cover,
the cuticle. There are marine members of the Chelicerata and Crustacea. The Hexapoda include
the insects and other clades that are minimally important in the marine environment. The
Ecdysozoa consists of a wide range of organisms including the Nematoda, Tardigrada, and
Arthropoda.

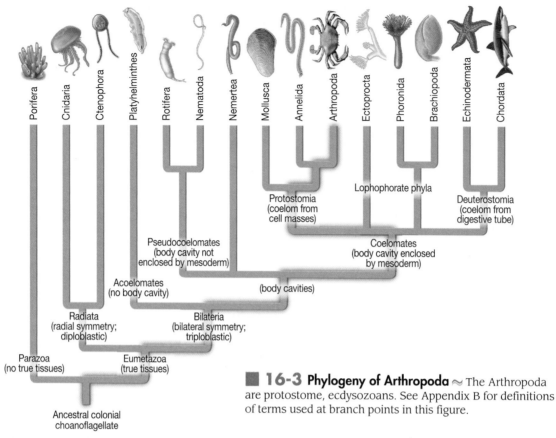

Porifera
Cnidaria
Ctenophora
Platyhelminthes
Rotifera
Nematoda
Nemertea
Mollusca
Annelida
Arthropoda
Ectoprocta
Phoronida
Brachiopoda
Echinodermata
Chordata

Protostomia
(coelom from
cell masses)

Lophophorate phyla

Deuterostomia
(coelom from
digestive tube)

Pseudocoelomates
(body cavity not
enclosed by mesoderm)

Coelomates
(body cavity enclosed
by mesoderm)

Acoelomates
(no body cavity)

(body cavities)

Radiata
(radial symmetry;
diploblastic)

Bilateria
(bilateral symmetry;
triploblastic)

Parazoa
(no true tissues)

Eumetazoa
(true tissues)

Ancestral colonial
choanoflagellate

■ **16-3 Phylogeny of Arthropoda** ~ The Arthropoda are protostome, ecdysozoans. See Appendix B for definitions of terms used at branch points in this figure.

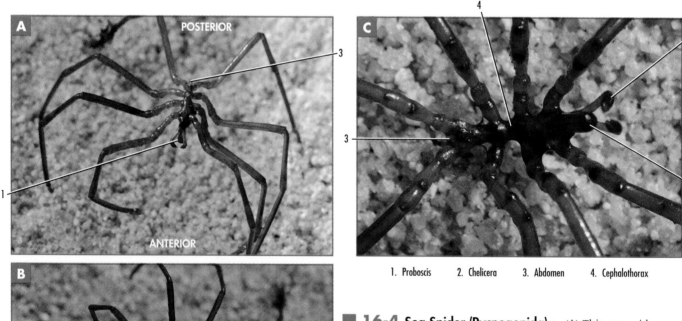

1. Proboscis   2. Chelicera   3. Abdomen   4. Cephalothorax

■ **16-4 Sea Spider (Pycnogonida)** ~ (A) This sea spider shows the characteristics that make these organisms members of the clade Chelicerata. Their body is composed of two segments: cephalothorax (prosoma) and a very small abdomen (opisthosoma). They generally have six pairs of cephalothoracic appendages that include a pair of mouthparts called chelicerae. Most chelicerates use their mouthparts to draw fluids from the bodies of their prey. (B) A dorsal view of the specimen. The Pycnogonida occur throughout all oceans but are most abundant in polar portions of the world's ocean. They occur from the littoral to depths of 7,000 m. (C) Ventral view of this specimen.

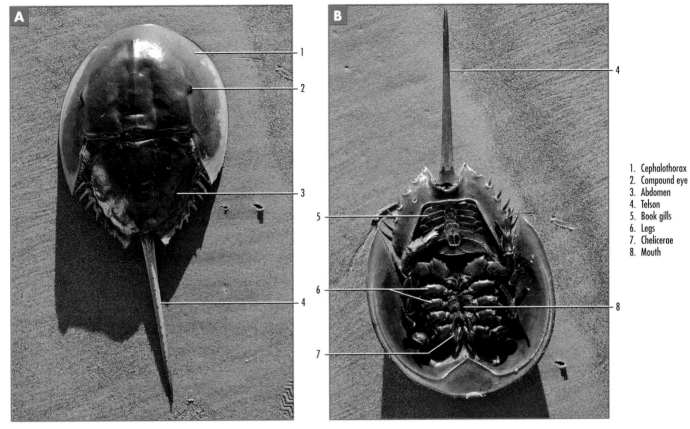

1. Cephalothorax
2. Compound eye
3. Abdomen
4. Telson
5. Book gills
6. Legs
7. Chelicerae
8. Mouth

■ **16-5 Atlantic Horseshoe Crab (Merostomata)** ≈ **(A)** This is a dorsal view of the horseshoe crab, *Limulus polyphemus*, which occurs along the Western Atlantic from Nova Scotia to the Yucatan Peninsula. The carapace covering the cephalothorax is a single, unsegmented piece and to some appears shaped like a horseshoe. They are nocturnal and omnivorous (the crab, not the persons who believe that it looks like a horseshoe). **(B)** In this ventral view, legs, telson, and book gills are visible.

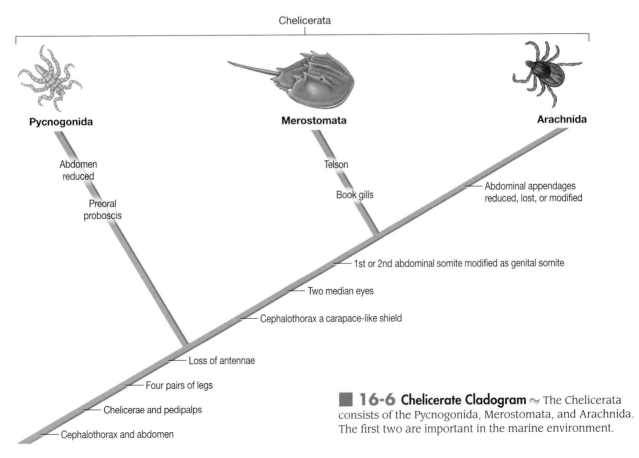

Chelicerata

Pycnogonida

Merostomata

Arachnida

Abdomen reduced

Preoral proboscis

Telson

Book gills

Abdominal appendages reduced, lost, or modified

1st or 2nd abdominal somite modified as genital somite

Two median eyes

Cephalothorax a carapace-like shield

Loss of antennae

Four pairs of legs

Chelicerae and pedipalps

Cephalothorax and abdomen

■ **16-6 Chelicerate Cladogram** ≈ The Chelicerata consists of the Pycnogonida, Merostomata, and Arachnida. The first two are important in the marine environment.

sometimes females), a long preoral tubular **proboscis**, multiple genital openings (gonopores), and a reduced abdomen.

Pycnogonid reproduction is sexual and fertilization occurs as eggs exit the female's gonopores. The male collects the eggs, attaches them to himself, and carries them on his ovigers. The male broods the eggs, and upon hatching a **protonymphon** larva emerges (similar to the nauplius of crustacea [see Figure 16-11], but nonhomologous), and continues to develop via molting.

A Chelicerate cladogram is depicted in Figure 16-6.

Crustacea

The crustaceans include familiar species, such as lobsters, crabs, and shrimp, as well as inconspicuous but ecologically important species, such as copepods. There are approximately 67,000 extant species, most of which are marine. Crustaceans are ubiquitous in the ocean, and can be found as epifauna and infauna nearshore, in the deep ocean, in the tropics, at the poles, and as plankton. Many crustaceans serve as the basis for economically important fisheries around the world.

Traits of the Crustacea include: double-branched (**biramous**) second antennae, two pairs of feeding appendages

(maxillae), compound eyes and/or ocelli (diminutive of *oculus*—eye) and a **nauplius larva** (see Figures 16-9 and 16-11). The body is typically divided into two parts, the cephalothorax and the abdomen.

The Subphylum Crustacea is extremely diverse and difficult to categorize based on morphology and feeding mechanisms. Sizes range from less than a millimeter to over 3 m (spider crab). One possible crustacean cladogram is represented in Figure 16-7.

Remipedia consists of approximately 20 species found only in caves with both freshwater and marine connections. Known only from a few locations, they were first discovered in the Bahamas in 1981. These crustaceans look similar to polychaete worms and feed as predators or scavengers.

Cephalocarida are epibenthic shrimp-like crustaceans approximately 2 to 4 mm in length. There are only about nine species discovered so far. They were first discovered in 1953. Cephalocarids are blind and feed on detritus.

Branchiopoda are mostly freshwater crustaceans, many of which are found in vernal pools and freshwater lakes. One group, the Cladocera, includes a few marine species.

Enclosed in a bivalve carapace, members of the class Ostracoda (Figure 16-8) resemble small clams. They are important in food chains and distributed worldwide.

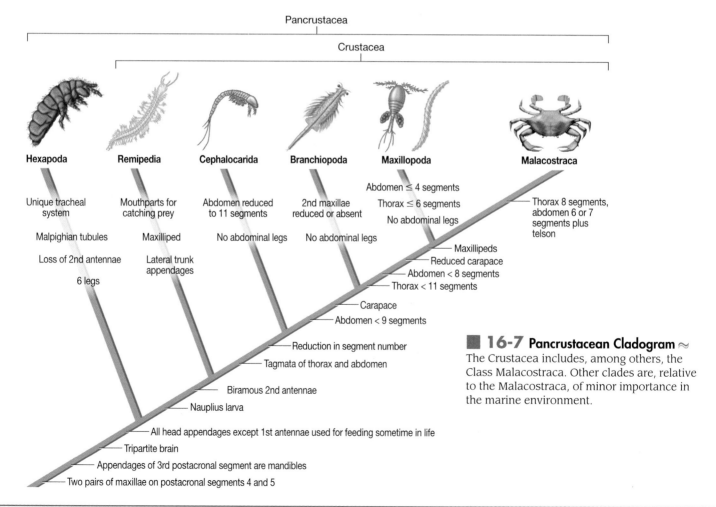

16-7 Pancrustacean Cladogram ≈
The Crustacea includes, among others, the Class Malacostraca. Other clades are, relative to the Malacostraca, of minor importance in the marine environment.

Species are highly variable in their ecological role, with some planktonic and others benthic. Most species have separate sexes and reproduce sexually, but there are parthenogenetic species.

Maxillopoda is a taxon encompassing the following groups: Copepoda, Mystacocarida, Tantulocarida, Cirripedia, Branchiura, and Pentastomida. Copepoda and Cirripedia are covered here. Maxillopoda share the following traits: a naupliar eye, an abdomen with four or less segments, a thorax with six or less segments, no abdominal legs, and genital appendages on the first abdominal segment.

Copepoda (Figure 16-9) are tiny (0.5 to 15 mm), essential herbivores in planktonic food webs, although there are carnivorous species. Most copepods are marine, and of those, most are planktonic, though parasitic and intertidal species exist. They display diurnal migration patterns, coming up to the surface to feed on phytoplankton each night, and retreating to depth during the day. Copepods are dioecious and most are sexually dimorphic with internal fertilization. In most species, eggs are brooded in sacs and carried by the female. There are six stages of nauplius larvae followed by five **copepodite** (larval stages resembling

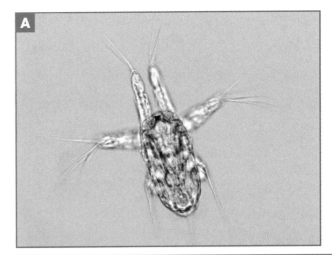

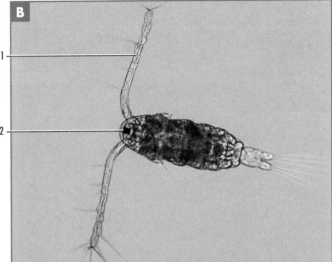

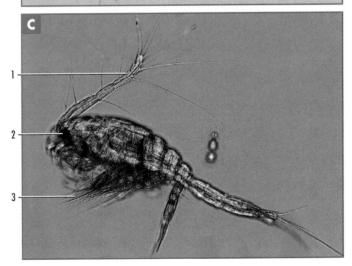

1. Antennule   2. Eye   3. Thoracic appendages

■ **16-9 Copepod (Copepoda)** ≈ As you examine these photos, note the spiny projections that help prevent sinking. (**A**) In the copepod order Calanoida, eggs hatch as a nauplius larva (seen in dorsal view) and will metamorphose into a copepodite larval form. (**B**) Extremely abundant in surface waters and as a result, in plankton tow samples, copepods (*Calanus*, seen here in dorsal view) are a major member of the marine zooplankton and a food source for other invertebrates and many vertebrates. For the most part, planktonic copepods are suspension feeders relying on phyto-planktors for food. (**C**) Shown is a lateral view of a second copepod.

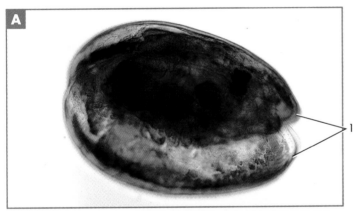

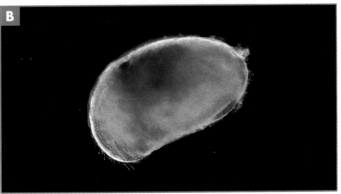

1. Shell

■ **16-8 Seed Shrimp (Ostracoda)** ≈ (**A**) Called seed shrimp, the ostracods have a bivalve carapace shell covering a body of highly fused segments. The "shell" may be chitinous or calcareous. (**B**) Because of their small size (frequently about 1 mm) and because the chitinous valves are often partially transparent, they are frequently overlooked by the casual observer. They are common in plankton tow samples.

the adult except they have an unsegmented abdomen and three pairs of thoracic limbs) larval stages of development.

Cirripedia (barnacles) are often mistaken for molluscs when closed up in their calcareous shell (Figure 16-10).

Barnacles are entirely marine and mostly benthic, though some commensal species exist. Barnacles are oriented upside down, with their head attached to the substrate. They use six pairs of **cirri** (thoracic appendages) to filter

Buckshot barnacle

Giant acorn barnacle

Red and white barnacle

Goose-necked barnacle

1. Cirri   2. Peduncle   3. Angular unicorn snail preying upon goose-necked barnacle   4. Mussel

■ **16-10 Barnacles (Cirripedia)** ≈ **(A)** *Chthamalus*, the buckshot barnacle, will cover large areas in the high littoral zone if space is available. **(B)** When feeding, cirripedia extend their jointed appendages into the water using a sweeping motion to suspension feed. **(C)** *Balanus tintinnabulum*, the red and white barnacle on the left, can be seen extending its thoracic appendages between its shell plates, whereas the one at the bottom has its plates closed. **(D)** (left) The goose-necked barnacle, *Pollycipes polymerus*, occurs in the Northeastern Pacific in the littoral zone. It is a stalked barnacle with a peduncle (middle) connecting the dorsal surface of the barnacle to the substrate. It frequently occurs in mixed beds with *Mytilus californianus*, and is frequently preyed upon by the angular unicorn snail (right), *Acanthina spirata*.

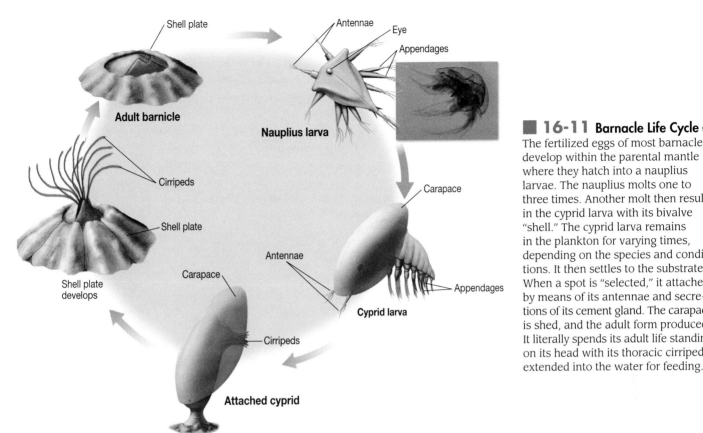

Shell plate

Adult barnicle

Nauplius larva

Antennae — Eye

Appendages

Cirripeds

Shell plate

Carapace

Antennae

Shell plate develops

Carapace

Appendages

Cyprid larva

Cirripeds

Attached cyprid

■ **16-11 Barnacle Life Cycle** ≈
The fertilized eggs of most barnacles develop within the parental mantle where they hatch into a nauplius larvae. The nauplius molts one to three times. Another molt then results in the cyprid larva with its bivalve "shell." The cyprid larva remains in the plankton for varying times, depending on the species and conditions. It then settles to the substrate. When a spot is "selected," it attaches by means of its antennae and secretions of its cement gland. The carapace is shed, and the adult form produced. It literally spends its adult life standing on its head with its thoracic cirripeds extended into the water for feeding.

feed and sweep food into their mouths. Barnacles are hermaphrodites and fertilization is internal. It is only upon examination of their nauplius larva that their relationship to crustaceans becomes apparent. During development, the nauplius larva is followed by a **cypris** larva. See Figure 16-11 for a generalized barnacle life cycle.

The Malacostraca includes approximately 29,000 extant crustacean species, and a diversity of large and familiar animals such as crabs, shrimp, lobsters, mantis shrimp, krill, amphipods, and mysids. Unifying characteristics of the group include an eight-part segmented thorax, an abdomen with six or seven segments, abdominal appendages, and a flattened telson. There are several groups (including isopods, Figure 16-12; amphipods, Figure 16-13; stomatopods, Figure 16-14; and euphausiids, Figure 16-15) included in the Malacostraca, but Decapoda will be used here as an example.

Benthic decapods include the true shrimp, crabs, and lobsters (Figure 16-16). There are approximately 1,000 extant species of decapods, most of which are marine, though some freshwater, and a few terrestrial species exist. Most decapods are both predators and scavengers and live epibenthic or infaunal lives. These are the largest crustaceans and many species are commercially important.

Decapods have two pairs of biramous antennae, a cephalothorax (head plus first three thoracic segments), three pairs of maxillipeds (mouth appendages) attached to the first three thoracic segments, stalked, compound eyes, a fused carapace enclosing the thorax and gills, and an abdomen (**pleon**) that protrudes from the posterior of the body.

Reproduction in decapods is sexual, and most species are dioecious. Fertilization is internal or external. Eggs may be released to the sea or brooded. Depending on the species, various larvae may hatch first, and there are often several larval stages. The ancestral types hatch out as nauplius or **metanauplius** larvae, and eggs of the more derived taxa start out as **zoea** or **protozoa**. See Figure 16-17 for a representative decapod life cycle.

■ **16-12 Isopods (Isopoda)** ≈ The flat-tailed isopod, *Idotea urotoma*, occurs in the middle and low littoral zone. Their color is highly variable, often matching their substrate. Commonly found under rocks, they may reach a length of 2 cm.

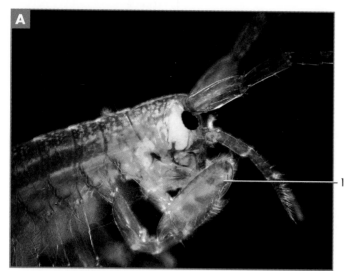

1. Gnatopod

16-13 Amphipod (Amphipoda) ≈ (A) *Parallorchestes ochotensis* is a common littoral inhabitant along the Northeastern Pacific. Note the lateral compression and large anterior gnatopods (*gnatho*—jaw, *pod*—foot), an appendage near the jaw. (B) This is an unidentified mudflat amphipod trapped in a sieve.

16-15 Krill (Euphausia) ≈ Commonly known as krill, there are 90 species of euphausiids. They are important in marine food chains as sources of food for a variety of large predators. Euphausiids feed on phytoplanktors.

Giant mantis shrimp

Oratosquilla oratoria

16-14 Mantis Shrimp (Stomatopoda) ≈ (A) The giant mantis shrimp, *Hemisquilla ensigera californiensis*, occurs in coastal regions of the Northeastern Pacific. It grows to 32 cm and spears/stuns its prey with the use of those large, praying mantis-like second thoracic appendages. It lives in burrows in sandy parts of its habitat. (B) *Oratosquilla oratoria* is a mantis shrimp occurring in the Western Pacific in coastal areas from 5 m to 60 m. It grows to 15 cm living in muddy bottoms where it constructs a burrow.

Red rock crab

1. Walking leg   2. Cheliped

16-16 Crabs (Decapoda) ≈ (A) The red rock crab, *Cancer productus*, occurs along the Northeastern Pacific coast. It inhabits the mid–littoral to sublittoral down to about 80 m. It is carnivorous. There are five pairs of appendages: four pair of walking legs and one pair of claws (chelipeds). *(continued)*

B 1. Male 2. Female

Fiddler crab

C Giant spider crab

D 1. Shell
2. Crab legs

Hermit crab

E 1. Staghorn hydrocoral
2. Hermit crab

Staghorn hermit crab

F Globose kelp crab

■ **16-16** **Crabs (Decapoda)** ≈ *(continued)* **(B)** (top, left) Fiddler crabs, *Uca crenulata*, occur in mudflats along the mid-Eastern Pacific. Note the enlarged claw of this male (used to signal females and to resist intrusion by other males). (top, right) This male is signaling a female and she is responding. Fiddler crabs live in burrows in the mud (bottom, left) and are easy to spot where they are active by the round balls of substrate they construct as they sift through the mud/sand in search of food (bottom, right). **(C)** The giant spider crab, *Macrocheira kaempferi*, is an inhabitant of coastal waters in the Northwestern Pacific at depths ranging from 50 to 600 m. It grows to a leg span of nearly 4 m and weighs up to nearly 20 kg. **(D)** Hermit crabs are omnivorous scavengers in the high littoral to sublittoral habitats. **(E)** *Manucomplanus varians*, the staghorn hermit crab, makes its "house" out of the staghorn coral, *Janaria mirabilis*. It occurs in sandy and rocky mixed habitats at depths from 6 m to 185 m in the Central Eastern Pacific. **(F)** The globose kelp crab, *Taliepus nuttali*, is associated with the large brown kelps and is found in intertidal habitats. *(continued)*

Shield-backed kelp crab

Striped shore crab

ANTERIOR

POSTERIOR

Pacific sand crab

1. Eggs
2. Telson

1

2

California spiny lobster

Caribbean spiny lobster

■ 16-16 Crabs and Lobsters (Decapoda) ~ *(continued)* (G) The

shield-backed kelp crab, *Pugettia producta*, occurs in kelp beds along the
Northeastern Pacific. It lives in the littoral and sublittoral to 75 m. (H) The
striped shore crab, *Pachygrapus crassipes*, is a common herbivore of the high and middle littoral zone. Their body may be up to 5.5 cm
wide. (I)(left) The Pacific sand crab, *Emerita analoga*, is one of a few relatively large (females up to 3.5 cm) invertebrates that are able to
survive on a sandy, exposed beach. It occurs on sandy beaches of the Northeastern Pacific. (right) Eggs can be seen on the ventral surface
of the female just underneath the V-shaped telson. (J) *Panulirus interruptus*, the California spiny lobster, is an Eastern Pacific organism that
can grow quite long (60 cm), but is generally around 35 cm as an adult. *P. interruptus* is a nocturnal species and occurs from the littoral
to depths of 60 m or more. (K) The Caribbean spiny lobster, *Panulirus argus*, forages at night along reefs. During the day, they can be found
under ledges and overhangs, often in groups of several individuals. They occur in the West Central Atlantic where they may grow up to 45
cm, but generally adults are 25 to 30 cm. *(continued)*

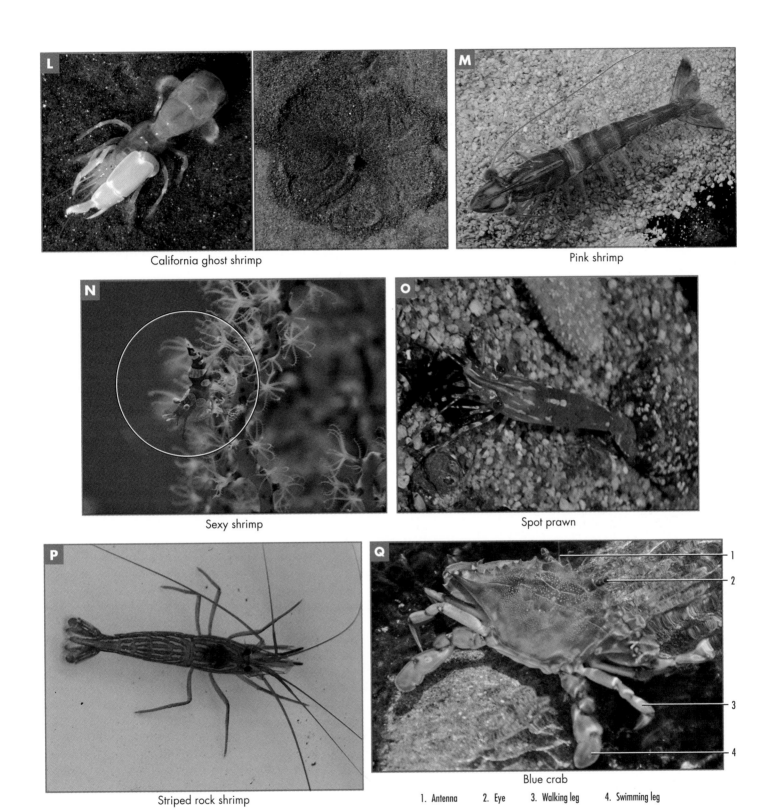

California ghost shrimp

Pink shrimp

Sexy shrimp

Spot prawn

Striped rock shrimp

Blue crab

1. Antenna   2. Eye   3. Walking leg   4. Swimming leg

■ **16-16 Shrimp and Crabs (Decapoda)** ∼ *(continued)* **(L)** (left) The California ghost shrimp, *Callianassa (Neotrypaea) californiensis*, is a common inhabitant of mudflats and back bays where wave action is low. (right) They burrow in the mud and leave telltale mounds. Their burrows can be extensive and complex, providing safety from predators and home for other organisms. Males are the larger sex and may grow to 10 cm. The single enlarged cheliped of the males may be on either side of the body. **(M)** The pink shrimp, *Penaeus duorarum*, is in fact, not generally pink. The color is highly variable–generally a gray, or slight blue, or even with a brown tinge. They occur in coastal waters of the mid-Northwestern Atlantic and are highly variable in morphology across this range. Females are larger than males and may obtain lengths of 28 cm. **(N)** The sexy shrimp, *Thor amboinensis*, occurs throughout the Caribbean and Indo-Pacific. They are small, up to 2 to 2.5 cm, and live on and within the tentacles of anemones. **(O)** The spot prawn, *Pandalus platyceros*, is a large shrimp occurring in the North Atlantic, from the low littoral to approximately 500 m. **(P)** The striped rock shrimp, *Lysmata californica*, occurs in the Eastern Pacific in the littoral and sublittoral habitats down to 50 m. This is one of many "cleaner" shrimp (species that remove ectoparasites and dead tissue from larger animals such as fish and lobsters). They may grow to 7.5 cm, but most are 5 to 5.5 cm. **(Q)** The blue crab, *Callinecters sapidus*, lives in the coastal Western Atlantic where it is an omnivore. This commercially important species may have a carapace up to 23 cm wide. *(continued)*

Dungeness crab

1. Walking leg
2. Antenna
3. Cheliped
4. Chela
5. Eye
6. Mouth appendage
7. Movable finger
8. Abdomen on male crab

■ **16-16 Crabs (Decapoda)** ≈ *(continued)* (**R**) The dungeness crab, *Metacarcinus magister*, lives in eel grass beds along the Northeastern Pacific where it reaches sizes up to 25 cm across their body (carapace). It is the most commercially important crab in the Northwestern Pacific.

■ **16-17 Crab Life Cycle** ≈ The reproductive cycle of a crab typically begins with a fertilized egg (zygote) that develops into a zoea larva. The zoea develops into a megalopa larva and then into a juvenile crab. In time, the juveniles develop into adults. This is the life cycle of the blue crab, *Callinecters sapidus* (Figure 16-16Q).

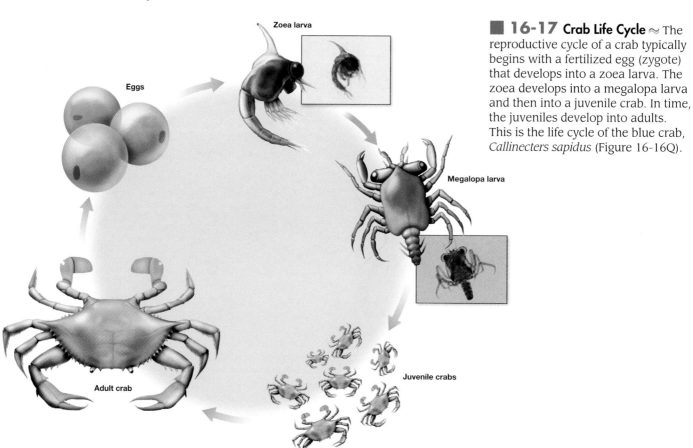

Zoea larva

Eggs

Megalopa larva

Juvenile crabs

Adult crab

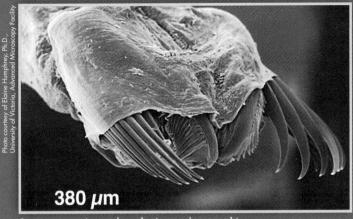

380 µm

Arrow worm (scanning electron micrograph)

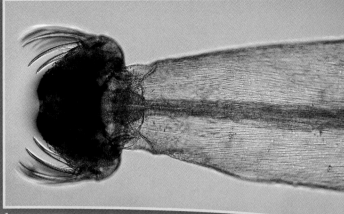

Arrow worm

17 Chaetognatha

The approximately 150 species of chaetognaths (also called arrow worms) are marine stealth predators. Most are important predators in planktonic food webs, though some are benthic, found attached to algae.

Chaetognaths are elongated and nearly transparent, arrow-shaped, dorsoventrally flattened animals with three fins: anterior lateral, posterior lateral, and caudal. Their visible gut runs from the head to the posterior lateral fin. For their small body size (typically 1-2 cm and up to 15 cm in some species) they have comparatively large grasping bristles, which they use to capture and inject poison into their main food source—unsuspecting copepods. The head and bristles are exposed only during feeding, otherwise they are covered by a hood. The head region is also covered by cuticle.

Arrows worms are hermaphroditic and reproduce sexually via internal fertilization. Eggs are released in most species, although *Eukrohnia* are brooders. Development is direct and can occur as quickly as one day.

Most of the relationships within the Chaetognath phylogeny have not been resolved. The Chaetognath clade may be placed within the Protostomia, or be closely related to the Nematoda. Furthermore, if placed within the Protostomia, morphological and molecular data are contradictory and do not resolve the precise placement within Protostomia. One interpretation of the data is shown in Figure 17-1 and an arrow worm is shown in Figure 17-4. Classes are listed in Table 17-1.

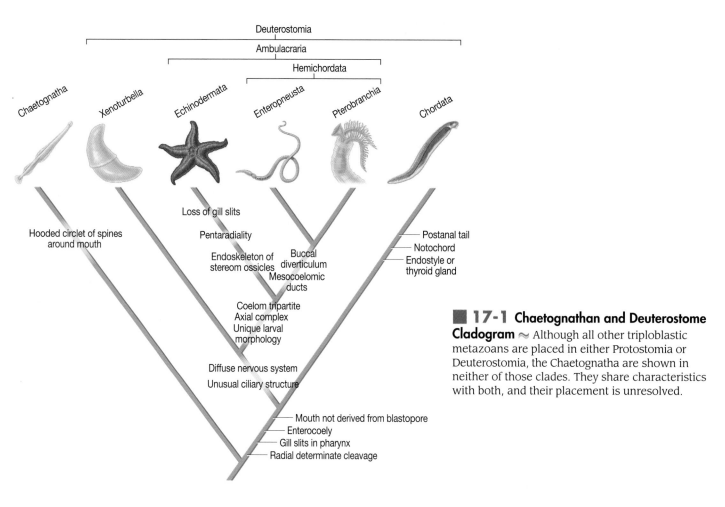

Deuterostomia
Ambulacraria
Hemichordata

Chaetognatha
Xenoturbella
Echinodermata
Enteropneusta
Pterobranchia
Chordata

Loss of gill slits

Pentaradiality

Hooded circlet of spines
around mouth

Endoskeleton of
stereom ossicles
Buccal
diverticulum
Mesocoelomic
ducts

Postanal tail
Notochord
Endostyle or
thyroid gland

Coelom tripartite
Axial complex
Unique larval
morphology

Diffuse nervous system
Unusual ciliary structure

Mouth not derived from blastopore
Enterocoely
Gill slits in pharynx
Radial determinate cleavage

■ 17-1 Chaetognathan and Deuterostome Cladogram ~ Although all other triploblastic metazoans are placed in either Protostomia or Deuterostomia, the Chaetognatha are shown in neither of those clades. They share characteristics with both, and their placement is unresolved.

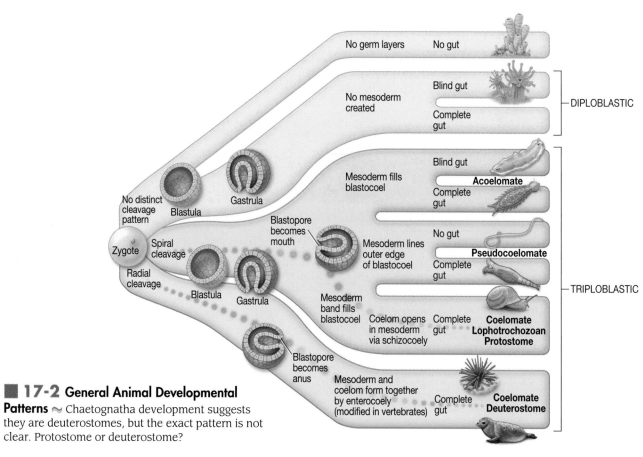

No germ layers — No gut

No mesoderm created — Blind gut / Complete gut — DIPLOBLASTIC

No distinct cleavage pattern — Blastula — Gastrula

Zygote

Spiral cleavage — Blastula — Gastrula

Radial cleavage — Blastula — Gastrula

Blastopore becomes mouth

Blastopore becomes anus

Mesoderm fills blastocoel — Blind gut / Complete gut — **Acoelomate**

Mesoderm lines outer edge of blastocoel — No gut / Complete gut — **Pseudocoelomate**

Mesoderm band fills blastocoel — Coelom opens in mesoderm via schizocoely — Complete gut — **Coelomate Lophotrochozoan Protostome**

Mesoderm and coelom form together by enterocoely (modified in vertebrates) — Complete gut — **Coelomate Deuterostome**

TRIPLOBLASTIC

■ 17-2 General Animal Developmental Patterns ~ Chaetognatha development suggests they are deuterostomes, but the exact pattern is not clear. Protostome or deuterostome?

PROTOSTOMES		DEUTEROSTOMES	
Spiral cleavage	Cleavage mostly spiral	Radial cleavage	Cleavage mostly radial
Cell from which mesoderm will derive	Endomesoderm usually from a particular blastomere designated 4d	Endomesoderm from pouches of primitive gut	Endomesoderm from enterocoelous pouching (except vertebrates)
Primitive gut / Mesoderm / Coelom / Blastopore	In coelomate protostomes the coelom forms as a split in mesodermal bands (schizocoelous)	Mesoderm / Coelom / Primitive gut / Blastopore	All coelomate, coelom from fusion of enterocoelous pouches (except vertebrates, which are schizocoelous)
Anus / Annelid (clamworm) / Mouth	Mouth forms from or near blastopore; anus a new formation. Embryology mostly determinate (mosaic). Includes phyla Platyhelminthes, Nemertea, Annelida, Mollusca, Arthropoda, Phoronida, Ectoprocta, Brachiopoda, minor phyla	Mouth / Anus	Anus forms from or near blastopore, mouth a new formation. Embryology usually indeterminate (regulative). Includes phyla Echinodermata, Hermichordata, Chordata

■ 17-3 Protostome and Deuterostome Developmental Patterns ~ Some chaetognath features, such as the position of the nerve cord, suggests a protostome pattern. The cleavage plane in early embryonic stages is similar to those in nematodes and crustaceans. Some genetic studies indicate that part of their development follows a pattern similar to both protostomes and deuterostomes, suggesting an origin before the protostome-deuterostome split. Bottom line . . . relationships are unresolved.

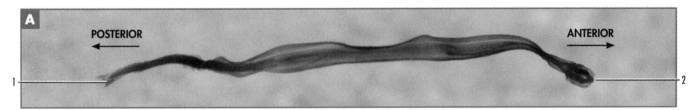

A — POSTERIOR ← → ANTERIOR — 1 — 2

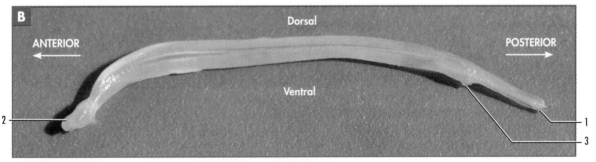

B — Dorsal — ANTERIOR ← → POSTERIOR — Ventral — 2 — 1 — 3

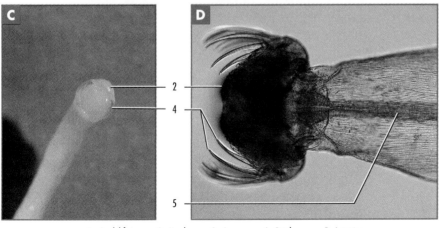

C

D

■ 17-4 Arrow Worms (Chaetognatha) ~ Arrow worms are predominantly members of the plankton, except for *Spadella*, which lives in shallow coastal water where it uses adhesive pads near the tail to cling to rocks and algae. Arrow worms are carnivores, feeding on fish larvae and other animals as they dart about. Their elongated bodies are transparent with paired fins and a caudal fin. All specimens in these photos are preserved; **A** has been stained. *(continued)*

1. Caudal fin   2. Hood   3. Anus   4. Bristles   5. Intestine

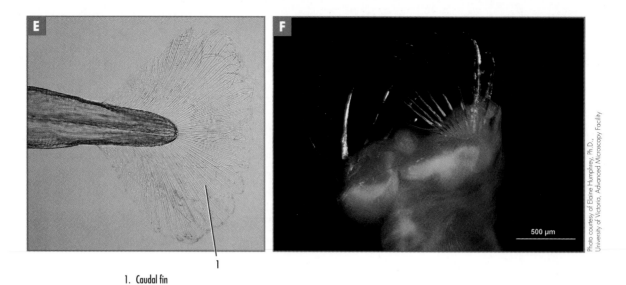

1. Caudal fin

■ **17-4 Arrow Worms (Chaetognatha)** ≈*(continued)* (E) This specimen is preserved. (F) In this living specimen, the extended bristles are evident.

■ Table **17-1** ≈ Chaetognath Classes

Class	General Description	Examples	Approximate Number of Species	Etymology
Archisagittoidea	All marine	*Caecosagitta*	20	*archi*—first, *sagitta*—arrow, *oidea*—ending of animal names
Sagittoidea (Figure 17-4)	Mouth with a margin of grasping bristles; body slender with lateral fins	*Sagitta, Eukrohnia*	130	*sagitta*—arrow, *oidea*—ending of animal names

Bat star

Purple urchin test

18 Echinodermata

Echinoderms are a unique animal group living throughout the marine environment. The 7,000 species of Echinodermata have a rich fossil record, and are represented by the following extant taxa: Asteroidea (sea stars), Echinoidea (sea urchins and sand dollars), Ophiuroidea (brittle stars and basket stars), Holothuroidea (sea cucumbers), and Crinoidea (feather stars and sea lilies). Most echinoderms are free-living benthic animals, though crinoids are attached, and some sea cucumbers are planktonic. Echinoderms have amazing regeneration abilities. Table 18-1 summarizes the Echinodermata classes.

As deuterostomes (Figure 18-1), echinoderms are the sister taxon to Chordata (Figure 18-2). Figure 18-3 shows a cladogram for echinoderms. Within the Echinodermata,

Table 18-1 ≈ Echinoderm Classes

Class	General Description	Examples	Approximate Number of Species	Etymology
Asteroidea (Figure 18-8)	Sea stars: adults with radial symmetry and arms and parts generally in fives or multiples, open ambulacral groove along arms; sea daisies: no arms, but a disk-shaped body with marginal podia	Sea stars: *Asterias* and *Pisaster*; sea daisies: *Xyloplax*	1,500	*aster*—start, *oid*—form, *ea*—characterized by
Echinoidea (Figure 18-9)	Globular or disk shaped; no arms, moveable spines, and closed ambulacral groove	Sea urchins: *Strongylocentrotus*; sea biscuits: *Lovenia*; sand dollars: *Dendraster*	950	*echinos*—sea urchin, *oid*—form, *ea*—characterized by
Ophiuroidea (Figure 18-10)	Star shaped with arms distinctly attaching to central disk; closed ambulacral grooves; tube feet without suckers	Brittle stars: *Ophiura*; basket stars: *Gorgonocephalus*	2,000+	*ophis*—snake, *oura*—tail, *oid*—form, *ea*—characterized by
Holothuroidea (Figure 18-11)	Shaped like a cucumber, with no arms, no spines	*Parastichopus* and *Cucumaria*	1,500	*holothourion*—sea cucumber, *oid*—form, *ea*—characterized by
Crinoidea	Tentacle-appearing tube feet used for feeding; five arms attaching at a base; no spines	*Crinoidea* and *Nemaster*	625	*krinon*—lily, *oid*—form, *ea*—characterized by

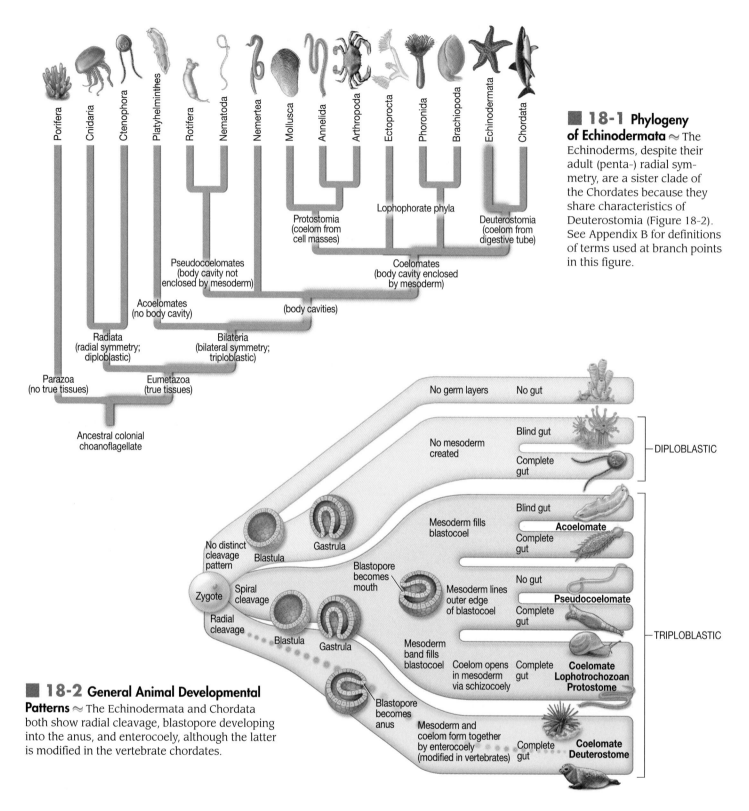

18-1 Phylogeny of Echinodermata ~ The Echinoderms, despite their adult (penta-) radial symmetry, are a sister clade of the Chordates because they share characteristics of Deuterostomia (Figure 18-2). See Appendix B for definitions of terms used at branch points in this figure.

18-2 General Animal Developmental Patterns ~ The Echinodermata and Chordata both show radial cleavage, blastopore developing into the anus, and enterocoely, although the latter is modified in the vertebrate chordates.

holothuroids and echinoids are generally considered to be sister taxa, while molecular evidence supports two disparate relationships for the remainder of the taxa.

As adults, echinoderms display secondary **pentaradial symmetry**, a type of radial symmetry where the symmetry is along five rays, (Figure 18-4), though some echinoids and holothuroids superficially appear bilateral. Unique to the phylum is their hydraulic water vascular system, which controls **tube feet** and thus locomotion. The endoskeleton of echinoderms is composed of porous calcium carbonate **ossicles** (calcareous plates variable in structure between classes). Mutable collagenous tissue (ligaments) occurs between the ossicles and can be softened and relaxed to allow the animal to lock into position with no effort, or as in the case of holothuroids, to basically turn their body into gelatinous material at will.

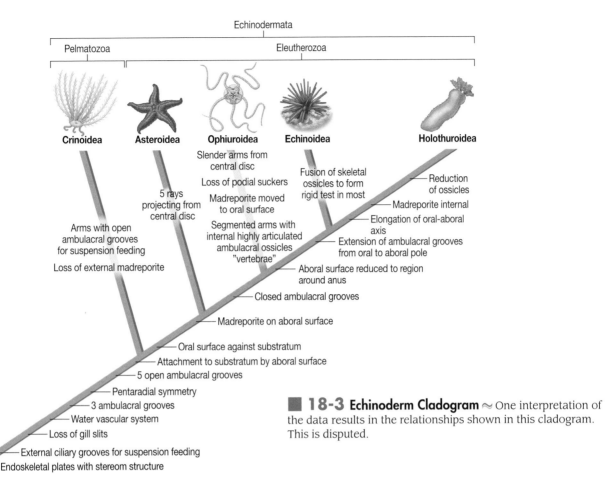

Echinodermata

Pelmatozoa | Eleutherozoa

Crinoidea — Asteroidea — Ophiuroidea — Echinoidea — Holothuroidea

Slender arms from central disc
Loss of podial suckers
Madreporite moved to oral surface
Segmented arms with internal highly articulated ambulacral ossicles "vertebrae"

Fusion of skeletal ossicles to form rigid test in most

Reduction of ossicles
Madreporite internal
Elongation of oral-aboral axis
Extension of ambulacral grooves from oral to aboral pole
Aboral surface reduced to region around anus

5 rays projecting from central disc

Arms with open ambulacral grooves for suspension feeding
Loss of external madreporite

Closed ambulacral grooves
Madreporite on aboral surface
Oral surface against substratum
Attachment to substratum by aboral surface
5 open ambulacral grooves
Pentaradial symmetry
3 ambulacral grooves
Water vascular system
Loss of gill slits
External ciliary grooves for suspension feeding
Endoskeletal plates with stereom structure

■ **18-3 Echinoderm Cladogram** ≈ One interpretation of the data results in the relationships shown in this cladogram. This is disputed.

■ **18-4 Ochre Sea Star (Asteroidea)** ≈ An ochre star, *Pisaster ochraceus*, is shown resting upon a bed of aggregate anemones (arrows), *Anthopleura elegantissima*, in the coastal rocky littoral environment. There is great variability of color between individuals. Note the pentaradial symmetry.

Asteroidea

Asteroids typically have five or more arms (rays) radiating broadly from a central disc and range in size from small and delicate (a few centimeters) to large (96 cm is the world record), heavily armored species. While most sea stars are predators or scavengers, filter feeders, detritivores, and suspension feeders are represented as well. Some sea stars

have the ability to evert their oral (gastric) stomach and feed extra-orally (outside of the body). There are approximately 1,600 extant species of asteroids. Sea stars play important roles in benthic ecosystems. The purple ochre sea star, *Pisaster ochraceus* (Figure 18-4), is the classic example of a **keystone species** (a species that plays an important, even critical, role in maintaining biodiversity and feeding relationships disproportionate to their abundance), while *Acanthaster planci*, the crown-of-thorns sea star, devours coral polyps and can **decimate** a reef community when its populations explode.

Asteroids are almost entirely dioecious (two sexes), though a few **protandric hermaphrodite species** (first males, then they develop into females) do exist. Reproduction is sexual, fertilization is typically external, and spawning usually occurs only once per year. As deuterostomes, cleavage is radial and coelom formation is enterocoelous (Figure 18-5). Echinoderms have complex life cycles; see Figure 18-6 for a representative asteroid life cycle. Some cold-water asteroids are brooders with direct development, but most juveniles develop from a bilaterally symmetrical planktotrophic (Chapter 6) larva. As adults, sea stars can regrow missing arms, and some can regrow new bodies from an arm with a partial disc (Figure 18-7).

Molecular and morphological characteristics have yielded two contrasting asteroid phylogenies. Representative asteroids are shown in Figure 18-8.

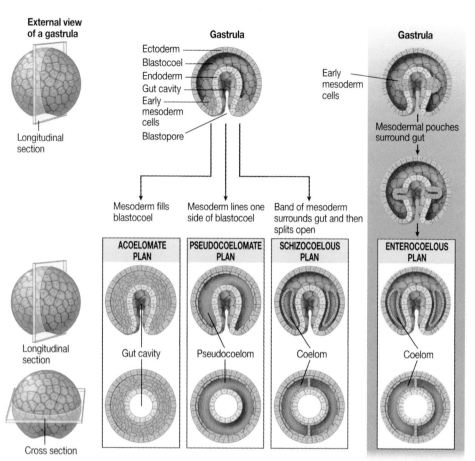

External view of a gastrula

Longitudinal section

Gastrula

- Ectoderm
- Blastocoel
- Endoderm
- Gut cavity
- Early mesoderm cells
- Blastopore

Longitudinal section

Cross section

Mesoderm fills blastocoel

Mesoderm lines one side of blastocoel

Band of mesoderm surrounds gut and then splits open

ACOELOMATE PLAN

Gut cavity

PSEUDOCOELOMATE PLAN

Pseudocoelom

SCHIZOCOELOUS PLAN

Coelom

Gastrula

Early mesoderm cells

Mesodermal pouches surround gut

ENTEROCOELOUS PLAN

Coelom

■ **18-5** Body Cavity Development ≈ The echinoderm and chordate developmental process is shown. Note the enterocoelous developmental pattern with mesodermally lined coelom.

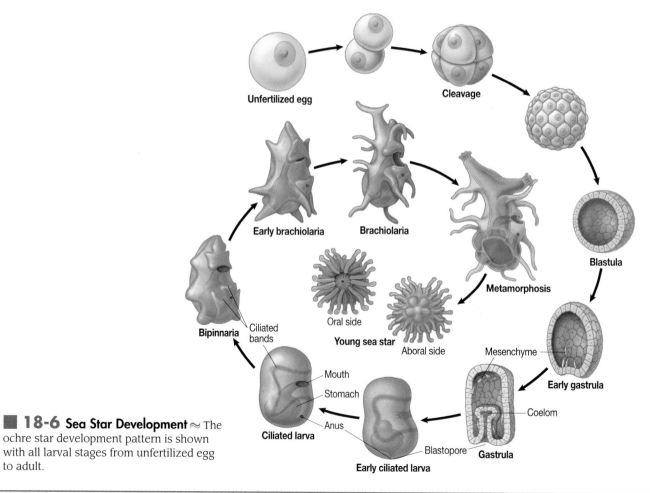

Unfertilized egg

Cleavage

Blastula

Early brachiolaria

Brachiolaria

Metamorphosis

Oral side

Young sea star

Aboral side

Mesenchyme

Early gastrula

Coelom

Bipinnaria

Ciliated bands

Mouth
Stomach
Anus

Ciliated larva

Early ciliated larva

Blastopore Gastrula

■ **18-6** Sea Star Development ≈ The ochre star development pattern is shown with all larval stages from unfertilized egg to adult.

■ 18-7 Regeneration in Sea Stars ≈ This ochre star, *Pisaster ochraceus*, is regenerating its missing parts (arrows). As long as part of the central disc is still attached to an arm, an entire individual will result. Note the color difference between this individual and the more purple ochre star above.

Bat star aboral surface

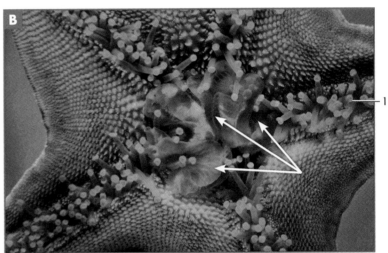

Bat star oral surface

1. Ambulacral groove with tube feet

Chocolate chip sea star

Knobby sea star

■ 18-8 Sea Stars (Asteroidea) ≈ (A) The bat star, *Asterina miniata*, is highly variable in color and a very common inhabitant of the rocky littoral and sublittoral habitats down to 40 m of the Northeastern Pacific. Individuals may reach 15.5 cm or more, but are generally around 10 cm. It is an omnivore, which is unusual for sea stars. (B) The bat star is capable of everting its stomach (arrows) and digesting organisms and other attached materials on the substrate. Note the open ambulacral grooves with tube feet, suckered tips of their tube feet, and scale-like plates making the surface rough. (C) The chocolate chip sea star, *Protoreaster nodosus*, occurs in the Indo-Pacific in the shallows of coastal waters. Individuals may reach 30 cm while feeding on sessile invertebrates like corals and sponges, and mobile invertebrates such as sea urchins and snails. (D) *Pisaster giganteus*, the knobby sea star, ranges along the Northeastern Pacific where it lives from the low littoral to about 50 m. It is comparable in size to the ochre star, *Pisaster ochraceus* (Figure 18-4) and feeds upon molluscs. *(continued)*

Sunflower star

1. Madreporite

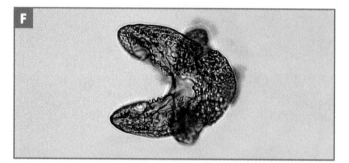

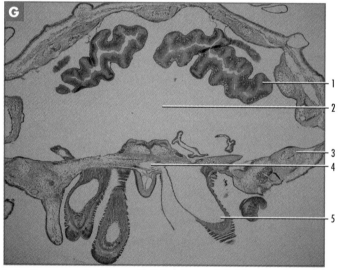

1. Hepatic caecum   2. Coelom   3. Skeletal plate   4. Radial canal   5. Tube foot

■ **18-8 Sea Stars (Asteroidea)** ≈ (E) The sunflower star, *Pycnopodia helianthoides*, feeds on snails, other sea stars, and abalone. This star inhabits the Northeastern Pacific coastal areas where it can reach a size of 60 cm in diameter and have as many as 24 arms. Note the obvious, light-colored madreporite on this specimen. (F) Sea star pedicellaria (a single pedicellarium) cover most sea stars on the oral and aboral surfaces. They are found around the spines and remove debris and small organisms, and move food to the mouth. Muscles move the pincer-like jaws. (G) A cross section of an *Asterina* arm shows the aboral surface at the top and a section through the coelom containing the hepatic caecum, radial canal, and tube feet.

Echinoidea

The echinoids (Figure 18-9) comprise two groups: the regular (sea urchins and pencil urchins) and irregular echinoids (sand dollars, heart urchins, and sea biscuits). Echinoids are adapted for living on both hard and soft substrates and use both tube feet and spines for movement. Species range in size from approximately 6 cm and up to the record 38 cm long. There are approximately 950 species of echinoids with a rich fossil record dating to the Ordovician. Sea urchins are herbivorous, while sand dollars are deposit feeders (Chapter 11). Urchins play a significant role as grazers in the marine food webs they inhabit, but can become a nuisance if their populations grow too large. Female gonads and their eggs are harvested and eaten as roe in Japanese cuisine.

Echinoids differ from other echinoderms in having a rigid skeleton of interlocking ossicles (test). The test is covered with either long spines (urchins) or tiny spines

Sand dollar

1. Holes for respiratory tube feet

Green sea urchin

■ **18-9 Sand Dollars and Sea Urchins (Echinoidea)** ≈ (A) (left) The sand dollar, *Dendraster excentricus*, inhabits the very low littoral to depths of 40 m. In low turbulence areas, they are on edge in the sand. In areas of higher wave action, they lie flat along the sandy bottom. There may be very large numbers of this species in some areas. They range along the Northeastern Pacific where they may grow to 10 cm. (right) The aboral surface of a dead sand dollar shows holes arranged in a flower petal pattern where respiratory tube feet project. (B) The green sea urchin, *Stronglylocentrotus droebachiensis*, occurs in northern coastal waters around the world, including the Atlantic and Pacific where it feeds on seaweeds. Individuals are generally around 8 to 9 cm. *(continued)* (sand dollars and relatives). If you could raise all five arms of an asteroid with all its arms and touch them together at a central **aboral** (opposite the mouth) point, you would have the basic anatomy of an urchin. For instance, the **ambulacral** (*ambularcum*—walking) plates and tube feet of an urchin run in five rows on the outside of the test. Five ocular plates (skeletal elements) surround the anus at the apex of the aboral surface. Various types of defensive, often pincer-like, **pedicellariae** (Figure 18-8F) are found on the test of echinoids. Urchins have the ability to regenerate lost or damaged spines. Most echinoids have five pairs of teeth arranged in a circle around their mouth in a structure called **Aristotle's lantern** (Figure 18-9E).

Echinoids are dioecious, and fertilization of eggs is external. Some cold-water species are **brooders**; eggs are carried externally and protected by spines. A planktotrophic larva (echinopluteus—Chapter 11) (Figure 18-9F) develops from the fertilized eggs of broadcast spawners (release their gametes into the water for external fertilization upon low probability encounters), and may feed for months before landing and metamorphosing into a juvenile urchin.

Long-spined black urchin

Purple sea urchin

West India sea egg

1. Aristotle's lantern   2. Oral surface

■ **18-9 Sea Urchins (Echinoidea)** ≈ *(continued)* (**C**) The long-spined black urchin, *Diadema antillarum*, may grow to 50 cm across their long spines. They are herbivorous urchins that feed on macroalgae, and live in the Eastern and Western tropical Atlantic. (**D**) The purple sea urchin, *Strongylocentrotus purpuratus*, occurs in the lower littoral and sublittoral, particularly in kelp beds. Individuals may grow to have a test (shell) of 20 cm, but appear much larger due to their spines. This species inhabits the coastal areas of the Northeastern Pacific. (**E**) (left) West Indian sea egg, *Tripneustes ventricosus*, occurs throughout the Caribbean and Florida coast where they principally inhabit sea grass beds, but they also occur on coral reefs. Individuals may grow to 15 cm in the littoral and sublittoral to a depth of 10 m. This urchin is omnivorous, feeding on macroalgae, plants, and invertebrates. (right) The oral surface of the West Indian sea egg shows the five pairs of teeth arranged in a circle around their mouth in a structure called Aristotle's lantern. (**F**) The pluteus larva occurs in echinoid broadcast spawners. Larval shape and number of "arms" varies between taxa. This is a sea urchin pluteus larva. *(continued)*

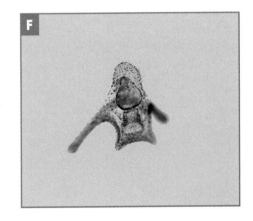

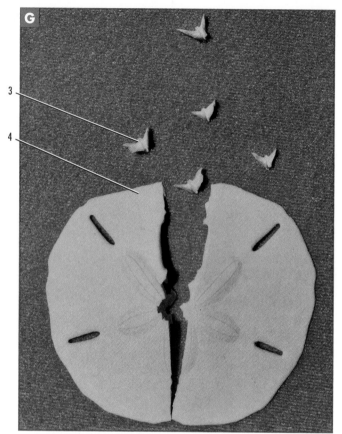

3. Tooth   4. Sand dollar test

■ **18-9 Sand Dollar (Echinoidea)** ≈ *(continued)* **(G)** This sand dollar test has been broken open showing the five pairs of teeth. Mounted and framed, it is a popular item at seaside souvenir stores.

Morphological studies have grouped the echinoids based upon their symmetry, plate rows, and respiratory pores (petals).

Ophiuroidea

Ophiuroids (Figure 18-10), brittle stars or basket stars, resemble asteroids, except that they have long, spindly, brittle, flexible arms that radiate distinctly from the central disc. The cryptic brittle stars are also the most diverse group of echinoderms, found in environments ranging from coral reefs to the abyssal plains; there are more than 1,600 extant species.

Ophiuroids differ from sea stars in that their calcite skeleton lacks pedicellariae, the ossicles form four large plates surrounding each arm or scale, and the epidermis, for the most part, is lacking in cilia. There is no exterior ambulacral groove. Instead, modified ambulacral ossicles (vertebrae) are internalized below the oral arm shield. They also lack an intestine and anus. They use several methods of feeding, including scavenging, predation, and deposit and suspension feeding. A graceful rowing motion is typical, with spines, and more rarely, tube feet assisting in propulsion.

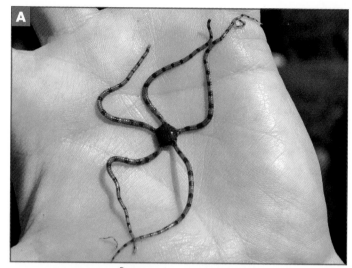

Panamanian serpent star

Spiny brittle star

■ **18-10 Brittle Stars (Ophiuroidea)** ≈ **(A)** *Ophioderma panamense*, the Panamanian serpent star, is a warm-water species, occurring in the Eastern Pacific between approximately 32 degrees north and south latitudes. It occurs in the mid to low littoral, and is the most abundant ophiuroid along the coasts of Southern California. **(B)** The spiny brittle star, *Ophiothrix spiculata*, is highly variable in color. The central disk of this suspension feeding ophiuroid is about 1.3 cm across. It occurs in the low littoral and sublittoral to 70 m, from mid-Northern latitudes across the equator of the Eastern Pacific.

Brittle stars have the ability to drop arms or segments of arms when attacked or threatened by relaxing their collagenous tissue. Some ophiuroids can reproduce by fission, though most reproduce sexually. Most species have separate sexes, but some are hermaphroditic (both simultaneous and protandric). Both spawning and internal brooding occur. Those eggs fertilized externally develop into a feeding **ophiopluteus** larva.

Holothuroidea

The worm-like sea cucumbers (Figure 18-11) least resemble other echinoderms. They are superficially bilateral, soft-bodied animals that can range in size from a centimeter to the longest, which is more than 3 m (*Synapta maculata*). Most are at least 10 cm. Sea cucumbers are ubiquitous throughout the ocean, fill more niches in more habitats than other echinoderms, and have reached their greatest species diversity on and around coral reef ecosystems. One-third of the approximately 1,200 holothuroid species are found in the deep ocean. Some economically important sea cucumbers are regarded as delicacies known as *trepang* and *beche-de-mer* in many Asian countries and overharvesting can destroy entire populations. Additionally, the pharmaceutical industry has become interested in several chemical compounds produced by sea cucumbers. Recently, a sea cucumber protein (lectin) was found to act as a toxin against malarial parasites, which has led to attempts to genetically engineer a mosquito to carry the toxin in hopes of one day eradicating malaria. Another protein found in species of Malaysian sea cucumber has been shown to possess antibacterial qualities. Other holothuroid chemicals are currently being studied for additional biomedical uses.

Natural selection has resulted in various morphologies, but sea cucumbers are generally oriented on their side and lack rays or arms. The side facing the substrate, the **sole**, includes three of the five ambulacral rows, which may or may not include tube feet. This orientation gives the body a superficial bilateral symmetry, which is found in all but burrowing species. Tube feet may be dispersed throughout the entire body surface, located on the dorsal surface modified into bumps, or papillae (Figure 18-11A), or entirely lacking. The mouth and anus are at opposite ends

Warty sea cucumber

Orange sea cucumber

Sweet potato sea cucumber

Sea apple

1. Buccal podia   2. Anus   3. Mouth

■ **18-11 Holothuroidea** ≈ **(A)** The warty sea cucumber, *Parastichopus parvimensis*, grows to 45 cm in length. The color is highly variable between individuals. It lives from the low littoral to sublittoral, including kelp beds and in bays on mud and eel grass beds, along the mid-Eastern Pacific. This species does not have tentacles. **(B)** *Cucumaria miniata*, the orange sea cucumber, shows its tentacles. It grows to 25 cm, including its tentacles, and occurs in the coastal Northeastern Pacific from the littoral to sublittoral down to 100 m. It is a suspension feeder. **(C)** The sweet potato sea cucumber, *Molpadia arenicola*, inhabits burrows in muddy or sandy coastal habitats. Unlike the other species shown, it does not possess tube feet, nor does it have tentacles. The sweet potato sea cucumber may burrow to 40 cm, but more frequently it is found near the surface. **(D)** The sea apple, *Pseudocolochirus violaceus*, grows to 18 cm. Individuals have three rows of tube feet along the ventral surface, and their curved body is positioned so that the tentacles point away from the substrate. These suspension feeders inhabit the Indo-Pacific on coral reefs to 12 m.

from one another (Figure 18-11C). The mouth has a circle of retractable **buccal podia** (Figures 18-11B and D), which are specialized tube feet modified into tentacle-like structures. They are used mainly for deposit or suspension feeding. Below the mouth, the muscular pharynx is surrounded by a calcareous ring of fused ossicles, which serves as an attachment for buccal podia and body wall muscles. Ossicles in holothuroids are microscopic and may vary significantly, even within species. A few species have large, plate-like ossicles on the functional dorsal surface.

Mobile holothuroids use their hydrostatic skeleton and musculature to move in a myriad of ways, including burrowing, swimming, and crawling. Some species have the ability to discharge sticky, stringy, and toxic **cuverian tubules** from their anus as defense against predators. The holothuroid is then able to regenerate the extruded tubules.

Most sea cucumbers are dioecious, but all possess only one gonad. The vast majority of species spawn and fertilization is external. However, several cold-water species brood eggs on their body wall. A few others are viviparous (producing young, which develop in the mother's body as opposed to laying eggs), having juveniles that burst forth from the mother's body wall. The fertilized eggs of non-brooding, oviparous (egg-laying) species develop into **auricularia** larvae, which are planktotrophic, and then into oblong **doliolaria** larvae. Metamorphosis then occurs, and the juvenile sea cucumber (**pentacula** larva) eventually settles and becomes an adult.

Recent molecular and morphological analysis places the Aspidochirotida and the Dendrochirotida together as sister taxa in the same clade. The remaining relationships within the Holothuroidea have not been resolved.

Crinoidea

Crinoids include both the stalked sea lilies and the free-living feather stars (cromatulids). The fossil record for this group is the best for the echinoderms, and extends to the Lower Ordovician. There are approximately 625 species of extant crinoids. Sea lilies are common in the deep ocean, while feather stars may be found at depths shallower than 200 m. Indo-Pacific coral reefs display an especially rich feather star biodiversity.

Crinoids are suspension feeders; their oral surface is exposed and includes both the mouth and the anus. The body of a crinoid consists of two main parts: the crown (disc) with a cup-like calyx at the base, and the stalk, which attaches the animal to its substrate. Only the top-most portion of the stalk is retained in adult cromatulids. The crown includes five branched feathery rays, open ambulacral (food) grooves, and large triplicate tube feet that assist with delivering food particles to the mouth. Most sea lilies' movements are restricted to bending, but feather stars crawl along substrate and some are capable of swimming. Crinoids have been found that range in size from 3 to 90 (*Heliometra glacialis*) cm.

Crinoids have the ability to regenerate lost arms and portions of the body, but do not reproduce asexually. Sexes are separate and fertilization is external. Eggs are brooded and the larvae are lecithotrophic (nutrition from egg yolk).

The phylogeny for the crinoids has not yet been resolved. Currently, it is thought that sea lilies are not a monophyletic group.

1. Arms   2. Cirri   3. Calyx

■ **18-12 Sea Lily (Crinoidea)** ≈ Shown are the skeletal remains of a sea lily. Note the jointed stalks and the calyx (body disc) from which the ten arms radiate.

Acorn worm

Pterobranch

Photos courtesy of Elizabeth Balser, Illinois Wesleyan University

19 Hemichordata

Members of the Hemichordata were long considered part of the Chordata based upon the presence of two hallmark chordate features: pharyngeal gill slits and what was interpreted as a dorsal notochord (Chapter 20). New evidence shows that the apparent dorsal notochord is, in fact, not homologous to the chordate notochord. Like Echinoderms (Chapter 18), they have a tripartite coelom. They are cosmopolitan in their distribution living on the bottom, most in shallow water. Table 19-1 summarizes this group.

Enteropneusta

Members of this class are called acorn worms (Figure 19-1). These worm-like creatures are free-living in burrows or under stones in mudflats or sandy areas of the littoral habitat. They are slow moving, *mucous-ciliary* (mucociliary) feeders. That is, they use their *proboscis* to probe their surroundings and trap food in mucus, which then conveys it to their mouth by cilia.

Sexes are separate, with external fertilization and a larval form very similar to that of echinoderms. The development of their hollow dorsal nerve cord is very similar to that of the chordates and has been cited as evidence of homology. That interpretation is disputed.

Pterobranchia

These small, sedentary organisms are colonial and, based upon superficial characteristics, were originally considered to be related to the Ectoprocta (Figure 19-2). However, their body plan and detail morphology greatly resembles the Enteropneusta. They live in tubes and use mucociliary feeding to remove food particles from the water. Each organism lives in its own separate tube independent of the others in its colony. Both sexual and asexual reproduction are common.

The cladogram in Figure 19-3 shows the relationship between the two classes of hemichordates and the other deuterostomes. The Ambulacraria is a clade of deuterostomes that includes the echinoderms and hemichordates, all sharing a unique larval form and a three-part coelom (Figure 19-4. In addition, each shares a specialized type of excretory organ. This presentation is disputed, and as more molecular data are available, may change.

Table **19-1** ≈ Hemichordate Classes

Class	General Description	Examples	Approximate Number of Species	Etymology
Enteropneusta (Figure 19-1)	Worm-like organisms with a distinct anterior proboscis, followed by a collar and then gill pores	*Balanoglossus* and *Saccoglossus*	75	*entero*—intestine, *pneustra*—for breathing
Pterobranchia (Figure 19-2)	Small colonial animals with, from posterior to anterior, a stalk, trunk, gill slits, collar, and tentacles	*Cephalodiscus* and *Rhabdopleura*	30	*ptero*—wing, *branchia*—gills

1. Trunk   2. Collar   3. Proboscis   4. Gill pores   5. Mouth

■ **19-1 Acorn Worm (Enteropneustra)** ≈ The trunk, proboscis, mouth, collar, and gill pores are shown. The organism is approximately 18 cm in length. They are near cosmopolitan in their distribution in shallow water, nearshore benthic habitats.

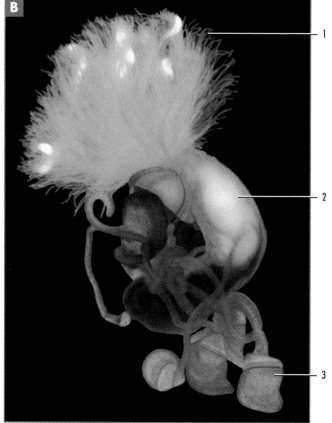

Photos courtesy of Elizabeth Balser, Illinois Wesleyan University

1. Tentacles   2. Zooid   3. Clone

■ **19-2 Pterobranchs (Pterobranchia)** ≈ (A) These sedentary colonial organisms are small, usually ranging from 1mm to 7 mm in length. Each individual is called a zooid and lives within a tube (arrow). (B) Zooids can contract into their tubes (as in A) or partially emerge from it and extend a crown of tentacles to feed. This specimen has been removed from its tube.

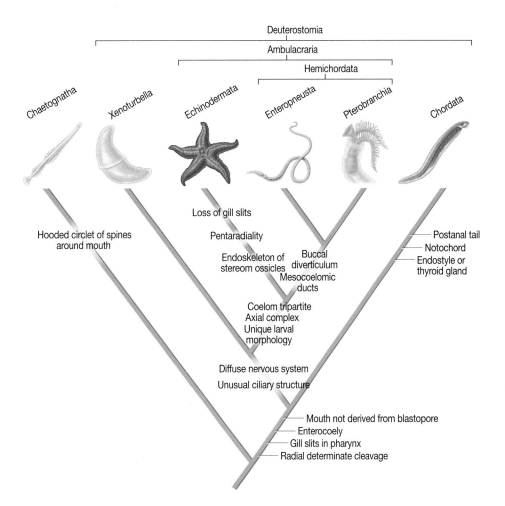

Deuterostomia

Ambulacraria

Hemichordata

Chaetognatha — Xenoturbella — Echinodermata — Enteropneusta — Pterobranchia — Chordata

Loss of gill slits

Hooded circlet of spines
around mouth

Pentaradiality

Buccal
diverticulum

Endoskeleton of
stereom ossicles

Mesocoelomic
ducts

Postanal tail
Notochord
Endostyle or
thyroid gland

Coelom tripartite
Axial complex
Unique larval
morphology

Diffuse nervous system
Unusual ciliary structure

Mouth not derived from blastopore
Enterocoely
Gill slits in pharynx
Radial determinate cleavage

■ **19-3 Hemichordate Cladogram** ≈ Together with the Echinoderms, the Hemichordata
are members of the clade Ambulacraria, and together with Chordata and Xenoturbella (disputed
based on anatomical and morphological characteristics, but supported by molecular data) are
members of the clade Deuterostomia. The Ambulacraria grouping is supported by a variety of
evidence, some of which is listed at this cladogram's branch points. Hemichordata's traditional
placement with Chordata was in large measure based upon the presence of gill slits in both and
the assumption that the stomochord (buccal diverticulum), an axial supportive rod, is homologous
to the notochord of chordates. Evidence now supports the stomochord as a synapomorphy of
hemichordates.

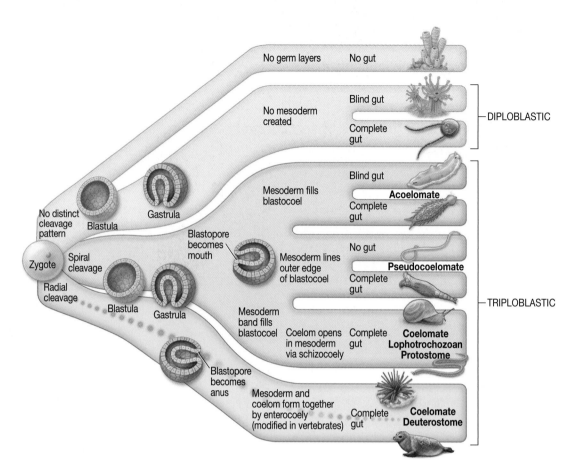

■ 19-4 General Animal Developmental Patterns ~ Hemichordate development most closely resembles that of echinoderms. There is an enterocoelous origin of the coelom, the anus develops from the blastopore, and there are other developmental and molecular similarities.

Humboldt penguin

Gray whale

20 Introduction to the Marine Chordata

Marine Chordata consist of a wide array of organisms (Figure 20-1) from the very familiar fish, birds, and whales to the more obscure sea squirts, salps (Urochordata), and lancelets (Cephalochordata). Despite their differences, all species placed within Chordata display, at some point in their life cycles, five hallmark anatomical features:

≈ a dorsal, tubular nerve cord

≈ a notochord (an axial skeleton)

≈ pharyngeal slits or pouches (the pharynx is between the mouth and the esophagus)

≈ a postanal tail

≈ an endostyle (a mucous-secreting lower portion of the pharynx).

These are illustrated in Figure 20-2. Table 20-1 summarizes the major groups within the phylum.

The organisms shown in this and subsequent chapters are common to the coastal habitats of North and South America and the Caribbean, with a particular emphasis on the West Coast of North America. Where possible, the hallmark characteristics of the phylum are illustrated, and the ecological and evolutionary significance of the taxon emphasized.

The cephalochordate amphioxus, comprising several genera including *Branchiostoma* (Figures 20-2, 20-3, and 20-4), will introduce the chordates. This is a minor group with about 25 species, but has historically played a very important role in helping us understand the evolutionary origin of the chordates. Cephalochordates inhabit shallow, coastal waters of both the temperate and tropical seas. They spend most of the time buried in the sand in "feeding" position with their head extending from the substrate. Six to 8 cm in length (8 cm is the Moby Dick of the amphioxus realm), they are used as food in some parts of the world. Because of their importance in understanding chordate evolution, one species, *Branchiostoma floridae,* is having its genome sequenced and a preliminary report has been published.

Chapters that follow look at the larger chordates, including pinnipeds (*pinna*—feather or wing, *pedi*—foot) such as the common harbor seal (*Phoca vitulina*) (Figure 20-5), cetaceans including the gray whale (*Eschrichtius robustus*) (Figure 20-6), and birds such as the common western gull (*Larus occidentalis*) (Figure 20-7).

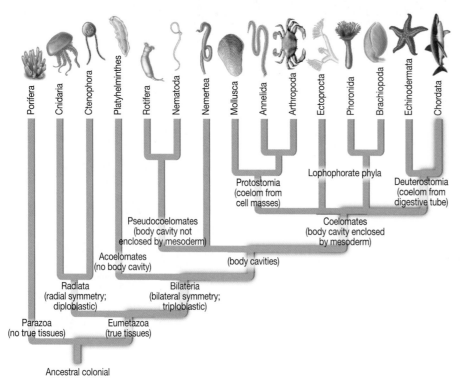

20-1 Phylogeny of Chordata ≈

The chordata is the last of the phyla covered in this atlas. All members are part of the coelomate Deuterostomia, although the developmental pattern is highly modified in some. This phylum contains most of the animals familiar to us: fish, amphibians, reptiles, birds, and mammals. But this phylum contains much more than these familiar forms. It contains an array of organisms that share common anatomical and morphological characteristics, and are important in ecosystems as food chain components and keystone species. See Appendix B for definitions of terms used at branch points in this figure.

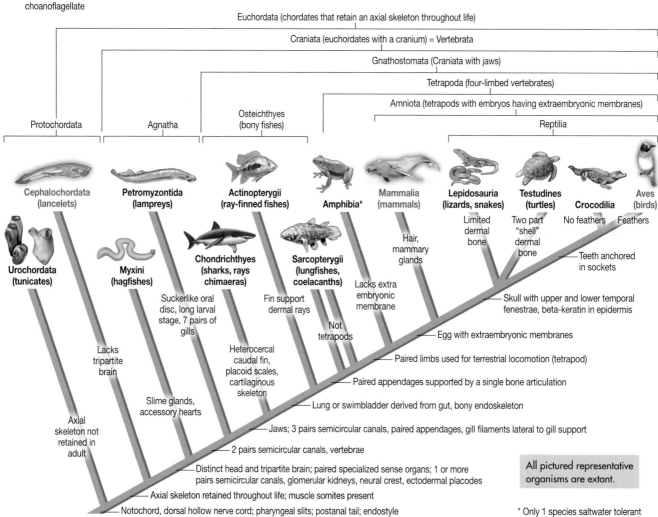

20-2 Chordate Cladogram ≈ Note the clades at the top of this diagram: Euchordata, Craniata, Gnathostomata, Tetrapoda, Amniota, and Reptilia. As you continue from this chapter through Chapter 27, these are important clades to remember. Photographs in this chapter include members of the taxa shown in highlight: Cephalochordata, Mammalia, and Aves. See Appendix C for definitions of terms.

Subphylum Class	General Description	Examples	Approximate Number of Species	Etymology
Urochordata	Highly variable; solitary, colonial, or compound organisms; incurrent and excurrent openings; benthic, planktonic, and pelagic forms; mostly filter feeders	Sea squirts, salps, and larvacea	1,600	*uro*—tail, *chorda*—cord
Cephalochordata Figures 20-3 and 20-4)	Slender animals that look like miniature lampreys up to 8 cm long	Lancelets	29	*cephalo*—head, *chorda*—cord
Craniata	Cranium surrounding tripartite brain			
Myxini	Eel-like body with no paired appendages or jaws; eyes degenerate; four pairs of tentacles around mouth	Hagfish	70	*myxa*—slime
Petromyzontida	Similar in appearance to hagfish, but generally larger and with keratinized teeth and seven pairs of gill openings	Lampreys	38	*petros*—stone, *myzon*—sucking
Chondrichythes	Jaws present; five to seven gill openings in most (four in a few); paired appendages	Sharks, skates, rays, and chimaeras	970	*chondros*—cartilage, *ichthys*—fish
Actinopterygii	Bony fish with single gill opening covered by an operculum; appendages with fin rays	Ray-finned bony fish (and therefore most bony fish)	27,000	*aktis*—ray, *pteryx*—fin
Sarcopterygii	Like other bony fish except appendages with stout internal skeleton compared to fin rays	Lobe-finned bony fish; paraphyletic without tetrapods	8	*sarkos*—flesh, *pteryx*—fin
Amphibia	Tetrapods with moist, water permeable skin; larval stage in most	Frogs, salamanders, and caecilians	5,500	*amphi*—double, *bio*—life
Reptilia—non-avian reptiles	Covered with scales; claws on digits; no larval stage; lays leathery-shelled egg	Lizards, snakes, turtles, crocodiles, alligators; paraphyletic without birds	8,100	*repere*—to creep
Aves—avian reptiles (Figure 20-7)	Feathers and endothermic; claws on leg digits; no larval stage; lays hard-shelled egg	Birds	9,700	*avis*—bird
Mammalia (Figures 20-5 and 20-6)	Hair and mammary glands; claws on digits of most, nails on others; no larval stage; most do not lay egg(s)	Egg-laying, marsupial, and placental mammals; an outgroup of reptiles	4,900	*mamma*—breast

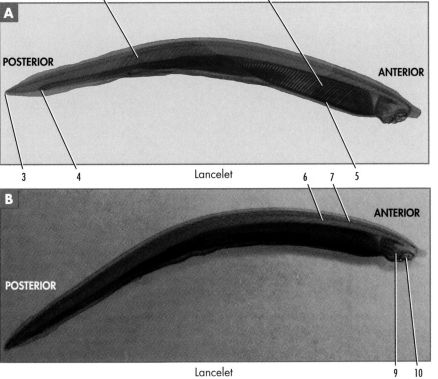

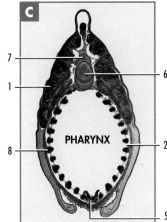

1. Myotomes (myomeres)
2. Pharyngeal gills and gill slits
3. Postanal tail
4. Anus
5. Endostyle (hypobranchial groove)
6. Notochord
7. Dorsal nerve cord
8. Gill
9. Wheel organ
10. Oral tentacles

■ **20-3** Photomicrograph of *Amphioxus* (Cephalochordata) ~ *Amphioxus* is a small, primitive chordate. Labels indicate the five hallmark anatomical features of chordates: dorsal tubular nerve cord, a notochord, pharyngeal slits or pouches, a postanal tail, and an endostyle. All of these features are present in *amphioxus*, but are not present in all adult chordates and are variously modified in some species. (**A** and **B**) These are photomicrographs of whole organisms. (**C**) This is a cross section through the pharynx of an adult.

ANTERIOR

POSTERIOR

Lancelet

1. Myotomes (myomeres)   2. Postanal tail   3. Gonad   4. Oral tentacles

■ 20-4 *Amphioxus* **(Celphalochordata)** ≈ Living specimens are translucent. This specimen's appearance is typical of individuals that have been collected in the wild and placed in preservative for later examination.

Harbor seal

■ 20-5 Harbor Seal (Mammalia) ≈ This is the common harbor seal (*Phoca vitulina*). Harbor seals are among the most widely distributed of seal species, being found in arctic and temperate oceans. Individuals generally inhabit a limited range and can be seen on sandy (**A**) and moderately rocky (**B**) shores. They feed on fish, squid, and some invertebrates.

Gray whale

■ 20-6 Gray Whale (Mammalia) ≈ The gray whale, *Eschrichtius robustus*, inhabits the Northeastern Pacific coastal waters from the Bering Sea to the lagoons of Baja California. The gray whale is a baleen whale that feeds on crustaceans and tube worms living in bottom sediments.

Western gull

■ 20-7 Western Gull (Aves) ≈ The common western gull (*Larus occidentalis*) is widely distributed along the Pacific Coast of North America from British Columbia to Baja California, although its range is rather limited for a gull. It is very different in appearance depending upon age. At about four years of age or older, the western gull has the appearance of the white and gray-to-black bird with pink feet shown here. As a juvenile, it has the appearance of the other bird shown in this photo. Each year, the juvenile will increasingly take on the appearance of the adult. (**A**) With a large yellow bill and a large red spot near the end, the adult shown is being pursued by the juvenile, who apparently won't give up orienting on the large red spot of the adult bill! (**B**) Feed me! Feed me!

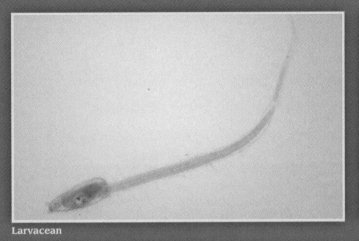

Larvacean

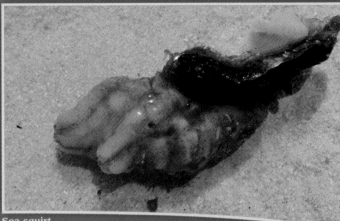

Sea squirt

21 Urochordata and Cephalochordata

These taxa are composed exclusively of marine species. See Figure 21-1 for a cladogram of these groups and their relationship to the Craniata (vertebrates). Table 21-1 summarizes the major groups within the two phyla.

Many species are important members of the biosphere, feeding on plankton by means of filter-feeding structures that generally use mucus to trap minute organisms. They range from strictly benthic to planktonic and pelagic. They may be singular, colonial, or **compound organisms** (more than one organism sharing a common structure such as a shell). The salps are particularly important in Antarctic seas, feeding on phytoplankton and in turn providing food for fish, marine mammals, and birds. At times, salps can outnumber krill in the Antarctic, and *Salpa aspera* has been seen covering 100,000 km² of sea surface area. Because of the number of phytoplanktors consumed by salps, at times salps may play an important role in the regulation of CO_2 levels in the atmosphere.

Urochordates

The Urochordates (*uro*—tail, *chorda*—cord) or tunicates (*tunica*—cloak or covering) possess a cellulose-containing tunic enclosing the organism. (They are the only animal

taxon capable of producing this large organic molecule usually associated with plants.) Most species only show all chordate hallmark features (Chapter 20) in their larval forms, and as adults, are highly modified for specialized life styles. As a taxon, they range throughout the seas and occur in a wide variety of habitats. (For example, see Fouling Communities, Chapter 33.) Several species are used as food in some parts of the world, and as of 2009 two species have had their genome sequenced. There are currently three classes (Table 21-1).

The Ascidiacea (*ascidia*—little bag, *acea*—group suffix), also called sea squirts (Figure 21-2), are sessile animals. Most are mucociliary filter feeders, feeding on a variety of planktonic forms, but some are predators. They are hermaphroditic (produce both egg and sperm) and generally show only two chordate characteristics in the adult form (pharyngeal slits and endostyle).

The Thaliacea (*thalia*—blooming or flourishing), also called salps, are pelagic organisms that are nearly transparent (Figure 21-3). In contrast to the sea squirts with siphons at the same end, most salps have siphons at opposite ends of their cylindrical bodies. They, too, filter feed using mucus, but the water stream is produced by muscular contractions rather than by cilia, as in the Ascidiacea.

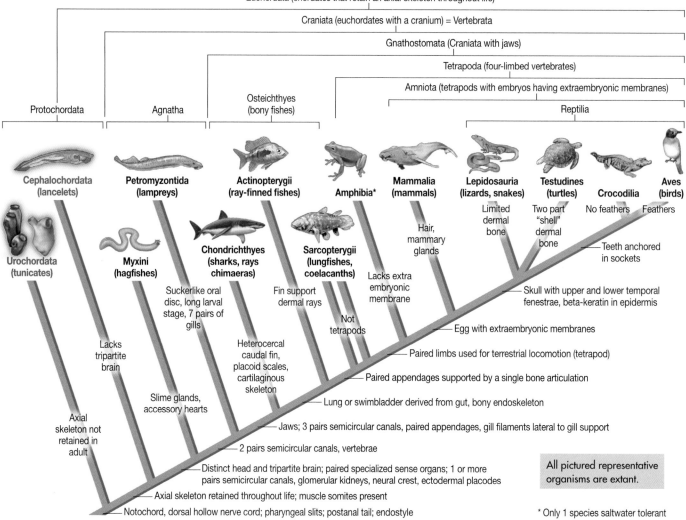

Euchordata (chordates that retain an axial skeleton throughout life)

Craniata (euchordates with a cranium) = Vertebrata

Gnathostomata (Craniata with jaws)

Tetrapoda (four-limbed vertebrates)

Amniota (tetrapods with embryos having extraembryonic membranes)

Protochordata   Agnatha   Osteichthyes (bony fishes)   Reptilia

Cephalochordata (lancelets)

Petromyzontida (lampreys)

Actinopterygii (ray-finned fishes)

Amphibia*

Mammalia (mammals)

Lepidosauria (lizards, snakes)

Testudines (turtles)

Crocodilia

Aves (birds)

Urochordata (tunicates)

Myxini (hagfishes)

Chondrichthyes (sharks, rays chimaeras)

Sarcopterygii (lungfishes, coelacanths)

Limited dermal bone

Two part "shell" dermal bone

No feathers   Feathers

Hair, mammary glands

Teeth anchored in sockets

Suckerlike oral disc, long larval stage, 7 pairs of gills

Fin support dermal rays

Lacks extra embryonic membrane

Skull with upper and lower temporal fenestrae, beta-keratin in epidermis

Lacks tripartite brain

Heterocercal caudal fin, placoid scales, cartilaginous skeleton

Not tetrapods

Egg with extraembryonic membranes

Paired limbs used for terrestrial locomotion (tetrapod)

Slime glands, accessory hearts

Paired appendages supported by a single bone articulation

Axial skeleton not retained in adult

Lung or swimbladder derived from gut, bony endoskeleton

Jaws; 3 pairs semicircular canals, paired appendages, gill filaments lateral to gill support

2 pairs semicircular canals, vertebrae

Distinct head and tripartite brain; paired specialized sense organs; 1 or more pairs semicircular canals, glomerular kidneys, neural crest, ectodermal placodes

All pictured representative organisms are extant.

Axial skeleton retained throughout life; muscle somites present

Notochord, dorsal hollow nerve cord; pharyngeal slits; postanal tail; endostyle

* Only 1 species saltwater tolerant

■ **21-1 Chordate Cladogram** ≈ All taxa represented here show the five hallmark characteristics of the chordata (extreme left of diagram). Note that the first branch (moving left to right) is based upon retention of an axial skeleton to the adult form. The second branch is based upon possession of a tripartite (*tri*—three, *partit*—divided) brain, a brain with three primary parts. The organisms leading to the left from these first two branches constitute the protochordates, which includes urochordates and cephalochordates. See Appendix C for definitions of terms.

■ **Table 21-1** ≈ Urochordate and Cephalochordate Subphyla and Classes

Subphylum Class	General Description	Examples	Approximate Number of Species	Etymology
Urochordata	Highly variable, solitary, colonial, or compound organisms; incurrent and excurrent openings; benthic, planktonic, and pelagic forms; most filter feeders	Sea squirts, salps, and larvacea	1,600	*oura*—tail, *chorda*—cord
Ascidiacea (Figure 21-2)	Attached animals; generally show only two chordate characteristics in the adult form (pharyngeal slits and endostyle)	Sea squirts	1,500+	*ascidia*—little bag, *acea*—group suffix
Thaliacea (Figure 21-3)	Pelagic organisms that are nearly transparent	Salps	30	*thalia*—blooming or flourishing, *acea*—group suffix
Appendicularia or Larvacea (Figure 21-4)	Paedomorphs, that is, they retain their larval form into adulthood	No common name	70	*appendic*—attached to
Cephalochordata (Figure 21-5)	Slender animals that look like miniature lampreys up to 7 or 8 cm long	Lancelets (amphioxus)	29	*cephalo*—head, *chorda*—cord

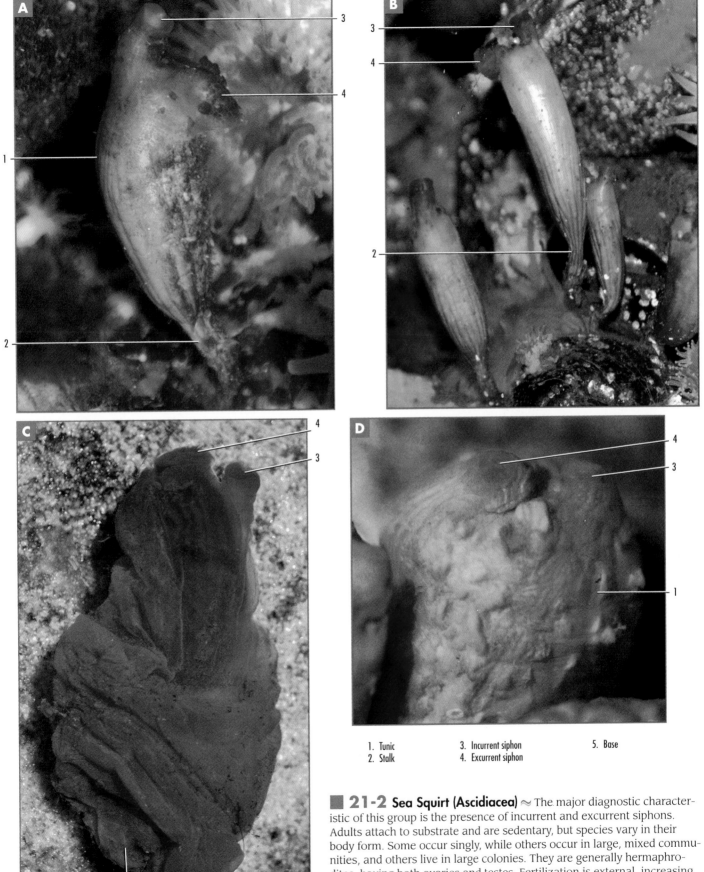

1. Tunic   3. Incurrent siphon   5. Base
2. Stalk   4. Excurrent siphon

■ **21-2 Sea Squirt (Ascidiacea)** ~ The major diagnostic characteristic of this group is the presence of incurrent and excurrent siphons. Adults attach to substrate and are sedentary, but species vary in their body form. Some occur singly, while others occur in large, mixed communities, and others live in large colonies. They are generally hermaphrodites, having both ovaries and testes. Fertilization is external, increasing the likelihood that fertilization will occur between unrelated individuals and maintaining genetic diversity. (**A** and **B**) *Styela montereyensis*, (**C**) *Ciona* (preserved specimen), and (**D**) *Mogula* (preserved specimen).

The Appendicularia (*appendic*—attached to) or Larvacea are **paedomorphs**, that is, they retain their larval form into adulthood (Figure 21-4). They also construct a unique feeding device composed of mucus and other materials, which form a filter. They have the smallest genome of any chordate based upon an incomplete draft genome sequence.

Cephalochordates

Five of the 25 cephalochordate species (*cephalo*—head, *chorda*—cord) occur in North America. These species are also known as amphioxus (*amphi*—both ends, *oxys*—sharp), (Figure 21-5). As mentioned earlier, these organisms played an important role in the development of our

understanding of Chordata and Craniata evolutionary relationships (Figure 21-1). They show all primary characteristics of the Chordata in a very straightforward, easily recognized form and share characteristics with tunicates and vertebrates. They are organic particle filter feeders, feeding from a half-buried position in the sandy bottom marine environment.

Evidence supports the hypothesis that amphioxus is the closest living relative of the vertebrates and shares a number of characteristics with them that are missing in the Urochordata. Because of their importance in our understanding of evolutionary relationships, the genome of amphioxus has been sequenced. In Chapter 22, we will compare amphioxus with the larva of the vertebrate lamprey.

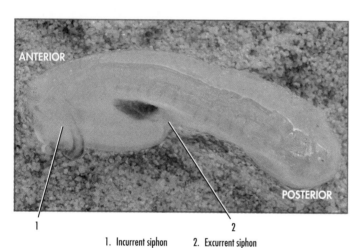

1. Incurrent siphon   2. Excurrent siphon

■ 21-3 Salp (Thaliacea) ≈ Salps vary widely in size, appearance, and distribution. All are more or less barrel shaped and are filter feeders, removing plankton as they pump water through their body. Like sea squirts, they have incurrent and excurrent siphons. However, their siphons are at opposite ends of their cylindrical body, and water is pumped through their bodies by muscular contractions. Salps' life cycles are complex and allow for very rapid population growth rates when their phytoplankton food source is abundant. This is a preserved specimen.

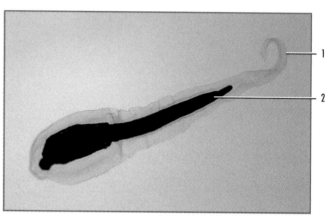

1. Tail   2. Dorsal nerve cord

■ 21-4 Larvacean (Larvacea) ≈ The larval larvacean body form (shown in this micrograph) is retained in the adult. However, adults build a mucous house for trapping food and in which they feed. The home is about the size of a walnut and must be replaced when it becomes clogged with materials suspended in the water. The specimen shown is about 1 mm in length.

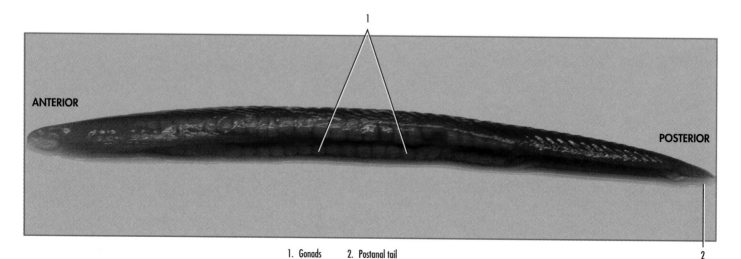

1. Gonads   2. Postanal tail

■ 21-5 Amphioxus (Cephalochordata) ≈ *Branchiostoma floridae* is abundant in coastal waters off Florida. It belongs to a group collectively known as "amphioxus." This is a preserved specimen.

Black oystercatcher

Mimic roundhead

22 Craniata

This taxon includes one non-vertebrate (invertebrate) group, the hagfish (Myxini; *myxa*—slime, mucus, Table 22-1), and all vertebrates. In this chapter, we will limit our look at vertebrates to the lamprey (Petromyzontida; *petros*—rock, *myzon*—sucking, Table 22-1). See Figure 22-1 for a cladogram of these groups and their relationship to the Urochordata and Cephalochordata.

The vertebrates are the most diverse group of Chordates and include all fish, amphibians, reptiles, birds, and mammals. The Craniata have a number of characteristics derived since their separation from a common ancestor with the Urochordata and Cephalochordata. They all possess a braincase (**cranium**) (Figure 22-2) and most have vertebrae (Figure 22-3), with hagfish being the exception, as mentioned previously. All groups have marine members

except the Amphibians, although there is a saline tolerant crab-eating frog (Figure 22-4).

Shared derived characteristics (synapomorphies) of the group include both an exoskeleton and endoskeleton of cartilage or bone. The endoskeleton has particular advantages over the exoskeleton and provides a strong scaffold upon which a large organism can be constructed. The result has been greater size in the Craniata than in phyla lacking an endoskeleton.

Associated with the development and increased importance of the endoskeleton has been the development of segmental muscles (Figure 22-5) and increased muscular folding (from the V shape of cephalochordates to the W shape of the vertebrates), which provides control over an extended body length.

■ Table 22-1 ≈ Agnathan Classes

Class	General Description	Examples	Approximate Number of Species	Etymology
Myxini (Figures 22-9, 22-11, and 22-12)	Jawless, eel-shaped organisms with no paired fins	Hagfish	70	*myxi*—slime
Petromyzontida (Figures 22-9 through 22-11, and 22-13 through 22-16)	Jawless, eel-shaped organisms with no paired fins; vertebrae as an arch	Lamprey	40	*petro*—stone, *myzon*—sucker

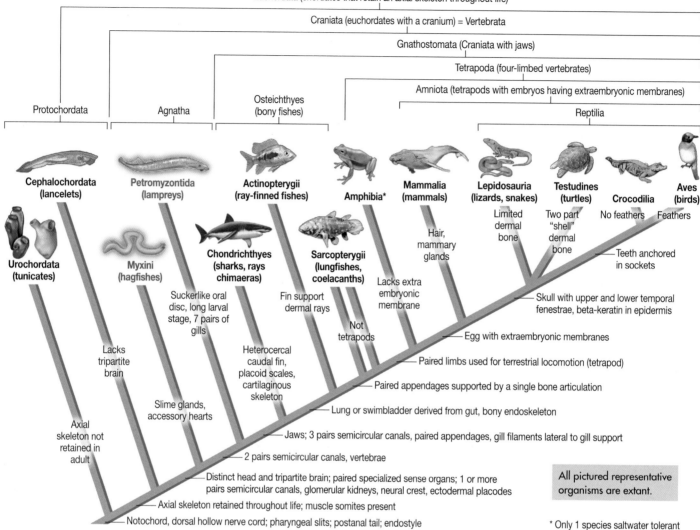

Euchordata (chordates that retain an axial skeleton throughout life)

Craniata (euchordates with a cranium) = Vertebrata

Gnathostomata (Craniata with jaws)

Tetrapoda (four-limbed vertebrates)

Amniota (tetrapods with embryos having extraembryonic membranes)

Protochordata

Agnatha

Osteichthyes (bony fishes)

Reptilia

Cephalochordata (lancelets)

Petromyzontida (lampreys)

Actinopterygii (ray-finned fishes)

Amphibia*

Mammalia (mammals)

Lepidosauria (lizards, snakes)

Testudines (turtles)

Crocodilia

Aves (birds)

Limited dermal bone

Two part "shell" dermal bone

No feathers   Feathers

Hair, mammary glands

Urochordata (tunicates)

Myxini (hagfishes)

Chondrichthyes (sharks, rays chimaeras)

Sarcopterygii (lungfishes, coelacanths)

Teeth anchored in sockets

Lacks extra embryonic membrane

Skull with upper and lower temporal fenestrae, beta-keratin in epidermis

Suckerlike oral disc, long larval stage, 7 pairs of gills

Fin support dermal rays

Not tetrapods

Egg with extraembryonic membranes

Lacks tripartite brain

Heterocercal caudal fin, placoid scales, cartilaginous skeleton

Paired limbs used for terrestrial locomotion (tetrapod)

Paired appendages supported by a single bone articulation

Slime glands, accessory hearts

Lung or swimbladder derived from gut, bony endoskeleton

Axial skeleton not retained in adult

Jaws; 3 pairs semicircular canals, paired appendages, gill filaments lateral to gill support

2 pairs semicircular canals, vertebrae

Distinct head and tripartite brain; paired specialized sense organs; 1 or more pairs semicircular canals, glomerular kidneys, neural crest, ectodermal placodes

All pictured representative organisms are extant.

Axial skeleton retained throughout life; muscle somites present

Notochord, dorsal hollow nerve cord; pharyngeal slits; postanal tail; endostyle

* Only 1 species saltwater tolerant

■ 22-1 Chordate Cladogram ≈ Note the derived characteristics that separate the Myxini and Petromyzontida from the other Chordata. Neither has jaws and is therefore not part of the Gnathostomata clade, while both are part of the Craniata and Agnatha. See Appendix C for definitions of terms.

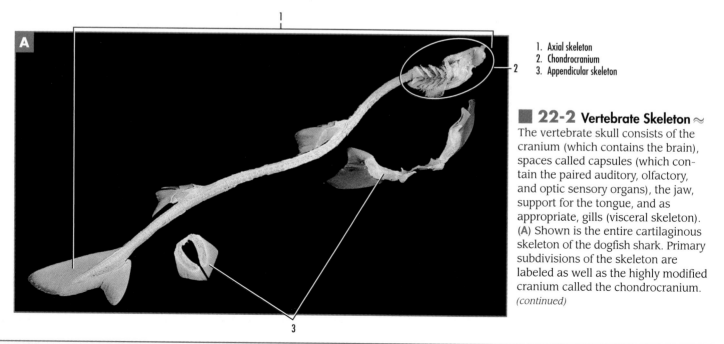

1. Axial skeleton
2. Chondrocranium
3. Appendicular skeleton

■ 22-2 Vertebrate Skeleton ≈ The vertebrate skull consists of the cranium (which contains the brain), spaces called capsules (which contain the paired auditory, olfactory, and optic sensory organs), the jaw, support for the tongue, and as appropriate, gills (visceral skeleton). **(A)** Shown is the entire cartilaginous skeleton of the dogfish shark. Primary subdivisions of the skeleton are labeled as well as the highly modified cranium called the chondrocranium.

(continued)

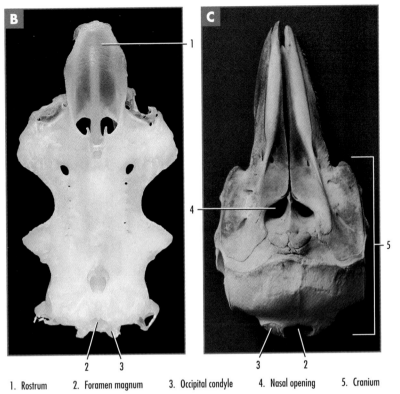

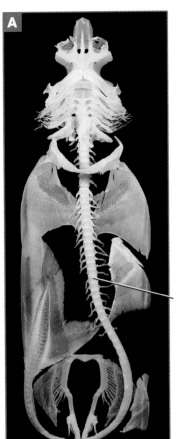

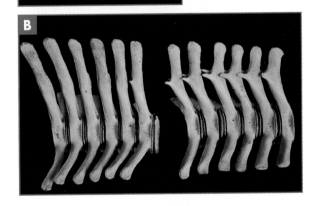

1. Rostrum   2. Foramen magnum   3. Occipital condyle   4. Nasal opening   5. Cranium

■ **22-2 Vertebrate Skeleton** ≈ *(continued)* **(B)** This is a dorsal view of the shark chondrocranium. Unique to the chondrocranium is the rostrum. Shared with other Craniata are structures such as the point at which the spinal cord and brain stem exit the cranium (foramen magnum) and a point at which the vertebral column touches (articulates) the cranium, the occipital condyle. **(C)** This is a dorsal view of a bony adult dolphin skull. Note the occipital condyles, which articulate with the first vertebra, the atlas.

■ **22-3 Craniata Vertebral Column** ≈ **(A)** The cartilaginous vertebral column of the dogfish. **(B)** Shown are two sections from the Pacific white-sided dolphin vertebral column.

1. Vertebral column

Crab-eating frog

■ **22-4 Crab-eating Frog (Amphibia)** ≈ *Fejervarya cancrivora* (formerly, *Rana cancrivora*) is the only *known* (emphasis on known) saline tolerant amphibian. It is native to Southeast Asia, inhabiting mangrove swamps, and has physiological mechanisms that allow it to spend short periods of time in salt water and in brackish water for extended periods.

This clade shows a general transition from cartilage to bone. Bone provides a number of advantages over cartilage. These include greater mechanical strength for muscle attachment and the physiological advantage of mineral regulation of calcium and phosphorus. It also provides greater predator protection as part of an exoskeleton.

Vertebrates possess an extensive exoskeleton (developed from the skin) that ranges from scales to cranial bones. Species in this clade also produce other dermal derivatives, ranging from scales to hair, feathers, claws, fingernails, and horns (Figure 22-6).

As a group, the Craniata show an increased metabolic rate coinciding with changes in all organ systems to support this modification. Synapomorphies include the development of a muscular pharynx for the exchange of carbon dioxide and oxygen (Figures 22-7A and 22-7B), development of a

1. Myomeres
2. Vertebral column

■ 22-5 Segmental Muscles ≈ Muscle segments (myomeres) run along the length of the vertebral column (axial skeleton) in fish. This bony fish is viewed from the ventral surface looking dorsally after all organs of the abdominal cavity have been removed. The vertebral column is labeled.

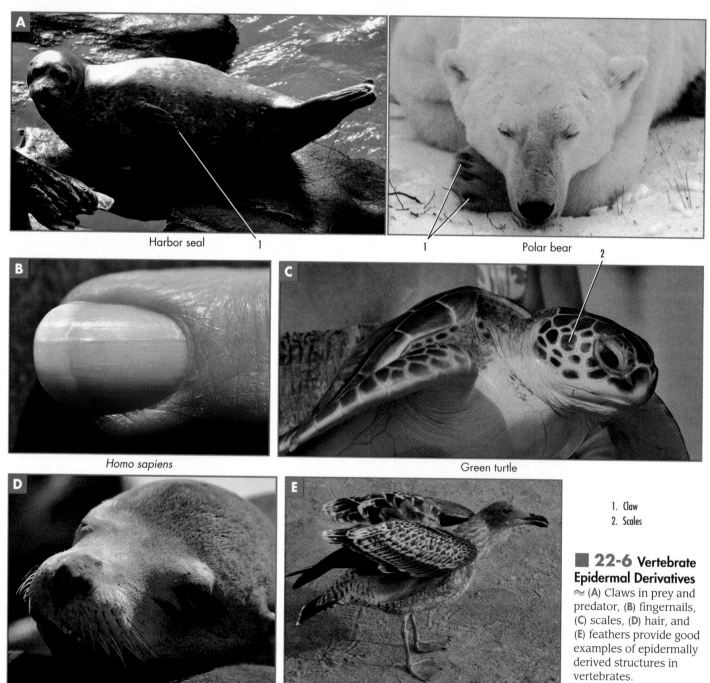

A Harbor seal 1

Polar bear 1 2

B *Homo sapiens*

C Green turtle

1. Claw
2. Scales

■ 22-6 Vertebrate Epidermal Derivatives ≈ (**A**) Claws in prey and predator, (**B**) fingernails, (**C**) scales, (**D**) hair, and (**E**) feathers provide good examples of epidermally derived structures in vertebrates.

D Harbor seal

E Juvenile gull

digestive system, which moves food by muscular contraction rather than ciliary action, and the addition of accessory glands such as a liver and pancreas (Figure 22-7C). This was associated with the development of a two-chambered, then a three-chambered, and eventually a four-chambered heart (Figure 22-7D), and the addition of blood cells (Figure 22-7E) and a protein molecule for the transport of oxygen. Finally, the clade possesses paired, glomerular kidneys (a tubule that surrounds a tuft of capillaries). See Figure 22-7F.

Associated with these changes and a shift from a filter-feeding life style to a predatory life style, a number of other changes occurred. Three areas at the anterior end of the nerve cord formed the brain, a cranium to protect the brain developed (Figures 22-2), and anterior sense organs, including eyes (Figure 22-8A), pressure receptors, taste and smell receptors, water vibration receptors, (Figure 22-8B) and electroreceptors (Figure 22-8C) developed.

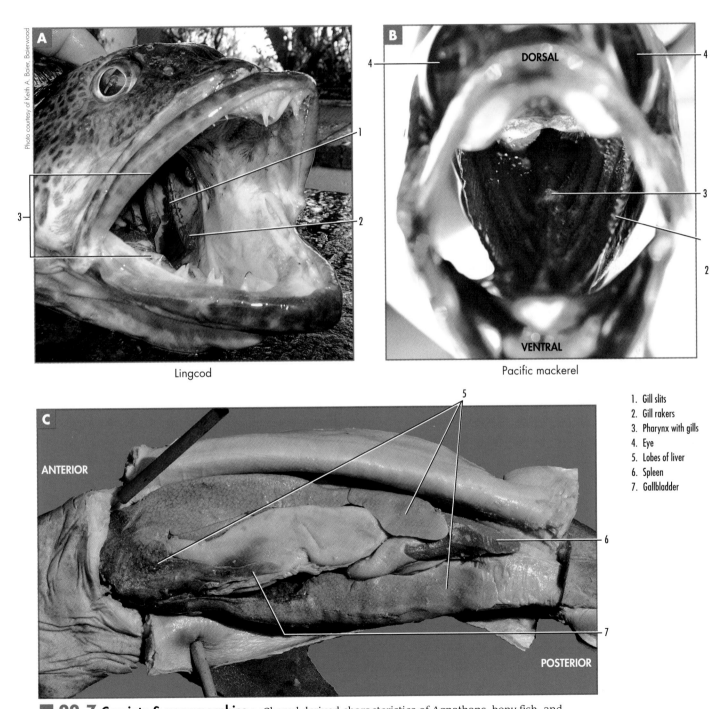

Lingcod

Pacific mackerel

1. Gill slits
2. Gill rakers
3. Pharynx with gills
4. Eye
5. Lobes of liver
6. Spleen
7. Gallbladder

22-7 Craniata Synapomorphies ≈ Shared derived characteristics of Agnathans, bony fish, and tetrapods are shown: (**A** and **B**) muscular pharynx in bony fish—lingcod, *Ophiodon elongates*, and Pacific mackerel, *Scomber japonicus*; (**C**) the liver, as seen in a preserved dogfish shark. *(continued)*

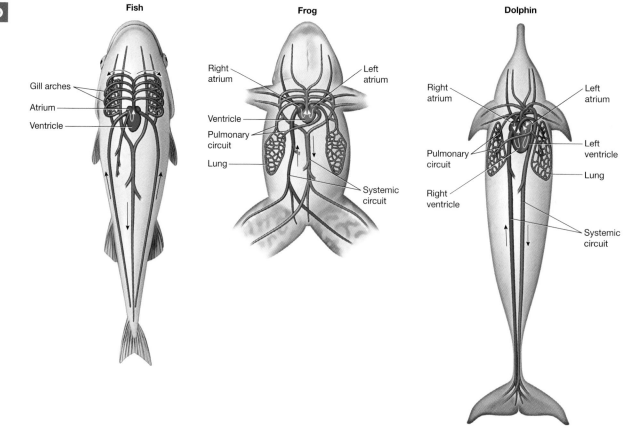

Fish

Gill arches

Atrium

Ventricle

Frog

Right atrium

Left atrium

Ventricle

Pulmonary circuit

Lung

Systemic circuit

Dolphin

Right atrium

Left atrium

Left ventricle

Pulmonary circuit

Lung

Right ventricle

Systemic circuit

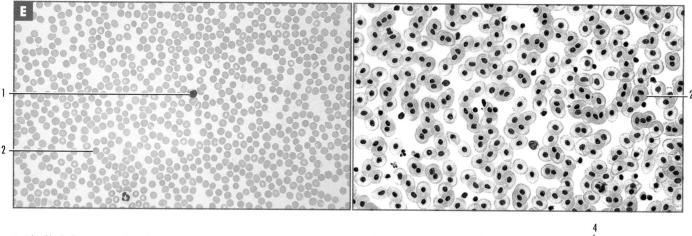

1

2

2

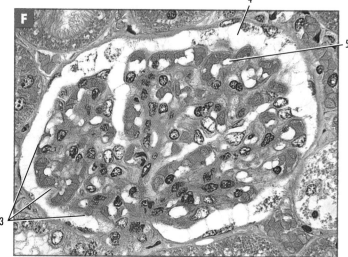

4

5

3

1. White blood cell
2. Red blood cell
3. Glomerulus
4. Space of Bowman's Capsule
5. Glomerular capillary lumen

■ **22-7 Craniata Synapomorphies** ≈ *(continued)* (D) Notice the difference in circulatory pathway from fish, to amphibian, to mammal. The general trend is from a single flow heart and circulatory pathway, to partial double pathway, and finally to complete double flow pathway. (E) On the left are mammalian blood cells; on the right are bony fish blood cells. Note that mammalian red blood cells have lost their nuclei by the time they enter general circulation, while those of bony fish retain their nuclei. (F) This section of a mammalian kidney shows a glomerulus, one of up to a million filtration structures in each mammalian kidney.

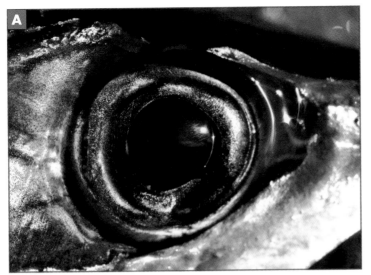

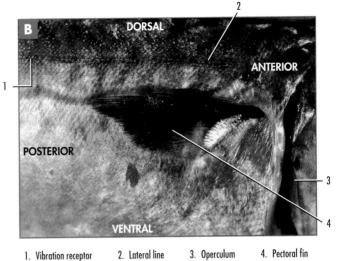

1. Vibration receptor   2. Lateral line   3. Operculum   4. Pectoral fin

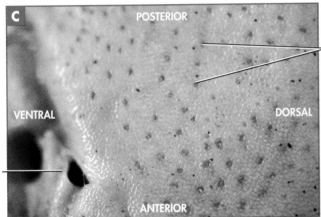

■ **22-8 Craniata Sense Organs** ∼ (A) The eyes in this bony saltwater fish are used in vision. (B) Vibration receptors of this saltwater bony fish, known as the lateral line, detect pressure changes. (C) The electroreceptors of this shark are known as **Ampullae of Lorenzini** and detect the electric field that surrounds living organisms.

1. Nostril
2. Electroreceptors (Ampullae of Lorenzini)

Jawless Fish

As a descriptive term, *fish* is nebulous at best. We will use the term to mean an organism with an endoskeleton, gills, and fins. Most have scales and a moist, generally mucous-covered skin. Aquatic habitats are dominated by the roughly 28,000 known fish species; there are more species of fish than all other vertebrates combined! The chordates described in this chapter are variously known as the jawless fish or **agnathans** (*a*—without, *gnathes*—jaw).

Agnathans include hagfish and lampreys (Figure 22-9), the Myxini and Petromyzontida, respectively. It is now difficult to call these fish vertebrates since hagfish lack vertebrae and the lamprey only has small bands of

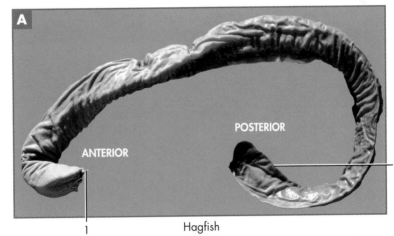

1. Tentacles
2. Caudal fin
3. Gill slits

■ **22-9 Hagfish and Lamprey (Agnathans)** ∼ Hagfish (A) and lampreys (B) are jawless fish ("jawless" does *not* mean "mouthless") that lack the paired appendages found in the Gnathostomata. These are preserved specimens.

cartilage along the dorsal side of the notochord, which partially surround the dorsal nerve cord (Figure 22-10), but it is a tradition that most textbooks continue. In both fish, the notochord remains the primary component of their axial skeleton. Both are cartilaginous fish, although the cartilages of hagfish and lampreys are unusual in that neither contains the protein **collagen** as a primary structural component, as in practically every other chordate. The primary protein components even differ between hagfish and lampreys. The molecular data support the hypothesis that collagenous cartilage is a derived characteristic of vertebrates originating after the separation of lampreys and the rest of the craniate clade.

Superficially, both groups lack scales, and their external gill openings are round holes rather than the elongated slits of other fish (Figure 22-11). Their body form is **anguilliform** (eel shaped).

Like the rest of Craniata, hagfish and lampreys have a cranium and other vertebrate derived characteristics, including an increased number of genes controlling several developmental pathways and clade specific embryonic structures producing parts of the cranium.

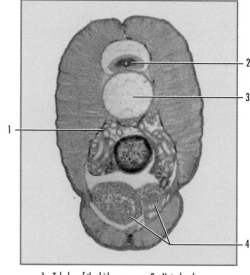

1. Tubules of the kidney	3. Notochord
2. Dorsal nerve cord	4. Heart chambers

■ **22-10 Lamprey Larval Notochord** ~ Note the notochord and dorsal nerve cord in this microscopic cross section of the lamprey ammocoetes larva. The notochord shown is about 250 μm in diameter.

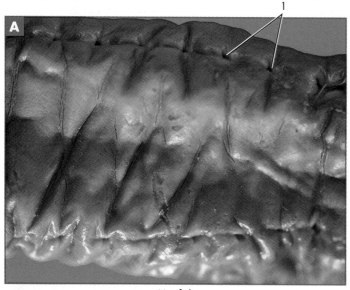

Hagfish

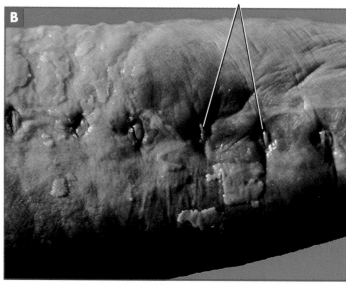

Lamprey

1. Gill slits

Nurse shark

■ **22-11 Craniata Gill Openings** ~ The multiple gill openings of this (**A**) hagfish and (**B**) lamprey are round to oval openings compared to the elongated slits of the (**C**) shark and bony fish. The shark in (**C**) is a nurse shark. (**A**) and (**B**) are preserved specimens.

Myxini

Hagfish only occur in cold, marine water. There are nearly 70 known species, all of which are scavengers feeding on living invertebrates and dead or dying fish. Often not appreciated for their ecological role, studies indicate they are present in sufficient numbers to have an important impact on many benthic communities, particularly with regard to nutrient recycling as an important consumer of nonliving organic and inorganic material (organic + inorganic = detritivore).

Their notochord is retained in the adult, and they have direct development with no larva. Hagfish excrete large amounts of slime from slime glands (up to several liters in a minute—as measured after contact with seawater), which covers their body. This appears to be a protective mechanism to avoid predation. In Figure 22-12, you can see the slime gland pores.

We are unaware of complete genome data on these organisms, but their mitochondrial DNA has been sequenced.

Petromyzontida

The lamprey notochord persists in the adult form (Figure 22-13). They have an attenuated body form like the hagfish and are scaleless. Although jawless, they do have a sucker-like oral disc and rasping tongue (Figure 22-14). They have seven pairs of gill openings, well-developed eyes, organs of taste and smell, and vibration receptors. Lamprey use external fertilization and have a long larval stage (Figure 22-15), which was originally thought to be a distinct species, and was given the name *Ammocoetes* (*ammo*—sand, *coetes*—whale) (Figure 22-16). Their larval form is still called an Ammocoetes and although the larval stage is smaller than the adult in most species, in some the reverse is true.

The larvae are freshwater only and have a lifestyle much like amphioxus: they burrow into a sandy bottom where they filter feed. They also look very much like amphioxus, showing the same simplified, easily visible chordate characteristics. They spend three to seven or more years as a larva, and then metamorphose into the adult form. Parasitic adults feed by attaching to live fish where they use their keratinized tongue-teeth (Figure 22-14) to rasp through the flesh and suck out body fluids, principally blood. Adults live for one to three years, depending on the species, then spawn and die. Nonparasitic forms do not feed as adults. They spawn and die within days or a few months.

Larval forms are an important food source for fish, sea otters, birds, and crayfish. Parasitic adults are important parasites of large fish and marine mammals; larger fish and birds eat them. The carbon passing through lampreys as part of the food chain is substantial.

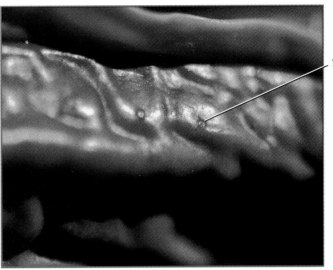

1. Slime gland

22-12 Hagfish Slime Glands ~ Large amounts of slime can be produced and then released from these glands, apparently as a protective mechanism against predation. The slime, which is released in a low volume form that swells upon contact with seawater, is produced in numerous glands on both sides of the body. In addition to slime, the secretions also contain fibers that may help to stabilize the mucus around the body.

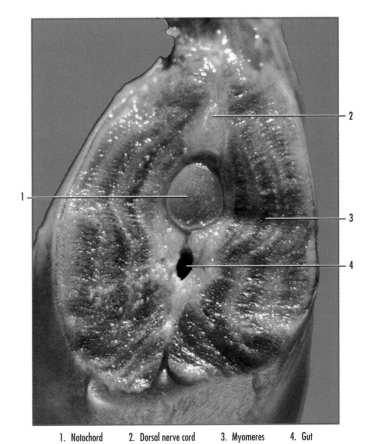

1. Notochord   2. Dorsal nerve cord   3. Myomeres   4. Gut

22-13 Lamprey Notochord ~ This preserved adult lamprey has been sectioned, revealing the notochord and dorsal nerve cord.

Lamprey show increased genetic complexity potentially associated with development in their vertebrate nervous system and skeleton, resulting in the production of vertebrae (although in the lamprey, they are poorly developed), and dorsal, ventral, and anal fins.

There are 35 known species. One species, *Petromyzon marinus*, has had its genome sequenced.

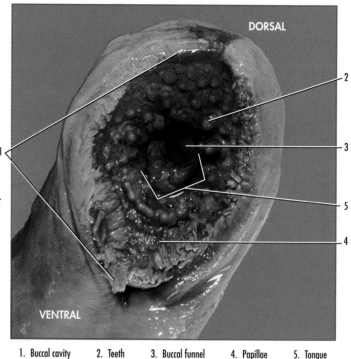

DORSAL

VENTRAL

■ 22-14 Lamprey Oral Cavity ≈

Although jawless, the adult lamprey has a buccal cavity and mouth that are effective for its feeding style. The oral disc is fringed by papillae that enable a tight seal on prey, and the buccal cavity is lined with teeth and ends at a rasping tongue. Anterior to posterior motion of the tongue opens and closes the buccal cavity. The mouth is at the rear of the buccal cavity, dorsal to the tongue, and the buccal funnel containing the teeth is the beginning of the mouth. This is a preserved specimen.

| 1. Buccal cavity | 2. Teeth | 3. Buccal funnel | 4. Papillae | 5. Tongue |

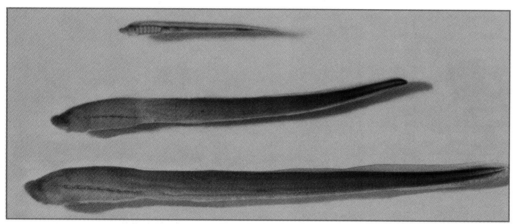

Lamprey larvae

■ 22-15 Lamprey Development ≈ This shows preserved lamprey ammocoetes larvae at three developmental stages.

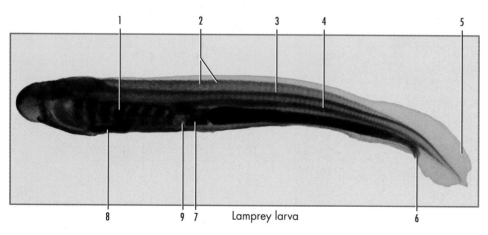

Lamprey larva

■ 22-16 Lamprey Ammocoetes Larva ≈ This stained whole mount of an early ammocoetes larva is shown slightly larger than life size. Note the pharynx, dorsal, hollow nerve cord, notochord, two-chambered heart, liver, and myomeres. In this larval form, the kidneys are not glomerular.

| 1. Gills | 3. Dorsal nerve cord | 5. Post anal tail | 7. Liver | 9. Heart |
| 2. Myomeres | 4. Notochord | 6. Anus | 8. Endostyle | |

Grey smooth-hound shark

Epaulette shark

23 Chondrichthyes

This chapter is the first in a series introducing the remaining Craniata, all of which have a mouth with jaws. Collectively these vertebrates are known as the **gnathostomes** (*gnathos*—jaw, *stoma*—mouth). The presence of jaws is the primary shared derived characteristic of this group (refer to Chapter 20), but others include changes in brain structures associated with increased sophistication of olfactory and visual organs, and for aquatic forms, the presence of the lateral line sensory system (Figure 22-8B).

The Chondrichthyes (*chondros*—cartilage, *ichthy*—fish) (Table 23-1) are predominantly **top carnivores** (the organism at the top of a food chain). They feed on everything from fish, squid, and marine mammals to mollusks, cetaceans, and plankton. However, a number of species are prey for seals and cetaceans.

The Chondrichthyes clade is an ancient group dating back more than 360 million years. They are vertebrates with major derived characteristics developed since beginning a separate evolutionary path from other cartilaginous fish, and in fact, their cartilaginous skeleton appears to be secondarily derived from bony ancestors. Other shared derived characteristics include paired appendages (Figure 23-1) and jaws (Figure 23-2) supported by cartilaginous or bone tissue proposed to be derived from the gill arches,

and skeletal support for the anterior pharyngeal gill slits. Their cartilaginous skeleton helps reduce their density and tendency to sink in an aquatic environment (Figure 23-2).

Chondrichthyes are a fairly diverse vertebrate group with nearly 1,000 known species. They are much better known than hagfish or lampreys, although some members are relatively obscure. Principally marine, there are 28 known freshwater species and some marine forms may wander into freshwater environments temporarily. According to the National Geographic Society, bull sharks have "... been spotted 2,500 miles (4,000 kilometers) up the Amazon River in South America and dwell in Lake Nicaragua, a freshwater lake in Central America. Bull sharks have traveled up the Mississippi River as far north as Illinois and are regularly spotted in India's Ganges."[1]

Their body is fusiform (*fusi*—spindle, *forma*—form) (Figure 23-3A) or is dorsoventrally depressed (Figure 23-3B). The pelvic fins of males are modified into **claspers** (Figure 23-4) and most species have unique **placoid scales** (*placo*—flat) (Figure 23-5), although they have been lost in the Chimaeras (Figure 23-6), Subclass Holocephali (*holo*—whole, *cephali*—head). They also use internal fertilization

---

[1] Brian Handwerk, "Bull Shark Threat: They Swim Where We Swim." *National Geographic News*, July 19, 2005.

Class / Subclass / Order	General Description	Examples	Approximate Number of Species	Etymology
Chondrichthyes	Cartilaginous fish; teeth independent of jaw; no swim bladder; claspers (modified pelvic fins) present in males	Sharks, skates, rays, and ratfish (chimaeras)	970	*chondros*—cartilage, *ichthy*—fish
Elasmobranchii	Five (to seven in some) gill slits; placoid scales; upper jaw not fused to cranium	Sharks, skates, and rays	937	*elasmo*—metal plate, *branchi*—gill
Rajiformes (Figures 23-17A and 23-19A)	Greatly enlarged pectoral fins; rajiform locomotion (waving of the pectoral fins)	Guitarfish and skates	260	*raji*—skate, flatfish, *forma*—form
Pristiformes (Figure 23-16)	Long snout with lots of teeth	Sawfish	7	*pristi*—sawed, *forma*—form
Myliobatiformes (Figures 23-3B, 23-17B, 23-18, and 23-19B)	Greatly enlarged pectoral fins; swim by flapping their pectoral fins	Sting rays, manta rays, eagle rays	180	*mylio*—millstone, *bati*—ray fish, *forma*—form
Torpediniformes	Capable of producing an electric discharge; enlarged pectoral fins	Electric rays	69	*torpe*—numb, *dini*—terrible, *forma*—form
Hexanchiformes	One dorsal fin; six or seven gill slits	Cow sharks, frilled sharks, and others	5	*hex*—six, *anchi*—gill, *forma*—form
Lamniformes (Figures 23-9A, 23-10, 23-13C, and 23-14A)	Two dorsal fins; five gills slits	Great white shark, thresher shark, basking shark, and others	20+	*lamni*—a predaceous fish, *forma*—form
Orectolobiformes (Figures 22-11 and 23-20)	Two dorsal fins; small gill slits, with the fourth and fifth overlapping	Whale shark, nurse shark, bamboo sharks, and others	40	*orecto*—stretched out, *lobi*—lobe, *forma*—form
Pristiophoriformes	Lengthened snout, shaped like a sword and edged with teeth; two dorsal fins but no anal fin	Sawsharks	9	*pristio*—sawed, *phori*—carry, *forma*—form
Squaliformes (Figures 23-4, 23-8, 23-10, and 23-13B)	Two dorsal fins (usually spines); no anal fin; five gills slits	Dogfish, lantern sharks, and others	80	*squali*—a dogfish, *forma*—form
Squatiniformes	Two dorsal fins; no anal fin; both pectoral and pelvic fins are broad; ventral portion of caudal fin larger than dorsal portion	Angel sharks	16+	*squatini*—a skate, *forma*—form
Carcharhiniformes (Figures 23-3A, 23-11, 23-12A, 23-12B and 23-13A)	Two dorsal fins; an anal fin; five gills slits; a nictitating membrane over the eye	Hammerhead sharks, bonnethead sharks, blacktip reef sharks, blue shark, tiger shark, bull shark, leopard shark, and others	270+	*charcharhini*—shark, *forma*—form
Holocephali (Figures 23-6 and 23-21)	Smooth skin lacking scales; upper jaw fused to cranium	Ratfish	65+	*holo*—whole, *cephali*—head

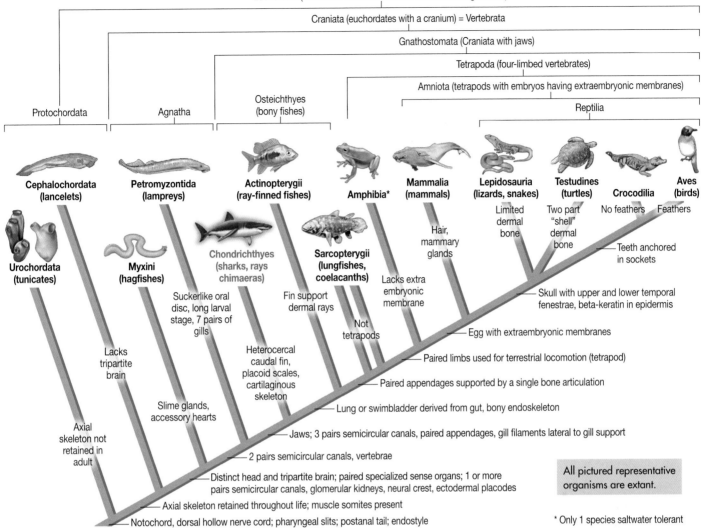

Euchordata (chordates that retain an axial skeleton throughout life)

Craniata (euchordates with a cranium) = Vertebrata

Gnathostomata (Craniata with jaws)

Tetrapoda (four-limbed vertebrates)

Amniota (tetrapods with embryos having extraembryonic membranes)

Reptilia

Protochordata   Agnatha   Osteichthyes (bony fishes)

Cephalochordata (lancelets)   Petromyzontida (lampreys)   Actinopterygii (ray-finned fishes)   Amphibia*   Mammalia (mammals)   Lepidosauria (lizards, snakes)   Testudines (turtles)   Crocodilia   Aves (birds)

Urochordata (tunicates)   Myxini (hagfishes)   Chondrichthyes (sharks, rays chimaeras)   Sarcopterygii (lungfishes, coelacanths)

Limited dermal bone

Two part "shell" dermal bone

Hair, mammary glands

No feathers   Feathers

Teeth anchored in sockets

Lacks extra embryonic membrane

Skull with upper and lower temporal fenestrae, beta-keratin in epidermis

Suckerlike oral disc, long larval stage, 7 pairs of gills

Fin support dermal rays

Not tetrapods

Egg with extraembryonic membranes

Lacks tripartite brain

Heterocercal caudal fin, placoid scales, cartilaginous skeleton

Paired limbs used for terrestrial locomotion (tetrapod)

Paired appendages supported by a single bone articulation

Slime glands, accessory hearts

Lung or swimbladder derived from gut, bony endoskeleton

Axial skeleton not retained in adult

Jaws; 3 pairs semicircular canals, paired appendages, gill filaments lateral to gill support

2 pairs semicircular canals, vertebrae

Distinct head and tripartite brain; paired specialized sense organs; 1 or more pairs semicircular canals, glomerular kidneys, neural crest, ectodermal placodes

All pictured representative organisms are extant.

Axial skeleton retained throughout life; muscle somites present

Notochord, dorsal hollow nerve cord; pharyngeal slits; postanal tail; endostyle

* Only 1 species saltwater tolerant

■ **23-1** **Chondrichthyes Cladogram** ~ Note the derived characteristics that separate the *Chondricthyes* from the *Myxini* and *Petromyzontida*, and from the other chordata, particularly the bony fish. Although their cartilaginous skeleton is included in this list, there is evidence that this was derived from bony ancestors. See Appendix C for definitions of terms.

and have direct development (no larval form). This differs from the hagfish and lamprey, both of which have larval forms (Figure 23-7).

Although Chondrichthyes are derived from ancestors with well-developed bone, members of this Class no longer have any bony elements in their skeleton. They do have mineralized tissues forming teeth, scales, and spines (Figures 23-8 and 23-9).

The ecological role of some members of this group is legendary (the great white shark comes to mind), while other extant species are not generally matters of public interest. Each species has its own particular position in the marine food chain, with specialized food sources ranging from plankton to invertebrates, fish, and marine mammals.

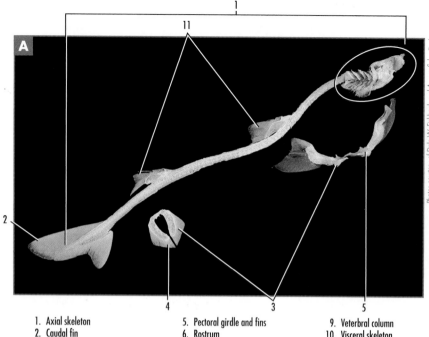

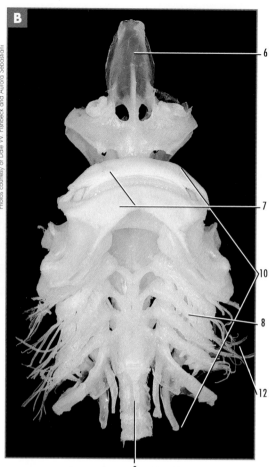

Photos courtesy of Dale W. Fishbeck and Aurora Sebastiani

1. Axial skeleton
2. Caudal fin
3. Appendicular skeleton
4. Pelvic girdle and fins
5. Pectoral girdle and fins
6. Rostrum
7. Jaws
8. Gill arches
9. Veterbral column
10. Visceral skeleton
11. Dorsal fin
12. Gill rays

23-2 Dogfish Shark Skeleton ≈ (A) This is the cartilaginous skeleton of the dogfish, *Squalus*. Both the axial (vertebral column and cranium) and appendicular (appendages) skeleton are shown, but they have been separated. In this photo, the caudal fin is to the left. (B) This is a ventral view of the encircled region in (A). Anterior elements of the shark skeleton, including the gills, jaws, and the anterior portion of the vertebral column are visible.

Bonnethead shark

Bat ray

23-3 Fusiform and Depressed Body Shapes of the Chondrichthyes ≈ (A) The fusiform body of this bonnethead shark, *Sphyrna tiburo*, is typical of sharks. (B) This bat ray, *Myliobatis californica*, illustrates the dorsoventrally depressed body typical of skates and rays. Note the prominent pectoral fins (the "wings").

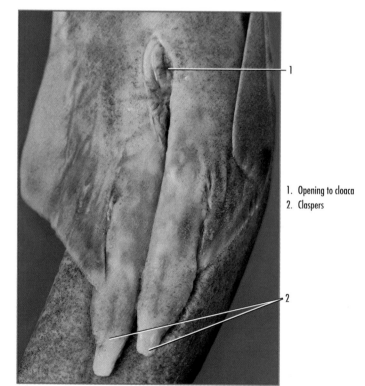

Dogfish shark

1. Opening to cloaca
2. Claspers

23-4 Claspers ≈ The pelvic fins of male Chondrichthyes are modified into claspers, which are used to transfer sperm during the internal fertilization of females. Shown is a preserved adult dogfish, *Squalus*.

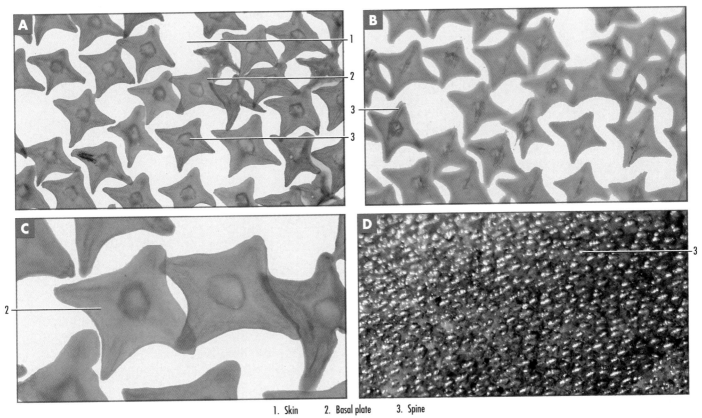

1. Skin   2. Basal plate   3. Spine

■ **23-5 Placoid Scales** ≈ The scales on most Chondrichthyes are placoid, although they have been lost in the Chimaeras. They are tooth-like in structure and are covered by enamel. (**A**) This micrograph is focused on the base of the scales, which are about 1 mm across at the base. (**B**) This micrograph is focused on the scale's raised spine. (**C**) This is an enlargement of (**A**). (**D**) The scales on *Squalus* are shown without the aid of a microscope.

Spotted ratfish

1. Spine
2. Lateral line
3. Mouth
4. Caudal fin

■ **23-6 Chimaera (Holocephali)**
≈ This is a preserved Holocephalian, *Hydrolagus colliei*. The shape of the tail resulted in the common name, ratfish. This specimen is about 35 cm in length. Note the dorsal spine.

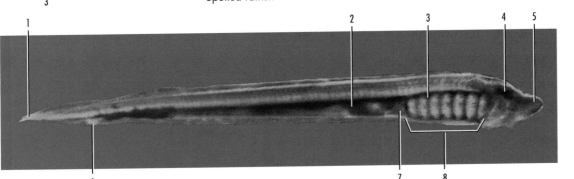

1. Postanal tail
2. Liver
3. Gill filaments
4. Eye
5. Oral hood
6. Anus
7. Heart
8. Pharynx

■ **23-7 Ammocoetes Larva of a Lamprey** ≈ This whole mount of an early ammocoetes larva is a little more than 1 cm in length. A number of structures are indicated, including its two-chambered heart.

1. Spine

■ **23-8 Dogfish** ≈ *Squalus* is commonly dissected in biology classes, and is one of the most widespread and widely studied shark species. Although primarily viewed as a nuisance, it is used as a food source and may be the "fish" in your fish and chips in Great Britain. This is a preserved specimen

Sand tiger shark

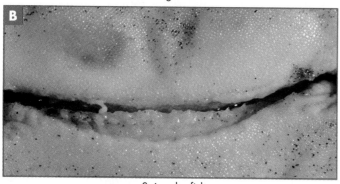

Spiny dogfish

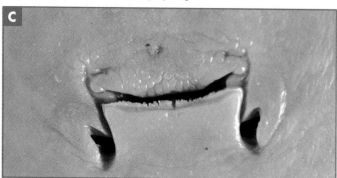

Round stingray

■ **23-9 Teeth of Chondrichthyes** ≈ (**A**) Teeth of a sand tiger shark, *Carcharias taurus*, are virtually identical in structure to placoid scales (Figure 23-5), except of course, in size. (**B**) Teeth of the spiny dogfish (this mouth is about 8 cm across), and of the (**C**) round stingray, *Urobatis halleri* (this mouth is about 1.5 cm across) are shown.

Elasmobranchii

The Subclass Elasmobranchii (*elasmo*—metal plate, *branchi*—gill) contains, by far, the greatest number of species. It includes the sharks, skates, and rays. The dogfish (Figure 23-8) is a widely distributed shark generally no more than 1 m in length and is commonly used in biology classes for dissection. They are often viewed as a nuisance by fishermen because they take bait intended for other species. In contrast to the dogfish, some elasmobranchs grow to 12 m.

Sharks have a fusiform body with an asymmetrical **heterocercal** (*hetero*—other, *cerco*—tail) caudal fin (Figure 23-10) and paired pectoral (*pectus*—chest) and pelvic (*pelvic*—referring to the hips) fins. Other fins are shown in Figure 23-11. Most sharks have five gill slits (Figure 23-12). They have well-developed sensory receptors, including olfactory, mechanoreceptors (lateral line—Figure 23-13A and Figure 23-13B), light receptors (lidless eyes—Figure 23-13C), and electroreceptors (Figure 23-13D). They are armed with an impressive supply of teeth, including rows

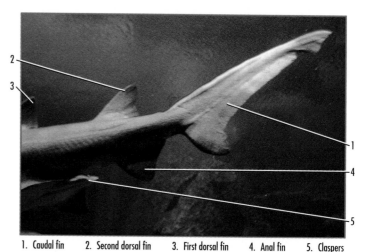

1. Caudal fin   2. Second dorsal fin   3. First dorsal fin   4. Anal fin   5. Claspers

■ **23-10 Heterocercal Caudal Fin** ≈ Shown is the heterocercal caudal fin of a sand tiger shark. You can also see the modified anal fins of this male, forming cigar-shaped structures called claspers. Claspers are involved in the transfer of sperm to a female.

of functional teeth followed by rows of developing teeth (Figure 23-14).

Although all organ systems are present and well developed, sharks do not have an organ dedicated to buoyancy maintenance equivalent to the swim bladder of bony fish. But they do accumulate oil in the liver, which aids in buoyancy, although most species still must move to avoid sinking. Natural selection favored a return to a cartilaginous

Leopard shark

1. Caudal fin   2. Second dorsal fin   3. First dorsal fin   4. Anal fin   5. Pelvic fin   6. Pectoral fin

■ **23-11 Fins of Sharks** ≈ The fins of a leopard shark, *Triakis semifasciatum*, are identified in this photograph. Leopard sharks are narrowly distributed in the Eastern Pacific. In some of those areas, large numbers gather during summer months for reasons that are not currently clear.

A — Sandbar shark

B — Pacific blacktip reef shark

C — Round stingray

1. Gill slits

■ **23-12 Shark and Ray Gill Slits** ≈ The presence of five gill slits is common in sharks. (**A**) Sandbar shark, *Carcharhinus plumbeus*, and (**B**) Pacific blacktip reef shark, *Carcharhinus melanopterus*. The sandbar and blacktip sharks are widely distributed species, with the blacktip often inhabiting shallow areas, including the intertidal. (**C**) Round stingray, *Urobatis halleri*. The gill slits on both sharks are located on the lateral portion of the body. Note the stingray's gill slits are located on the pale, ventral surface on either side of the body midline. In addition to these, rays have another pair of "gill slits" (spiracles) on their dorsal surface posterior to their eyes.

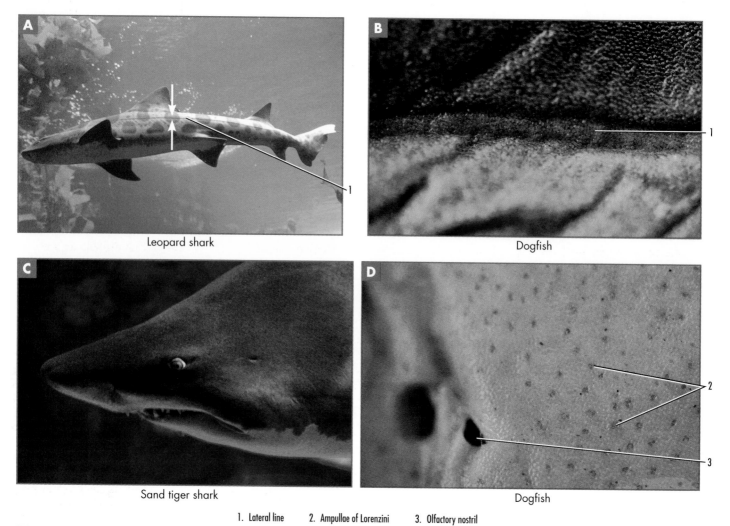

Leopard shark

Dogfish

Sand tiger shark

Dogfish

1. Lateral line   2. Ampullae of Lorenzini   3. Olfactory nostril

■ **23-13 Sensory Receptors of Sharks** ≈ (**A**) The lateral line of a leopard shark, *Triakis semifasciatum*, is visible (arrows). (**B**) The dogfish lateral line is shown in a close-up view. (**C**) The eye of a sand tiger shark, *Carcharias taurus*. (**D**) This is a close-up of the electro-receptors (Ampullae of Lorenzini) of the dogfish and its olfactory nostrils.

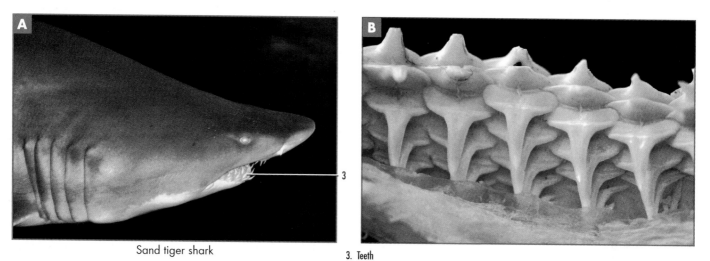

Sand tiger shark

3. Teeth

■ **23-14 Shark and Ray Teeth** ≈ (**A**) Notice the angle of the teeth of this sand tiger shark, *Carcharias taurus*. As they move across the jawline, teeth will be lost and those from behind will replace those lost. In aquaria housing sharks, teeth collect on the bottom of the tank and are washed out with discarded water. (**B**) Rows of teeth can be seen in the preserved jaw of this shark. This view is from the inside of the jaw. The rows of teeth move up and over the jawline at the top of the photograph. From the inside of the mouth looking forward to the anterior end of the shark, the teeth can be seen as they move "up and out." The lower jaw is seen at the bottom of the photograph.

skeleton in the freshwater, bony fish ancestors of the Chondrichthyes.

Water and salt regulation generally results in blood with a water content similar to seawater, although some species maintain blood with a higher salt content than seawater. This is accomplished by maintaining high concentrations of urea and trimethylamine oxide in the blood (nitrogen compounds where the nitrogen content is derived by removing it from the amino acids contained in dietary protein).

Although all members of this clade use internal fertilization, strategies for offspring support are highly variable. All skates and some sharks lay eggs after fertilization and are said to be **oviparous** (*ovi*—egg, *parous*—giving birth to), including those that lay "a mermaid's purse" (Figure 23-15). They have direct development and some species take up to two years to grow into an adult, the longest direct development time of any vertebrate.

Some sharks retain their young within their uterus where yolk provides a food source for development. This is termed **ovoviviparous** (*ovo*—egg, *vivi*—alive, *parous*—

giving birth to). This is also known as aplacental viviparity. Others give nourishment to their developing embryo through a placenta or secretions called "uterine milk." These are called **viviparous** (*vivi*—alive, *parous*—giving birth to).

The rays constitute more than half the species in Elasmobranchii. They include the skates, stingrays, sawfish (Figure 23-16), electric rays, and manta rays (Figure 23-17). Generally, their body form is adapted to life on the ocean bottom and is dorsoventrally flattened (Figure 23-17) with enlarged pectoral fins, although some species such as the manta ray (Figure 23-18) are pelagic. Their gill slits are located ventrally and their teeth are adapted for crushing prey. To avoid sediment intake to the gills, they have a modified first gill slit (spiracle) on their dorsal surface (Figure 23-19).

The largest of the Elasmobranchii and the largest extant fish is the whale shark (Figure 23-20), *Rhincodon typus*. It is a filter-feeding pelagic species occurring in tropical and warm water subtropical areas.

■ **23-16 Green Sawfish (Pristiformes)** ≈ Although having a body similar to a shark, the green sawfish, *Pristis zijsron*, is a ray.

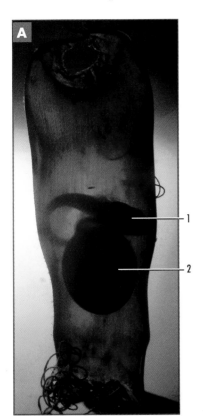

1. Developing shark
2. Yolk sac

■ **23-15 Shark Eggs**
≈ (**A**) A mermaid's purse contains a developing shark embryo and is produced by some oviparous sharks. The developing shark pup and the yolk sac can be clearly seen in this backlit photograph. (**B**) A mermaid's purse with a cutout window shows the developing swell shark inside.

Shovel nose guitarfish

Bluespotted stingray

1. Pectoral fins

■ **23-17 Ray Body Form** ≈ The (**A**) shovel nose guitarfish, *Rhinobatus productus*, and the (**B**) bluespotted stingray, *Taeniura lymna*, illustrate the body form of rays. Note the dorsoventrally flattened morphlogy and enlarged pectoral fins.

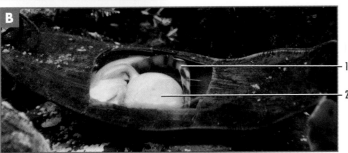

■ **23-18** Manta Ray (Myliobatiformes)
≈ The manta ray, *Manta birostris* is a pelagic filter feeder and is the largest ray species. Found in tropical waters, manta rays may grow to 1300 kg and over 7.5 m.

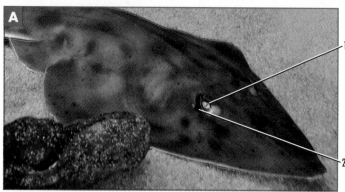

Shovel nose guitarfish

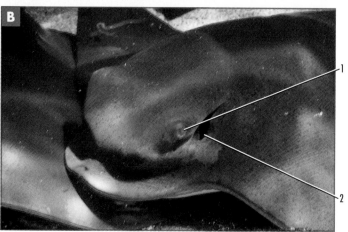

Bat stingray

1. Eye   2. Spiracle

■ **23-19** Spiracles ≈ Respiratory spiracles located directly behind the eyes are visible in the (**A**) shovel nose guitarfish, *Rhinobatus productus*, and the (**B**) bat stingray, *Myliobatis californica*.

■ **23-20** Whale Shark (Orectolobiformes) ≈ *Rhincodon typus*, the whale shark, is a large pelagic species reaching over 12 m and 35 Mg. This filter feeder has a very wide mouth (up to 1.5 m across) with reduced teeth.

Holocephali

Members of this group have many shared characteristics with the sharks, skates, and rays. They also have many unique characteristics, including jaws bearing flat plates, a smooth, scaleless skin, and fusion of their upper jaw to their cranium, a very unusual anatomical feature in fish. Commonly known by a number of names, there are over 30 extant species of chimaeras (*chimera*—goat or monster) or ratfish (Figure 23-21). As a clade, they diverged from the elasmobranchs over 300 million years ago and the number of species has been in decline over at least the last 50 million years. The decline may not be as severe as once thought, because previously unknown species have been discovered in recent years.

■ **23-21** Chimaera (Holocephali) ≈ This Ratfish, one of about 33 modern species, shows the rabbit-shaped face typical of the genus, and inspired the genus name *Hydrolagus* (*hydro*—water, *lago*—hare) for this species. (A little poetic license must be given here, since rabbits and hares are not the same thing.) This species, *Hydrolagus colliei*, is common to the Eastern North Pacific, living near the bottom from nearshore to depths over 900 m. Note the single dorsal fin, venomous hard spine, unusually small number of teeth forming plates (not visible), the prominent lateral line, and pits along the snout where Ampullae of Lorenzini are found (not visible). The eyes are very large for an animal this size. This specimen is about 28 cm long.

Grunt sculpin

Weedy scorpionfish

24 Osteichthyes

Although traditionally called the Class Osteichthyes (*oste*—bone, *ichthyes*—fish), this name is now used as a descriptive term rather than a taxon. Bony fish are part of a clade that includes the vast majority of extant fish species and all tetrapods (Chapter 25). Collectively, this clade's shared derived characteristics include bone, which replaces cartilage as it develops (endochondral bone: *endo*—within, *chondral*—cartilage), development of a gut out-pocketing, which forms a swim bladder or a lung, a shared developmental pattern for specific skull bones, a common mechanism of tooth formation, and a number of molecular synapomorphies.

The Classes Actinopterygii (*actis*—a ray, *pteryx*—fin or wing) (Table 24-1 and Figure 24-1) and Sarcopterygii

Table 24-1 ≈ Osteichthyes Classes, Subclasses, and Orders

Class
  Subclass
    Order
	General Description	Examples	Approximate Number of Species	Etymology

Sarcopterygii	Bony skeleton with a single gill opening covered with an operculum; paired fins with well-defined internal skeleton and associated muscles	Paraphyletic unless tetrapods are included	8	*sarkos*—flesh, *pteryx*—fin
Actinopterygii	Bony skeleton with a single gill opening on each side covered by an operculum; membranous fins	Most bony fish	27,000	*actis*—ray, *pteryx*—fin
Neopterygii	Skeleton primarily bone; usually homocercal caudal fin; mostly cycloid or ctenoid scales	Most bony fish	27,000	*neo*—new, *pteryx*—fin
Lepisosteiformes (Figure 24-9)	Elongate bodies covered with ganoid scales; heterocercal tail; able to gulp air with a vascularized swim bladder	Gars	7	*lepis*—scale, *osteo*—bone, *forma*—shape

(continued)

Class Subclass Order	General Description	Examples	Approximate Number of Species	Etymology
Elopiformes (Figure 24-10)	Eel-like larvae; single dorsal fin; strongly forked tail; wide gill openings	Tarpons, tenpounders and ladyfish	8	*ellops*—sea fish, *forma*—shape
Anguilliformes (Figure 24-11)	Long slender body with small gill openings; anal, caudal, and dorsal fins continuous; scales small or not present	Eels, moray eels, and gulper eels	790	*anguila*—eel, *forma*—shape
Clupeiformes (Figure 24-12)	No spiny rays in fins; open duct from swim bladder to pharynx; pelvic fins on abdomen; mostly filter feeders using gill rakers	Anchovies, sardines, shad, herrings, and others	300	*clupea*—sardine, *forma*—shape
Cypriniformes (Figure 24-13)	Head generally scaleless; mouth toothless; pharyngeal teeth grind against a chewing pad at the base of the skull	Carps, minnow, goldfish, electric fishes, chubs, and suckers	3,300	*kyprinos*—goldfish, *forma*—shape
Salmoniformes	Last three vertebrae turned upward; tetraploid karyotype (four of each kind of chromosome present per cell nucleus rather than the more common two of each type); small cycloid scales	Salmon and trout	66	*salmo*—salmon, *forma*—shape
Lophiiformes (Figure 24-14)	Spines on anterior dorsal fin; first ray, when present, modified into a lure for attracting prey; tetrapod-like base to pectoral fin; light organs in deepwater species	Angler fish and frogfish	322	*lophos*—crest, *forma*—shape
Mugiliformes (Figure 24-15)	Dorsal fin with spines and soft dorsal fin widely separated; pelvic fin behind the abdomen; head blunt; teeth small	Mullets	72	*mugil*—mullet, *forma*—shape
Atheriniformes (Figure 24-16)	Usually two dorsal fins; anal fin generally with an anterior spine; pelvic fins abdominal; dorsal fin above anal fin	Silversides, isonids, rainbowfishes, blue eyes, surf sardines, and others	393	*atherine*—smelt, *forma*—shape
Beloniformes (Figure 24-17)	Dorsal and anal fins posteriorly located; streamlined body shape; jaw morphologies and relative lengths of upper and lower jaws highly variable within order	Needle fishes, flying fishes, ricefish, halfbeaks, and sauries	186	*belone*—needle, *forma*—shape
Beryciformes (Figure 24-18)	Probably a polyphyletic group, but generally show similarities in the number of caudal fin rays (19 principal rays)	Lanterneye fishes, fangtooth, spinyfins, squirrelfishes, soldier fishes, pinecone fishes, and slimeheads	219	*Beryci*—the alfonsino (a species of fish), *forma*—shape
Gobiesociformes (Figure 24-19)	Highly modified pelvic fin specialized into an abdominal disc used to adhere to the substrate; scaleless	Clingfish and singleslits	120	*gobius*—goby, *esox*—pike, *forma*—shape
Syngnathiformes (Figure 24-20)	Elongated body with bony rings along the length; small mouth at the end of a tube-shaped snout (absent in one genus)	Pipefishes, seahorses, trumpetfishes, cornetfishes, and others	240	*syn*—with, *gnathos*—jaw, *forma*—shape
Tetraodontiformes (Figure 24-21)	Scales variously modified into plates, spines, or shields; swim bladder in most; some able to take in large amounts of water and enlarge body; teeth usually strong incisors	Triggerfish, trunkfish, puffers, porcupine fish, burrfish, boxfish, triplespines, spikefish, and filefishes	353	*tetra*—four, *odous*—teeth, *forma*—shape
Pleuronectiformes (Figure 24-22)	Not bilaterally symmetrical; one eye moves across the cranium to the other side during development; body highly compressed; swim bladder almost always absent	Flatfish (soles, Southern flounders, left-eyed flounders, citharids, tongue fish, large-tooth flounders, right-eyed flounders, Psettodids, crested flounders, and turbots)	456	*pleura*—similar, *nektos*—to swim, *forma*—shape

(*continued*)

Class Subclass Order	General Description	Examples	Approximate Number of Species	Etymology
Scorpaeniformes (Figure 24-23)	Head and body spiny or with bony plates; pectoral fin usually rounded; caudal fin variable but usually rounded	Scorpionfish, sculpins, poachers, sablefish, velvetfish, oilfish, pigfish, lumpfish, gurnards, cowfish, sea ravens, greenlings, snailfish, prowfish, rockfish, stonefish, waspfish, searobins, and flatheads	1,326	*skorpaina*—diminutive of scorpion, *forma*—shape
Perciformes (Figure 24-24)	Largest order of fishes, but probably not monophyletic; fin spines usually present; pectoral fins well above ventral surface, pelvic fins well anterior; swim bladder lacks duct	Sunfishes, perches, remoras, surfperches, chichlids, barracudas, gobies, mackerels, tunas, swordfish, marlin, and others	>8,000	*perke*—perch, *forma*—shape

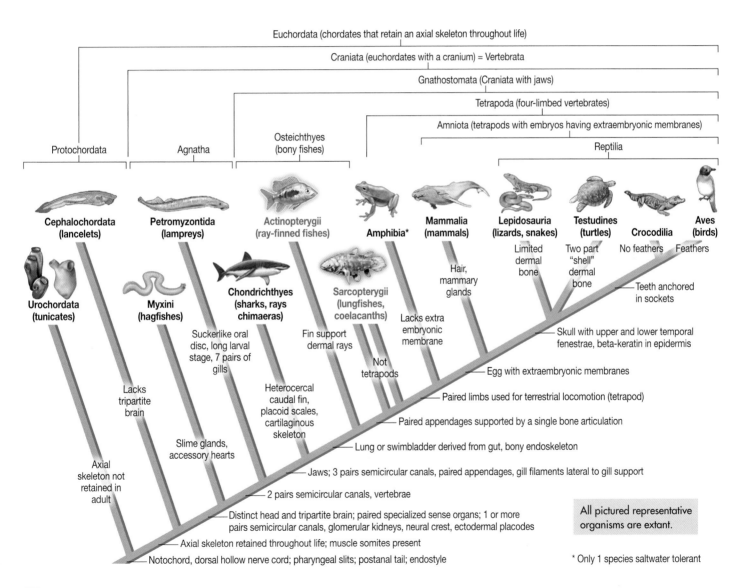

■ **24-1 Chordate Cladogram** ∼ Note bony fish (Osteichthyes) are part of the Gnathostomata along with the Chondrichthyes and consist of at least two primary groups: Actinopterygii and Sarcopterygii, which differ in that the Sarcopterygii have unique supportive elements in the skeleton or girdle of their appendages. Osteichthyes also includes the tetrapods. See Appendix C for definitions of terms.

(*sarkos*—flesh, *pteryx*—fin or wing) (Figure 24-1) show several unique derived characteristics not present in the other members of this clade, specifically the tetrapods. One is the presence of an operculum (a cover or lid) composed of bony plates attached to muscles covering the gills (Figure 24-2). It provides protection for the blood-rich, delicate gill tissues (Figure 24-3) and aids in the flow of oxygen-containing water across the gills. This clade (including the tetrapods) also shows increased specialization of jaw muscles, jaw bones, and the presence of an esophageal derivative used for gas exchange (lung) or as a means of achieving neutral buoyancy in water (swim bladder—Figure 24-4).

Although it has long been proposed that lungs evolved from the swim bladder, the evidence now supports the reverse evolutionary history: the swim bladder evolved from lungs.

Most bony fish are carnivorous, but there are herbivores (rare), suspension feeders, scavengers, detritivores, and parasites.

Most fish reproduce by means of sexual reproduction, but there is much variation on what we think of as the "usual" means of sexual reproduction. Generally, there tend to be separate sexes, with external fertilization and development. However, there is every imaginable variation on this theme.

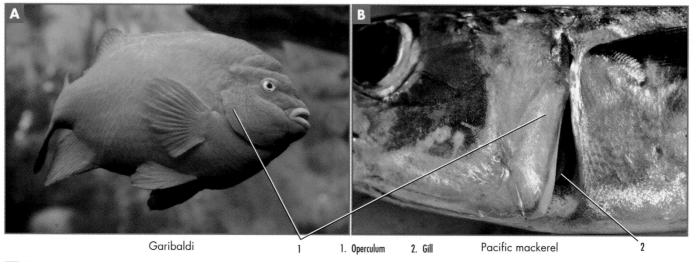

Garibaldi   1   1. Operculum   2. Gill   Pacific mackerel   2

■ **24-2 Operculum** ≈ The operculum is a derived characteristic of Osteichthyes. It covers the gills and aids in movement of water across them. It is shown in the (**A**) Garibaldi, *Hypsypops rubicundus*, and (**B**) the Pacific mackerel, *Scomber japonicus*.

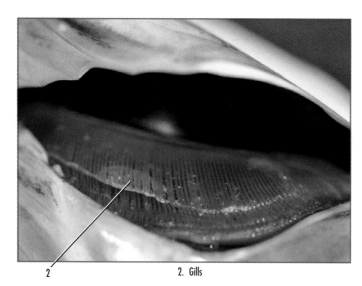

2   2. Gills

■ **24-3 Gills** ≈ Gills form the respiratory surfaces of fish where gas exchange occurs. These are the gills of a Pacific mackerel, *Scomber japonicus*.

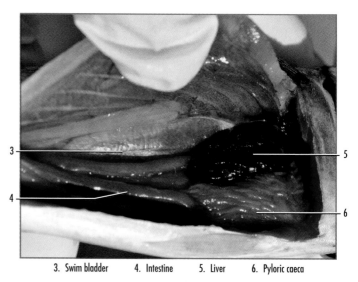

3. Swim bladder   4. Intestine   5. Liver   6. Pyloric caeca

■ **24-4 Swim Bladder** ≈ The swim bladder is a derived characteristic and is used in buoyancy. This is the swim bladder of a Pacific mackerel, *Scomber japonicus*.

Actinopterygii

This is the largest vertebrate class based on the number of known species. Ray-finned fish are characterized by having mucous glands and dermal scales (Figure 24-5), which are **ganoid** in ancestral forms, and **cycloid, ctenoid,** or absent in derived forms. Swim bladders are present with or without a duct connecting to the esophagus. They have a single circulatory path (Figure 24-6) and nucleated red blood cells (**erythrocytes**) (*erythro*—red, *cyte*—cell) (Figure 22-7E). Their fins are supported by dermal rays (skin bones) and moved with musculature in the body. Dermal rays (Figure 24-7) consist of bilateral pairs of segmented, concave dermal bones facing each other. Rays are called **lepidotrichia** (*lepido*—scale, *tricho*—hair) and support webs of skin. Pelvic and pectoral fins link to other dermal bones called **radials**, which connect to the pelvic and pectoral girdles.

The ancestors of this class gave rise to other clades, including the Cladista (*cladi*—branch), which have ganoid scales (Figure 24-8). All extant species are freshwater fish and have lungs. A second clade is Chondrostei (*chondro*—cartilage, *osteon*—bone), which primarily have a cartilage

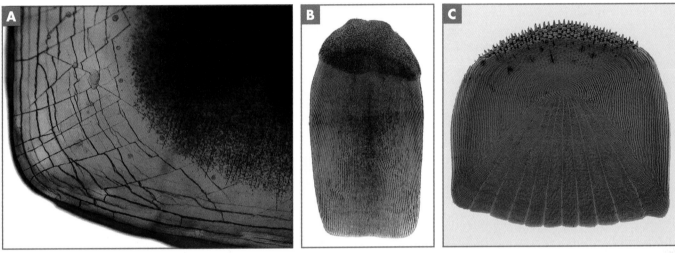

■ **24-5 Dermal Scales** ≈ Three scale types are seen in the Osteichthyes: (**A**) ganoid, (**B**) cycloid, and (**C**) ctenoid. In (**B**) and (**C**), the free edge is at the top and the attached edge at the bottom. These are photomicrographs with epidermis removed.

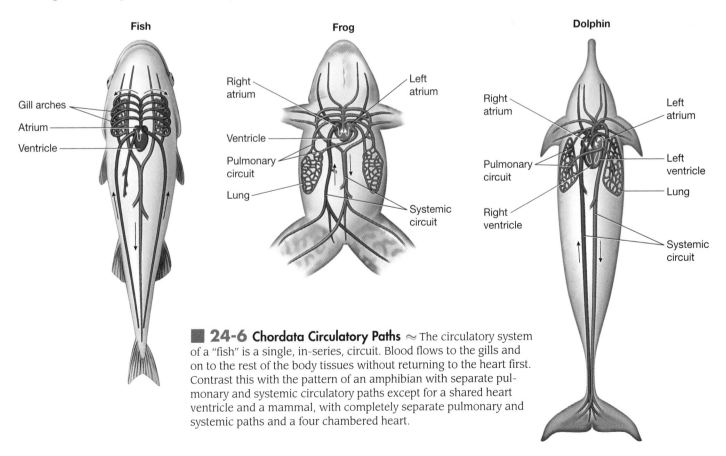

■ **24-6 Chordata Circulatory Paths** ≈ The circulatory system of a "fish" is a single, in-series, circuit. Blood flows to the gills and on to the rest of the body tissues without returning to the heart first. Contrast this with the pattern of an amphibian with separate pulmonary and systemic circulatory paths except for a shared heart ventricle and a mammal, with completely separate pulmonary and systemic paths and a four chambered heart.

skeleton, a heterocercal (*hetero*—different, *cerco*—tail) caudal fin and ganoid scales. Many extant Chondrostei species are freshwater, but some spend most of their adult life in saltwater, then migrate up rivers or streams to spawn. This lifestyle is called **anadromous** (*anadromos*—running upward). These are represented by paddlefish and sturgeon. A third clade includes the Neopterygii (*neo*—new, *pteryxgii*—fin) where the skeleton is principally bone, the caudal fin is generally **homocercal** (*homo*—like, *cerco*—tail), and scales are cycloid, ctenoid, and seldom ganoid (Figures 24-5 and 24-8).

Two extant neopterygean genera are included in the Order Lepisosteiformes. Both are freshwater fish with ganoid scales (Figure 24-8) and are nonteleosts (*non*—not, *tele*—perfect, complete, *osteon*—bone). The rest are the teleosts ("perfect bone").

The number of teleosts is not known, but it exceeds 27,000 with nearly 200 new species described each year (Figures 24-9 through 24-24). This clade has a number of anatomical and morphological adaptations that allowed them to adaptively radiate into a wide variety of habitats. These include lighter-weight scales and a homocercal caudal fin allowing for rapid motions. Modifications in other fins increased flexibility and maneuverability. There were also changes in swim bladder physiology and feeding efficiency.

1. Dermal ray   Pajama cardinalfish

■ **24-7 Dermal Rays** ≈ Dermal rays form a bony skeleton within the fins and are attached to muscle, allowing for movement. The dermal rays are clearly seen in the caudal fin of this pajama cardinalfish, *Sphaeramia nematoptera*.

Alligator gar

Longnose gar

■ **24-8 Ganoid Scale** ≈ (A) The skin of an alligator gar, *Lepisosteus (Atractosteus) spatula*, shows a pattern common in fish with ganoid scales. (B) This ganoid scale, shown in a close-up, has had all the epidermis and dermis removed.

■ **24-9 Gars (Lepisosteiformes)** ≈ (A) This alligator gar, *Lepisosteus (Atractosteus) spathula*, although principally a freshwater fish, occurs in bays, bayous, and brackish waters, and is much more than an occasional inhabitant of saltwater. It possesses the heterocercal caudal fin (although in gars it is a symmetrical heterocercal fin) of this group (arrow) and enlarged ganoid scales (Figures 24-5 and 24-8). (B) The longnose gar, *Lepisosteus osseus*, is principally a freshwater species, but also inhabits estuaries, other brackish waters, and ocean bays and deeper bayous.

Tarpons

Ladyfish

■ **24-10 Tarpon (Elopiformes)** ≈ (**A**) These tarpons, *Megalops atlanticus*, are a large-eyed fish growing up to 2.5 m and weighing over 140 kg. They are sought by sports anglers. (**B**) The ladyfish, *Elops saurus*, inhabits coastal areas in the tropical Western Atlantic and Indo-Pacific Oceans. They are generally around 60 cm long, but may reach nearly 1 m and weigh 7 kg. In both species, note the single dorsal fin and strongly forked caudal fin.

Leopard moray

Goldentail moray

Green moray

California moray

■ **24-11 Eels (Anguilliformes)** ≈ (**A**) The leopard moray, *Enchelycore pardalis*, ranges across the Indo-Pacific Ocean. Note the bright colors and curved jaw typical of this species. (**B**) The goldentail moray, *Gymnothorax miliaris*, is distributed throughout the Caribbean along shallow reefs. (**C**) The green moray, *Gymnothorax funebris*, is found along the West Central Atlantic in habitats from rocky shores to seagrass. (**D**) The California moray, *Gymnothorax mordax*, is distributed along the Eastern Pacific. Morays do not have pectoral or pelvic fins. (**E**) Here you can see directly into the moray's gills because they lack an operculum.

Anchovy

Sardine

■ 24-12 Anchovy and Sardine (Clupeiformes) ≈ (A) Anchovies are a typical fish of this taxon. The word "anchovy" refers to a family of fish, the Engraulidae. There are nearly 140 species worldwide. (B) The Pacific sardine, *Sardinops sagax*, is a coastal pelagic species often occurring in schools of millions of individuals. It currently ranges off North America in the Eastern Pacific Ocean. Note the absence of spiny rays in both species.

Koi

■ 24-13 Koi (Cypriniformes) ≈ The common koi, or carp, *Cyprinus carpio*, is a domesticated freshwater fish derived from western Asia, specifically, the Caspian Sea. The carp is a freshwater species representative of this order. It shows the characteristic scaleless (arrow) head and teeth placed exclusively outside their mouth.

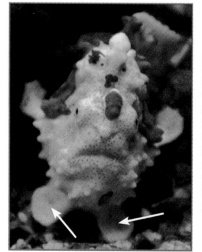

Warty frogfish

■ 24-14 Frogfish (Lophiiformes) ≈ The warty frogfish, *Antennarius maculates*, inhabits sheltered rocky reefs in the Southeastern Pacific. It can be found in association with sponges. Arrows indicate pectoral fins, which in the Lophiiformes, have a tetrapod-like base.

Pacific striped mullet

Atlantic striped mullet

Striped mullet

Diamondscale mullet

■ 24-15 Mullets (Mugiliformes) ≈ (A) Visitors to lagoons and estuaries often see a fish jumping from the sloughs and narrow channels. These are mullets, specifically the striped mullet, *Mugil cephalus*. (B) The striped mullet is widely distributed in coastal tropical and subtropical waters, but is absent from the Caribbean. They can also be found in freshwater where they have entered from the sea. They are widely used as a food source by people, particularly in the lagoons of Baja California. (C) This is a striped mullet after having been caught by hand netting. (D) The diamondscale mullet is widely distributed throughout the Indo-Pacific. It inhabits lagoons and other shallow water habitats, including mangroves. Note the pelvic fin behind the abdomen and the blunt head.

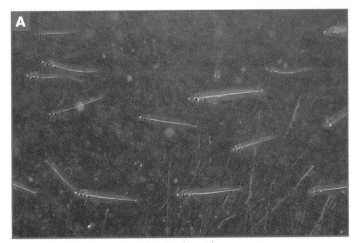

Atlantic silversides

Topsmelt

Grunion

■ **24-16 Silversides (Atheriniformes)** ≈ **(A)** These Atlantic silversides, *Menidia menidia*, are a widely distributed species. They generally reside near the water's edge, but may also be found in areas at depth and in seagrass. **(B)** Topsmelt, *Atherinops affinis*, occur in estuarine and marine environments. They are common in a variety of coastal environments. Note the dorsal fin above the anal fin and the abdominal pelvic fins. **(C)** Grunion, *Leuresthes tenuis*, are best known for coming near the low-tide zone to lay their eggs. One of two species, *L. tenuis*, occurs in the Eastern Pacific. They are oviparous. In this photo you see two males surrounding a female (arrow) buried in the sand. Each has released its semen, visible as a white milky substance on the sand.

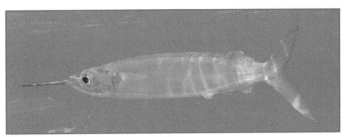

Ballyhoo

■ **24-17 Ballyhoo (Beloniformes)** ≈ The ballyhoo, *Hemiramphus brasiliensis*, is distributed along the coastal Eastern and Western Atlantic, principally in tropical areas. Note the streamlined body shape and the extreme posterior position of the dorsal and anal fins characteristic of the order.

Longjaw squirrelfish

■ **24-18 Squirrelfish (Beryciformes)** ≈ The longjaw squirrelfish, *Holocentrus adscensionis*, is a Caribbean species that occurs in shallow coral reefs and offshore habitats, although some references indicate that it is widespread throughout the Western and Eastern tropical and temperate Atlantic. It is nocturnal.

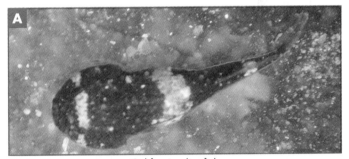

California clingfish

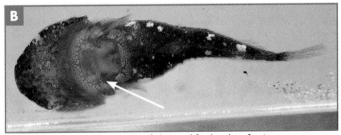

California clingfish (modified pelvic fins)

■ **24-19 Clingfish (Gobiesociformes)** ≈ The California clingfish, *Gobiesox rhessodon*, is a small, rocky intertidal inhabitant. Its range extends to the shallow subtidal. **(A)** Dorsal view. **(B)** Ventral view. Note the sucker derived from the highly modified pelvic fin (arrow).

Trumpetfish

Leafy seadragon

Big-belly seahorse

Pipefish

Yellow-banded pipefish

Weedy seadragon

■ **24-20 Seahorses and Allies (Syngnathiformes)** ≈ (A) The trumpetfish, *Aulostomus maculates*, is found throughout the Caribbean in back reef and fore reef areas. (B) The leafy seadragon, *Phycodurus eques*, can be found in temperate waters around Australia's shallow, sandy bottom seas where kelp can attach to rocky outcroppings. (C) The big-belly seahorse, *Hippocampus abdominalis*, is one of the largest seahorses found around New Zealand and Australia. It lives in shallow water around rocky reefs and among seaweeds. This is a male showing his brood pouch. (D) The pipefish, *Syngnathus leptorhynchus*, lives in lagoons, coral reefs, and seagrass habitats. Pipefish are weak swimmers because only the dorsal fin is used to propel them through the water. (E) The yellow-banded pipefish, *Dunckerocampus pessuliferus*, is a Central Western Pacific species where it inhabits coastal waters, including estuaries. (F) The weedy seadragon, *Phyllopteryx taeniolatus*, inhabits the Indo-Pacific along coral reefs to 50 m where it grows to 46 cm. In all species, note the elongated, bony-ringed bodies and prominent tube-shaped snout characteristic of the order.

Scrawled filefish

Bridled burrfish

Spot-fin porcupinefish

Spotted trunkfish

Queen triggerfish

■ **24-21 Porcupinefish and Allies (Tetraodontiformes)** ~ (A) The scrawled filefish, *Aluterus scriptus*, inhabits the Western Atlantic as well as the Gulf of Mexico. Coloration is highly variable within the species. The most striking individuals are bright green with bright blue dots and stripes, and some black dots. They inhabit lagoons and seaward reefs across the entire tropical seas, including the Caribbean and Indonesian areas. (B) The bridled burrfish, *Chilomycterus antennatus*, inhabits seagrass beds and reefs in the Western and Eastern tropical Atlantic. This species is capable of inflating itself to intimidate predators. Note enlarged scale at arrow. (C) Spot-fin porcupinefish, *Diodon hystrix*, are circumtropical, occurring in lagoons and reefs. It, too, can enlarge its body by taking in large quantities of water. Note the spine-like enlarged scale at the arrow. (D) The spotted trunkfish, *Lacophrys bicaudalis*, inhabits the Caribbean and Gulf of Mexico. It occurs around coral reefs. (E) The queen triggerfish, *Balistes vetula*, inhabits coastal areas in the Western and Eastern Central Atlantic. This colorful fish can be seen in rocky or coral reef areas. Note the mouth. It is equipped with heavy teeth and powerful jaws for crushing the shells of crustaceans, echinoderms, and mollusks.

Diamond turbot

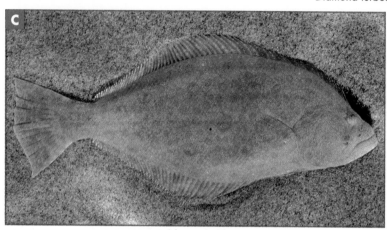

California halibut

Starry flounder

■ **24-22 Flounders and Allies (Pleuronectiformes)** ≈ (**A** and **B**) *Pleuronichthys guttulatus*, the diamond turbot, occurs in the Eastern Pacific on sandy and muddy bottoms, particularly in bays, lagoons, and estuaries. (**C**) The California halibut, *Paralichthyus californicus*, occurs in the Eastern Pacific from Baja California to central California and occasionally to northern Washington. It principally lives on sandy bottoms, particularly in bays, lagoons, and estuaries. (**D**) The starry flounder, *Platichthys stellatus*, occurs in the North Pacific Ocean from Japan, Alaska, and California. It may occur in both freshwater and saltwater habitats, particularly in shallow water. When in freshwater, it has entered from the ocean through an estuary. It may occur on sandy, muddy, or gravel bottoms. Young may occur in the intertidal zone. In all species, note the flattened bodies and asymmetry produced by eye migration from one side of the body to the other.

Lumpfish

Red lionfish

■ **24-23 Scorpionfish and Allies (Scorpaeniformes)** ≈ (**A**) The lumpfish or lumpsucker, *Cyclopterus lumpus*, is found in the Arctic, North Pacific, and Atlantic Oceans. Its pelvic fins are modified into adhesive disks used to attach to objects on the ocean floor. Their odd appearance is the reason for the family name Cyclopteridae, which means "circle wing." This specimen is attached to a rock. (**B**) Red lionfish, *Pterois volitans*, occur naturally in the Western Pacific, but can be found as an exotic along coastal Florida north to Long Island, New York. They inhabit harbors, offshore reefs, and lagoons. Pectoral and dorsal fins have long spines with venom glands in grooves along the spines. Spines (arrow) are used in catching prey and as a means of deterring predators. *(continued)*

Spotted scorpionfish

Tidepool sculpin

Blue rockfish

Lingcod

Photo courtesy of Keith A. Baier

■ **24-23 Scorpionfish and Allies (Scorpaeniformes)** ≈ *(continued)* (**C**) Spotted scorpionfish, *Scorpaena plumieri*, have venomous pelvic, dorsal, and anal fins. Their coloration helps this predator surprise prey as they lie motionless on a rocky or sandy bottom. (**D**) The tidepool sculpin, *Oligocottus maculosus*, is a tidepool resident of the Western and Eastern Pacific. The common name "rockfish" applies to a large number of fish species. In North America it most often refers to a specific family, the Sebastidae (controversial and not universally recognized), in the order Scorpaeniformes. One-third of all species in this order are placed in this family. (**E**) The blue rockfish, *Sebastes mystinus*, is representative of the Sebastidae. It is an Eastern Pacific species occurring from the surface to depths of just over 500 m associated with reefs and kelp beds. They are viviparous. (**F**) Lingcod, *Ophiodon elongates*, is unique to the Northeastern Pacific. Specimens may reach 150 cm and 60 kg. Note the presence of spines (arrows), particularly on the dorsal fins of these Scorpaeniformes.

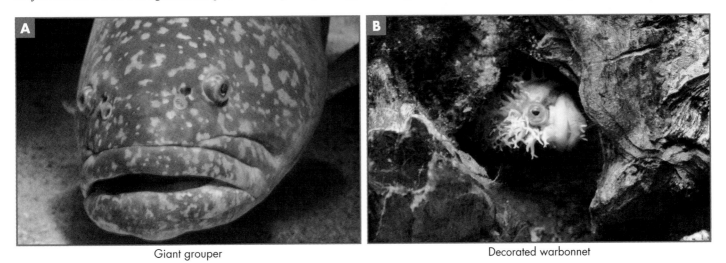

Giant grouper

Decorated warbonnet

■ **24-24 Perch and Allies (Perciformes)** ≈ (**A**) The giant grouper, *Epinephelus lanceolatus*, occurs throughout the Indo-Padific. They may grow to 27 m in length and weigh up to 600 kg. (**B**) The decorated warbonnet, *Chirolophis decoratus*, has numerous, branched appendages (cirri) emerging from its head region that extend to its dorsal fin. It is found in temperate waters of the North Pacific, usually hiding among rocks and algae. *(continued)*

Saddle anemonefish

Queen angelfish

Whitetail dascyllus

Yellow tang

Great barracuda

Bluestriped grunt

■ **24-24 Perch and Allies (Perciformes)** ≈ *(continued)* **(C)** Saddle anemonefish, *Amphiprion ephippium*, occurs in the Eastern Pacific in coastal water, such as protected bays. They are usually found in pairs. **(D)** *Holacanthus ciliaris*, the queen angelfish, occurs in the Western Atlantic and throughout the Caribbean. It is found on coral reefs and feeds on sponges as an adult. Note how far anterior the pelvic fins (arrow) are. **(E)** The whitetail dascyllus, *Dascyllus aruanus*, is found principally across the tropical Indian and Pacific Oceans. It is a small reef species inhabiting shallow lagoons and subtidal reef areas. Its black and white stripes are a means of camouflage called disruptive coloration, a useful adaptation in a varied habitat such as a reef. **(F)** In the tropical Pacific Ocean, the yellow tang, *Zebrasoma flavescens*, inhabits coral lagoons and the seaward side of coral reefs. **(G)** The great barracuda, *Sphyraena barracuda*, is also a member of the Perciformes. It ranges around the globe in tropical and temperate coastal and open seas, where it is an aggressive predator growing to nearly 2 m. **(H)** The bluestriped grunt, *Haemulon sciurus*, occurs over coral and rocky reefs in the Western Atlantic from Florida to Brazil and in turtle grass (*Thalassia*—Chapter 32). *(continued)*

Sailor's grunt and a bluestriped grunt

Stoplight parrotfish

Male yellowhead jawfish

Red hind

Atlantic wolffish

Mudskipper

■ **24-24 Perch and Allies (Perciformes)** ≈ *(continued)* **(I)** Sailor's grunts, *Haemulon parra*, and a bluestriped grunt gather in turtle grass beds and here are taking advantage of the cover provided by a pier along the Florida coast. Both species are common in the Western Central Atlantic. **(J)** The initial phase of the stoplight parrotfish, *Sparisoma viride*, may be either male or female. All individuals change to male and go from the colors you see here to a bright green fish with several bright yellow spots—hence the name "stoplight" fish! **(K)** Male yellowhead jawfish, *Opistognathus aurifron*, brood a female's eggs in their mouth. They are territorial along coral reefs in the Caribbean. Note the absence of any neighbors close by! **(L)** The red hind, *Epinephelus guttatus*, is in the grouper family and inhabits the Caribbean and Gulf of Mexico where it lives in shallow coral and rocky reefs. **(M)** Atlantic wolffish, *Anarhichas lupus*, lives on rocky bottoms, but can be seen over sand or mud. They live in the North Atlantic on both eastern and western sides, and are generally found in water near freezing (1-2°C). **(N)** Mudskippers are unusual fish showing a variety of anatomical and behavioral adaptations to an amphibious lifestyle. The common name "mudskipper" refers to fish placed in nine different genera, all of which are active in intertidal habitats. In this photo, an individual of the genus *Periophthalmus* is shown pulling itself up onto a muddy shore. It shows a wide range of anatomical, morphological, physiological, and behavior modifications to this lifestyle. In fact, these modifications to terrestrial life result in impaired oxygen exchange underwater. This necessitates a return to the surface and gulping of air when submerged. There are 18 species in this genus.

Sarcopterygii

Members of this clade are known as the lobe-finned fish and their paired fins are supported by an internal skeleton made of a single basal skeletal element with short dermal rays, and musculature within the appendage. Their caudal fin is **diphycercal** (*diphy*—two fold, *cerco*—tail) (Figure 24-25). This group is not monophyletic unless tetrapods are included, but we will only discuss the non-tetrapod members in this chapter.

Unlike other fish, lobe-finned fish have a heart with a pair of atria and a partially divided ventricle. This double circulation pattern is like the tetrapods (Figure 24-6-frog) and unlike the Actinopterygii's single circulation pattern (Figure 24-6-fish).

There are eight extant species; all are lungfish or coelacanths (Figure 24-25). The lungfish are freshwater and the two known coelacanth species are marine.

Known only from fossils, the coelacanths were thought to be extinct until one extant species was discovered in 1938; a second was discovered in 1998. They have direct development, hatching from a 9 cm diameter egg. These are the largest eggs known in the Osteichthyes.

The ancestral connection between Sarcopterygii and tetrapods, and the associated transition from an aquatic habitat to a terrestrial one raises questions about how physical conditions in the two environments compare and how these differences influenced the evolution of aquatic and terrestrial vertebrates.

Salient physical features of the aquatic habitat are listed below and those of the terrestrial environment in Chapter 25.

Life in water offers various challenges and advantages. The advantages include

≈ a near zero gravitational force to overcome while moving and supporting the body
≈ low energy cost per unit of body weight for body support
≈ food opportunities

Challenges include

≈ difficulty in moving through a high viscosity substance (water)
≈ high costs of temperature maintenance
≈ tendency to sink
≈ detection of sound and other vibrations
≈ gas exchange, particularly O_2 absorption
≈ osmoregulation

Tetrapods— Sarcopterygii With Limbs

We will begin discussing the tetrapods in Chapter 25.

■ **24-25 Coelacanth (Sarcopterygii)** ≈ Shown is a member of the extant genus *Latimeria*. They are remnants of a group that were thought to have gone extinct 70 million years ago until an individual was recovered off the coast of Africa in 1938, with others taken from various sites off South Africa and Madagascar in later years. A second species was recovered off Indonesia during the last decade. Notice the diphycercal caudal fin typical of the Sarcopterygii. These marine species are descendants of freshwater fish living 400 million years ago.

Green sea turtle

Brown pelican

25 Amphibia and Reptilia

The most obvious derived character of this clade is four limbs used for locomotion in a terrestrial environment (*tetra*—four, *podo*—foot), although many tetrapod lineages have secondarily lost one or both of their limb pairs and/or they have been modified into flippers or wings (Table 25-1 and Figure 25-1).

Remember, tetrapods are part of the gnathostome clade, most closely related to the Sarcopterygii and sharing derived characteristics with them, including strengthened limbs, muscles within limbs, and a swim bladder or lungs connecting to the back of the throat (pharynx). Some extinct Sarcopterygii and tetrapods share derived characteristics not present in extant Sarcopterygii (the coelacanth and lungfish—Chapter 24), including the presence of a pair of passages from each nostril to the pharynx—internal nares (Figure 25-2). The clade, including these extinct sarcopterygians and the tetrapods, shared characteristics that ultimately proved important in meeting some conditions of a terrestrial life.

The terrestrial environment offers some challenges and provides some improvements in the physical conditions (**abiotic** conditions) with which life must contend and to which it must adapt. Opportunities include

≈ The greater abundance of oxygen: Air contains 21% oxygen while water is exceptional if it contains 0.0008% oxygen. This is not important if you do not require oxygen, but is important to the majority of familiar life-forms. Oxygen is much more available in the terrestrial environment.

≈ Warmer habitats: The terrestrial environment has portions that are much warmer than the greatest proportion of aquatic environments. For example, the average temperature of the ocean is about 3.5°C while the terrestrial tropics average about 20°C. Not a big thing until you remember that for every 10°C increase in temperature, the rate of a chemical reaction doubles! Life after all, depends upon chemical reactions.

≈ A difference in viscosity: Air is much less viscous than water, making it much easier to move through air than water.

≈ Sunlight availability: As you are undoubtedly learning in your marine biology class, sunlight is used by some organisms (photoautotrophs, *photo*—light, *auto*—self, *troph*—feeder) as an energy source to produce food. The portion of sunlight important in food production is absorbed by water and quickly disappears at depth, while it passes through the atmosphere with little change.

Class Order	General Description	Examples	Approximate Number of Species	Etymology
Amphibia	Four limbs in most; moist, glandular skin acting as primary respiratory organ; double circulatory pattern with three-chambered heart; sensory organs modified for terrestrial environment; external fertilization	Caecilians, frogs and toads, and salamanders	6,000+	*amphi*—double, *bio*—life
Urodela (Figure 25-11)-	Four limbs; separate head and trunk; tail in adults	Salamanders	550	*uro*—tail, *delos*—evident
Anura (Figures 22-4, 25-6A, 25-7A, 25-8B, 25-9A)	Head and trunk are fused; no tail in adults; two pairs (pelvic and pectoral) of unequal limbs; four digits on front limbs; scaleless, moist skin	Frogs and toads	5,300	*an*—without, *oura*—tail
Reptilia—Nonavian	Keratinized epidermal scales; two pairs of limbs; three-chambered heart in most, but ventricle partially divided, and some with four-chambered heart; amniotic eggs; internal fertilization	Snakes, lizards, turtles, crocodiles and alligators	8,200+	*reptili*—creep or crawl
Testudines (Chelonia) (Figures 25-17 and 25-20)	Body enclosed by bony plates, fused to axial skeleton; beak instead of teeth; no temporal openings in skull	Turtles	300	*testudo*—turtle *testa*—shell
Squamata (Figures 25-9B, 25-14, 25-19 and 25-21)	Skin dry and keratinized; shedding of epidermal scales; internal fertilization with paired copulatory organs	Snakes and lizards	7,800+	*squamatus*—scaly
Crocodilia (Figures 25-7B, 25-15, 25-16, 25-22, and 25-23)	Secondary palate separating nasal and oral cavities; four-chambered heart; thickened scales; aquatic; large muscular tail	Crocodiles and alligators	23	*crocodiles*—crocodile

These advantages come with a price (isn't there always!). Disadvantages of the terrestrial environment are listed below.

≈ Although air contains more molecular oxygen (O_2), air is very drying.

≈ Not only are major parts of the terrestrial environment warmer than aquatic habitats, they are much more variable in temperature. The **specific heat capacity** (the amount of heat energy that must be added to a given volume of a substance to raise the temperature of that substance by 1°C) of water is much greater than air, and as a result, the air easily changes temperature. Large variability in temperatures proves to be a much more difficult adaptive hurdle than does cold temperature.

≈ There appears to be no disadvantage to the increased available sunlight in the terrestrial environment except its drying effect and damage to biomolecules such as DNA.

≈ Water provides about 1,000 times more buoyancy than air, therefore air provides little support of the body.

≈ Water provides a medium through which sperm may swim to eggs to achieve fertilization. Air provides a drying medium and does not support the movement of unprotected sperm to the egg.

≈ Air dries unprotected tissues and cells, such as those of respiratory organs, sperm, egg, zygote, and embryo.

≈ Sensory receptors adapted for aquatic life are not well adapted for the terrestrial environment.

The bones and limb muscles of Sarcopterygii provided an innovation and the structural variability upon which natural selection could act. The result has been the evolution of support structures for the terrestrial body.

The air sacs connecting with the pharynx and paired internal nares provided a respiratory surface that was an **invagination** (*in*—into, *vagina*—sheath) rather than an **evagination** (*e*—out of)(as in gills), reducing respiratory water loss and providing a surface appropriate for the exchange of gases in air. These adaptations were aided by the double circulation of the Sarcopterygii, which separated oxygen rich and oxygen poor blood (Figure 25-3), increasing the efficiency of oxygen distribution to the body tissues.

Sarcopterygii and early tetrapods showed little adaptation to the problems of terrestrial fertilization and development, and if modern amphibians are an indicator, the problem was avoided entirely by returning to an aquatic habitat for fertilization and development. Terrestrial

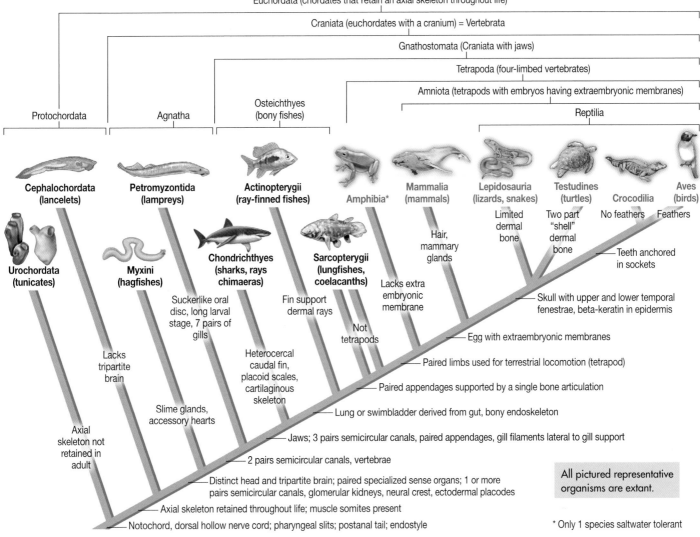

Euchordata (chordates that retain an axial skeleton throughout life)

Craniata (euchordates with a cranium) = Vertebrata

Gnathostomata (Craniata with jaws)

Tetrapoda (four-limbed vertebrates)

Amniota (tetrapods with embryos having extraembryonic membranes)

Reptilia

Protochordata

Agnatha

Osteichthyes (bony fishes)

Cephalochordata (lancelets)

Petromyzontida (lampreys)

Actinopterygii (ray-finned fishes)

Amphibia*

Mammalia (mammals)

Lepidosauria (lizards, snakes)

Testudines (turtles)

Crocodilia

Aves (birds)

Limited dermal bone

Two part "shell" dermal bone

No feathers

Feathers

Urochordata (tunicates)

Myxini (hagfishes)

Chondrichthyes (sharks, rays chimaeras)

Sarcopterygii (lungfishes, coelacanths)

Hair, mammary glands

Teeth anchored in sockets

Suckerlike oral disc, long larval stage, 7 pairs of gills

Fin support dermal rays

Lacks extra embryonic membrane

Skull with upper and lower temporal fenestrae, beta-keratin in epidermis

Lacks tripartite brain

Heterocercal caudal fin, placoid scales, cartilaginous skeleton

Not tetrapods

Egg with extraembryonic membranes

Paired limbs used for terrestrial locomotion (tetrapod)

Paired appendages supported by a single bone articulation

Axial skeleton not retained in adult

Slime glands, accessory hearts

Lung or swimbladder derived from gut, bony endoskeleton

Jaws; 3 pairs semicircular canals, paired appendages, gill filaments lateral to gill support

2 pairs semicircular canals, vertebrae

Distinct head and tripartite brain; paired specialized sense organs; 1 or more pairs semicircular canals, glomerular kidneys, neural crest, ectodermal placodes

Axial skeleton retained throughout life; muscle somites present

Notochord, dorsal hollow nerve cord; pharyngeal slits; postanal tail; endostyle

All pictured representative organisms are extant.

* Only 1 species saltwater tolerant

■ **25-1 Chordate Cladogram** ~ The tetrapods include the Amphibia through the Mammalia. Although there are members of each taxon that lack feet (poda), they all share an ancestor with four legs and five digits. Most (except the Amphibia) have extraembryonic membranes. See Appendix C for definitions of terms.

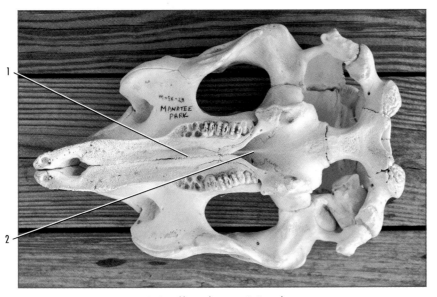

1. Second bony palate   2. Internal nares

■ **25-2 Florida Manatee Internal Nares** ~ Shown is the skull of a Florida manatee. We are looking at the roof of its mouth, which is formed by a sheet of bone (secondary bony palate) that separates the nasal passages from the mouth cavity. The bony palate allows simultaneous chewing and breathing. The internal nares deliver air to the pharynx (*pharynx*—throat), a short, common passageway for the respiratory and digestive tracts. Ultimately, air and food follow separate paths to the stomach and lungs via the esophagus and trachea, respectively.

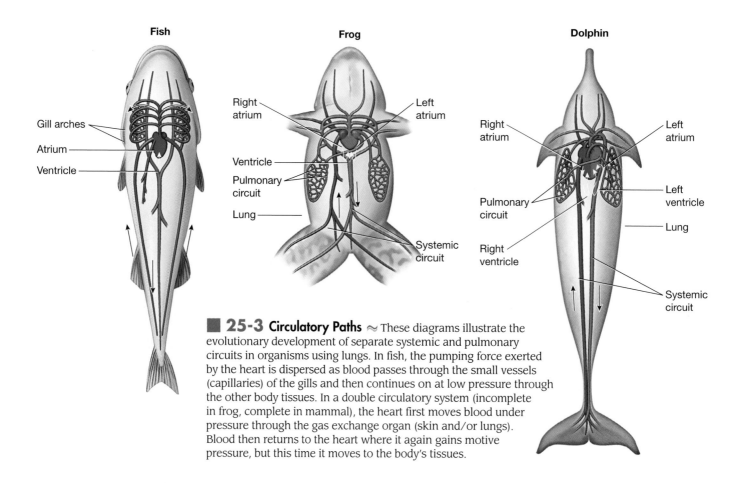

Fish

Gill arches
Atrium
Ventricle

Frog

Right atrium
Left atrium
Ventricle
Pulmonary circuit
Lung
Systemic circuit

Dolphin

Right atrium
Left atrium
Pulmonary circuit
Left ventricle
Right ventricle
Lung
Systemic circuit

■ **25-3 Circulatory Paths** ～ These diagrams illustrate the evolutionary development of separate systemic and pulmonary circuits in organisms using lungs. In fish, the pumping force exerted by the heart is dispersed as blood passes through the small vessels (capillaries) of the gills and then continues on at low pressure through the other body tissues. In a double circulatory system (incomplete in frog, complete in mammal), the heart first moves blood under pressure through the gas exchange organ (skin and/or lungs). Blood then returns to the heart where it again gains motive pressure, but this time it moves to the body's tissues.

adaptations such as a copulatory organ (Figure 25-4) to deliver sperm, an egg covering resistant to water loss (Figure 25-5), and/or internal development emerged later in tetrapod evolution.

Sarcopterygii and early tetrapods show a similarity in shoulder structure and skull structures. In early tetrapods, the general anatomy included a limited number of digits (fingers/toes), with five becoming the standard for most extant species except in most modern amphibians and birds (Figure 25-6). They originally had a single neck vertebra allowing for vertical (dorsal, ventral) motion of the head and later possessed a second vertebra, which allowed side-to-side motion (Figure 25-7). Associated with these tetrapod changes were increases in vertebral strength, greater muscle development associated with limbs and vertebrae, and strengthening of shoulder and hip bones, among others.

Although controversial, one interpretation of current data includes three groups of tetrapods: temnospondyls, lepospondyls, and anthracosaurs. The temnospondyls include ancestors of modern amphibians (Lissamphibia; *liss*—smooth, *amphi*—on both sides, or double), and based upon skull structure, the lepospondyls and anthracosaurs are more closely related to the Amniotes: reptiles and the two groups that evolved from reptiles, the birds and mammals. A description of marine reptiles appears later in this

chapter and a description of birds and mammals in following chapters.

Lissamphibia

Lissamphibia (frogs and toads, salamanders and caecilians) have terrestrial adaptations, which include skeletal modifications to support the body in air, lungs as opposed to gills in the majority of adult forms, limbs associated with a well-developed musculoskeletal system (Figure 25-8), and sensory systems adapted to air. However, because their skin is a major point of water loss (Figure 25-9), they depend upon returning to water for fertilization and development, and many larval forms use gills as their respiratory organ.

At this time, it is unclear if Lissamphibia is a monophyletic or paraphyletic group. However, it does contain all extant species of amphibians, none of which occupy a strictly marine habitat. Ironically, the group that shares more characteristics than any other modern group with extinct, early tetrapods and has an ancestry important in the transition of aquatic vertebrates (both marine and freshwater) into a terrestrial habitat, no longer has a fully marine species. However, there is a frog that can survive in brackish water (estuarine) habitats as tadpoles and adults, principally inhabiting mangrove swamps (Figure 25-10)

■ 25-4 Copulatory Organ

Organ ≈ Most land vertebrates have internal fertilization as an adaptation to a dry environment. A copulatory organ transfers sperm into the female body. Turtles and crocodilians have a single penis, as do mammals. Snakes and lizards have two structures used singly to deposit sperm into the female's body. The copulatory organs of a lizard, a pair of penises (hemipenes) are shown. During mating, one is everted to deposit sperm within the cloaca of a female.

1. Hemipenes   2. Testes   3. Ductus deferens

■ 25-5 Tetrapod Eggs

Tetrapod Eggs ≈ **(A)** The leathery shell of a Honduran milksnake, *Lampropeltis triangulum hondurensis*, is shown with the young snake about to emerge. **(B)** The hard protein and calcium carbonate shells of the domestic chicken, *Gallus domesticus* (left), and emu, *Dromaius novaehollandiae* (right) are shown for size and color comparisons. All three shells protect the embryo from desiccation and microorganisms while allowing gas exchange and providing the food and raw materials needed for the developing young.

■ 25-6 Digits of Frog

and Birds ≈ **(A)** The skeleton of the amphibian bullfrog, *Rana catesbeiana*, shows the standard tetrapod condition of five digits on its posterior appendages (left) and the derived condition of four on its anterior appendages (right). The feet of the Caribbean flamingo, *Phoenicopterus ruber* **(B)**, and this American bittern, *Botaurus lentiginosus* **(C)**, show the reduced number of digits typical of the birds.

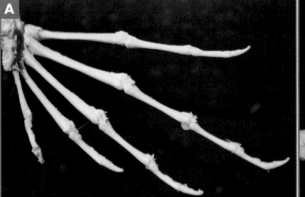

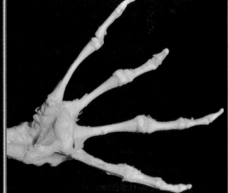

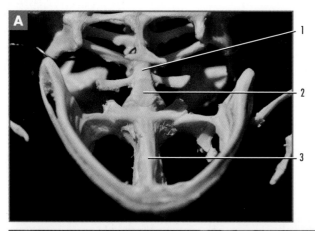

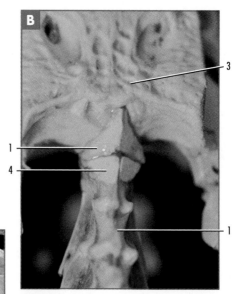

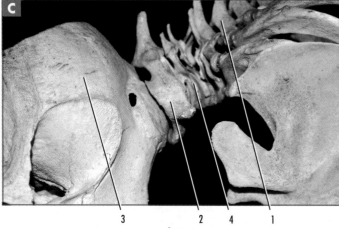

1. Vertebral column
2. Atlas
3. Skull
4. Axis

■ **25-7 Neck Vertebrae** ≈ The atlas bone shown in this frog (**A**), and the atlas and axis of this American alligator, *Alligator mississippiensis* (**B**), and the Pacific white-sided dolphin (**C**), illustrate the structural differences within tetrapods that result in various degrees of head movements. These range from strictly an up-and-down motion (frog), to both up-and-down and side-to-side motions (alligator), to complete rotation of any degree along the dorso-ventral and lateral planes. Cervical (neck) vertebrae of dolphins and most whales have secondarily fused to varying degrees, restricting motion in all planes.

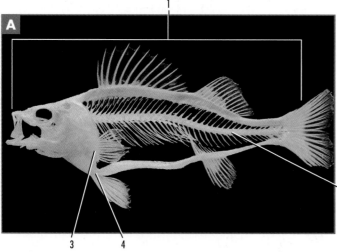

1. Axial skeleton   2. Vertebral column   3. Pectoral girdle   4. Pelvic girdle

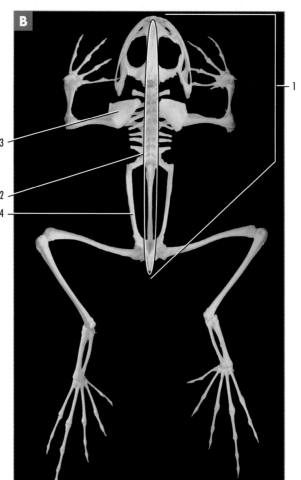

■ **25-8 Skeleton of Teleost and Tetrapod** ≈ The (**A**) skeleton of a teleost fish (yellow perch, *Perca flavescens*), and that of a (**B**) bull-frog, *Rana catesbeiana*, are shown. These illustrate the striking axial and appendicular skeletal differences between the teleost fish and early tetrapods. The axial skeleton consists of the skull, vertebral column, and ribs including the sternum. The appendicular skeleton consists of the limb bones and their bony anchors to the axial skeleton, the pectoral and pelvic girdles.

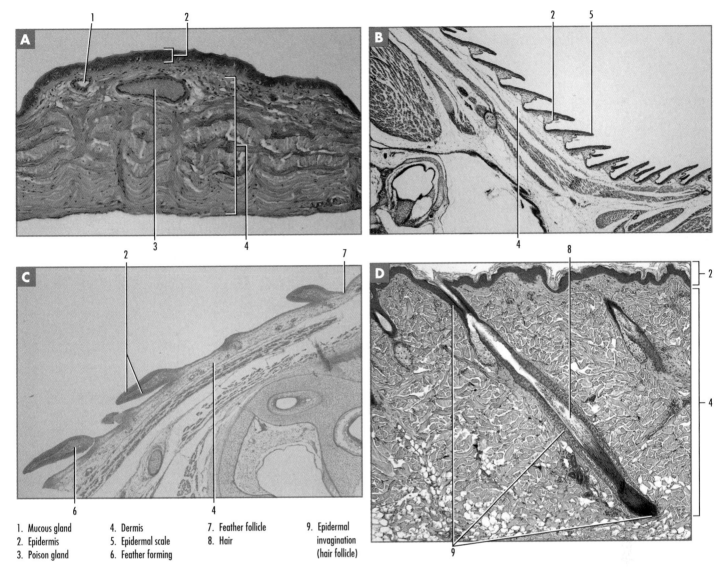

1. Mucous gland
2. Epidermis
3. Poison gland
4. Dermis
5. Epidermal scale
6. Feather forming
7. Feather follicle
8. Hair
9. Epidermal
   invagination
   (hair follicle)

■ **25-9 Tetrapod Skin** ≈ (**A**) Skin (integument) from a frog is thin. Since the skin is a primary respiratory organ, it has numerous mucous glands to keep it moist, a feature necessary for gas exchange. The two layers shown are the outer epidermis (*epi*—upon, *derma*—skin) and the underlying dermis. The vertebrate epidermis is a thin, densely cellular, avascular layer that gives rise to important structures such as (**B**) reptilian scales, (**C**) avian feathers, and (**D**) mammalian hair. The dermis is the vascularized layer of the skin where pigments, fat cells, and nerves are found. Common structures like claws, beaks, and horns are composed of combinations of dermis and epidermis.

where the salinity is greater than freshwater, but lower than the open ocean. *Bufo marinus* is one, but its most frequently used common name, cane toad, indicates it is principally a terrestrial organism that is an opportunistic user of the estuarine habitat. *Rana cancrivora* (or *Fejervarya cancrivora*) (Figure 22-4) is another species that is found in portions of the marine habitat. Known as the crab-eating or mangrove frog, it is found in the brackish water of mangrove streams and in surrounding grassy areas of Southeast Asia. Tadpoles of this species tolerate salinities

up to 39 parts per thousand (the open ocean habitat is ±35 parts per thousand) and adults tolerate salinities up to 28 parts per thousand.

The Lissamphibia include Apodans (caecilians), salamanders (Urodela—Figure 25-11), and frogs and toads (Figure 22-4). Collectively there are more than 6,100 species in this group.

As of late 2009, the genomes of 504 amphibians (including 284 frogs and 217 salamanders) have been, at least in part, determined.

■ 25-10 Mangroves ≈ A major coastal habitat of tropical and subtropical areas, mangroves offer a diverse community consisting of several different mangrove species mixed with shrubs (Chapters 32 and 33). They are limited to tropical and subtropical regions where they form a thick, wooded area that stabilizes coastal sediments and reduces the force of waves while capturing organic rich sediments and extending the shoreline. Mangroves comprise as much as 75% of world tropical coastlines. Various marine amphibians call this habitat home.

■ 25-11 Salamander (Urodela) ≈ Salamanders are members of the Order Urodela (Caudata). In many ways they are typical amphibians with an amphibian circulatory system utilizing skin and lungs as respiratory surfaces. However, their development in terrestrial species is direct, bypassing a larval stage. There are no known marine species.

Amniotes

Amniotes (*amnio*—a fetal membrane) are a monophyletic group containing organisms with improved adaptations to the terrestrial environment as compared to the Lissamphibia and showing a complete break from an aquatic environment for reproduction and development, although many have secondarily adapted to the marine environment. The primary shared derived characteristic is a series of membranes surrounding the developing embryo called **extra** (*extra*—outside of) **embryonic membranes** (Figure 25-12). They include the **amnion** with fluid bathing the embryo, the **allantois**, **yolk sac**, and enclosing the others, the

chorion. The outermost layer of their egg is a porous shell; leathery in the reptiles (Figure 25-5A), hard and brittle in birds (Figures 25-5B and 25-12), and variable in mammals, although most extant mammals do not have a porous shell and retain the embryo without a shell within the uterus.

Other derived characteristics include internal fertilization by penis or cloaca, ventilation of lungs by negative

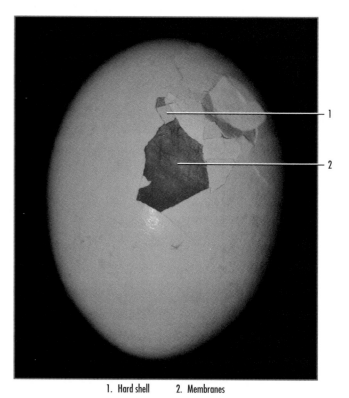

1. Hard shell   2. Membranes

■ 25-12 Amnion ≈ A portion of the hard, calcium shell of this domestic chicken egg has been peeled away exposing membranes of this amniote.

pressure formed by the contraction of rib muscles surrounding the thoracic cavity and for some, posterior muscles such as the diaphragm, and thickened, waterproof skin.

The available evidence suggests that the amniotes are most closely related to the anthracosaurs. Anthracosaurs were more completely adapted to the terrestrial environment than other taxa of vertebrates lacking extra-embryonic membranes (**anamniotes**), including the Lissamphibia.

The fossil record shows the first amniotes were small and lizard-like in their appearance. Their adaptive radiation led to three patterns of skulls: the Anapsida, Diapsida and Synapsida.

The first of these is the anapsids (*an*—not or without, *apsis*—arch), which do not have openings forming an arch behind the eye orbit (Figure 25-13). This is what is seen in the earliest amniotes and in modern turtles, although some evidence suggests its presence in turtles is nonhomologous, a relationship called **homoplasy**, (*homo*—same, *plasi*—form).

The Diapsida (*di*—double, *apsis*—arch) skull has two openings behind each eye orbit (Figure 25-13), although the ancestral condition has been variously modified, as is perhaps the case in extant turtles. Diapsids include extant crocodiles, alligators, lizards, snakes, birds, and possibly turtles.

The Synapsida (*syn*—together, *apsis*—arch) have a single opening behind each eye orbit (Figure 25-13). The only extant group within this clade is the mammals.

Muscles used in raising the lower jaw pass through these skull openings. The appearance of these openings in the amniotes may have allowed the adaptive radiation of these groups to fill a variety of ecological niches with different food sources.

Reptiles (Except Birds)

Reptiles (*reptili*—creep or crawl) have traditionally included snakes, lizards, crocodiles, alligators, and turtles. However, they share a number of derived characteristics with birds and the evidence shows reptiles are a paraphyletic group *without* birds. In fact, the crocodilians and birds are a monophyletic group and are therefore in a clade apart from the other amniotes. However, we will consider the birds in Chapter 26.

As a group, the reptiles are **homeothermic ectotherms**, (*homo*—same, *thermo*—heat and *ecto*—outside). That is, they use heat from the environment to regulate their body temperature and have behaviors that maximize heat gain. (Figure 25-14). They have claws on their digits (Figure 25-15) and, except for turtles (the upper left photo on the Chapter 25 title page shows what serve as teeth for a turtle), possess well-developed teeth (Figure 25-16). They are covered with thickened layers of a unique reptilian version of the protein **keratin** (*kerat*—horn) in and on the epidermis that forms scales (Figure 25-17). Note these scales are quite different in their origin and structure from those of fish: they are epidermal as opposed to the dermal scales in fish (Figure 25-18).

Reptiles have a more complex nervous system than amphibians although their brain is relatively small compared

■ 25-13 Amniote Skull Anatomy ≈

The monophyletic amniotes diversified into three primary patterns of holes in the skull behind the eye orbits: no openings (anapsid), two openings (diapsid) on each side, and one opening on each side (synapsid). These openings are associated with large muscles that raise the lower jaw. They provide the force necessary for a feeding style that requires biting off large pieces of food and then grinding it as a first step in digestion. Note the anapsid skull is the ancestral condition, the synapsid skull is mammalian, and the diapsid skull is present in the reptiles and birds.

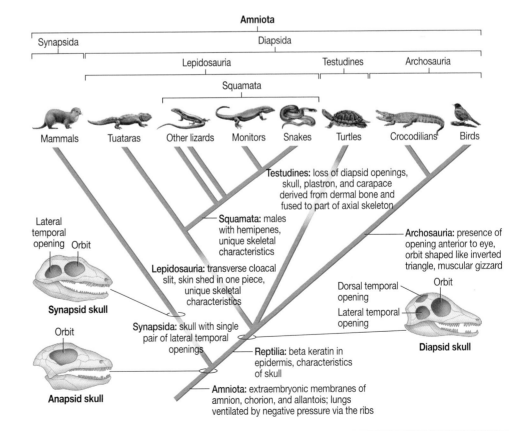

Sungazer lizard

■ 25-15 American Alligator Claws ≈ Note the large scales and claws on this American alligator (*Alligator mississippiensis*). Claws at the ends of digits are characteristic of most tetrapods.

■ 25-14 Homeothermic Ectotherm ≈ This sungazer lizard, *Cordylus giganteus*, like most lizards, spends considerable time regulating body temperature by absorbing heat from its environment, principally in the form of sunlight. The name sungazer comes from their habit of facing the sun at the entrance to their burrow. Note the large, epidermally derived scales.

1. Tooth

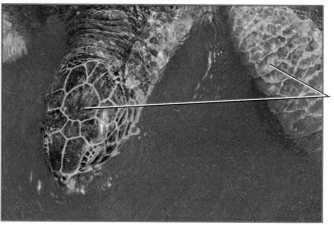

1. Scale

■ 25-16 American Alligator Teeth ≈ Note the teeth of this American alligator (*Alligator mississippiensis*). Most tetrapods have well-developed teeth (turtles and birds being the exceptions).

■ 25-17 Reptilian Scales ≈ *Chelonia mydas*, the green sea turtle, shows fairly typical reptilian scales on its head and flippers, but highly modified scales on its shell. Like all turtles, they share derived characteristics that include loss of the diapsid skull openings and a bony shell derived from epidermal scales and dermal bone (scutes). Scutes (*scutum*—oblong shield) are fused to part of their axial skeleton.

Striped mullet

■ 25-18 Fish Scales ≈ This is a striped mullet, *Mugil cephalus*. Note the large scales (arrow) along the middorsal line. Fish scales are produced by the dermis (Figures 24-5 and 24-9B) in contrast to the epidermally derived scales of reptiles, including birds.

to the other amniotes. Lizards and snakes have a well-developed **olfactory** (*olfactare*—to smell) organ in the roof of their mouth (Jacobson's organ).

Reptiles also have a more efficient circulatory system (three- or four-chambered heart) and higher blood pressure than amphibians, more efficient physiological means of conserving water, and a dry, scaly skin that protects from water loss due to the presence of a number of lipids (fats and oils) embedded in the epidermis. Associated with their improved circulatory efficiency are lungs with greater surface area per unit of body volume for improved gas exchange and negative pressure respiration instead of the positive pressure respiration of the amphibians (reptiles inhale rather than gulp air).

Marine reptiles have secondarily adapted to the marine habitat while retaining their terrestrial shared derived characteristics. They include a single lizard, the marine iguana of the Galapagos Islands, more than 65 species of sea snakes, the saltwater crocodiles, the American crocodile, and seven species of sea turtles.

The marine iguana (Figure 25-19) is probably the least marine of the reptiles and the sea turtle the most (Figures 25-17 and 25-20), with all species tied to land to a greater or lesser extent. Iguanas primarily enter water to feed, while other species may only return to land to lay eggs (females only).

Galapagos marine iguana

■ **25-19 Marine Iguana (Squamata)** ≈ The Galapagos marine iguana (*Amblyrhynchus cristatus*) can reach 1.3 m in length for males and 0.6 m for females, including their tail. They feed on marine algae in the cold water of the Humboldt Current off the Galapagos Islands. One of their greatest threats is hypothermia resulting from time spent feeding in the ocean surrounding the islands. They spend a great deal of time gaining heat from the sun directly and from the dark volcanic rocks of the Galapagos shoreline after and before feeding excursions into the local sublittoral habitat. They are the only lizard that feeds in seawater and possess several adaptations to this lifestyle.

Green sea turtle

Hawksbill turtle

Olive ridley sea turtle

■ **25-20 Sea Turtles (Testudines)** ≈ (**A**) *Chelonia mydas*, is the green sea turtle, one of seven sea turtle species. All sea turtles have shells that are lighter and more hydrodynamic in shape than their terrestrial relatives. They also have limbs that are modified into flippers. The green turtle occurs across tropical and subtropical seas. It is descended from terrestrial ancestors that returned to the sea about 150 million years ago. Females return to land only to lay eggs. The (**B**) olive ridley sea turtle, *Lepidochelys olivacea*, appears to have the greatest number of nesting females of any sea turtle species. Compared to other sea turtles, they are relatively small: to 79 cm and 45 kg. They are globally distributed across tropical oceans. (**C**) The hawksbill turtle, *Eretmochelys imbricata*, has a shell (carapace) that is serrated toward the posterior lateral portions (arrow). The shell is also noticeably yellow on the ventral portion. Its name comes from the hawk-like appearance of its head and jaw. Hawksbill turtles are distributed throughout tropical oceans of the world feeding largely on a limited number of sponge species.

Turtles are in the Order Testudines (Chelonia), the lizards (iguana) and snakes (Figure 25-21) in the Order Squamata, and crocodiles and alligators (Figures 25-15, 25-16 and 25-22) in the Order Crocodilia.

The crocodilians have a secondary palate like the mammals (Figure 25-23). This means the internal nares are in the rear of the mouth (pharynx) so they can breathe when something is in their mouth (like food!). They also have a four-chambered heart as in the birds and mammals, as opposed to the two-chambered heart of fish and the three-chambered heart of most amphibians (Figure 25-3).

Birds (Avian Reptiles or Aves)

Birds and crocodilians form a monophyletic group. We consider the birds—Aves (*avis*—bird)—in the next chapter.

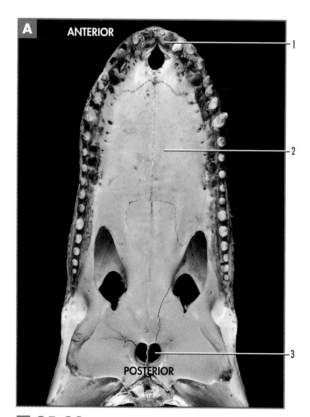

■ **25-21 Sea Snake (Squamata)** ≈ The banded sea krait, *Laticauda colubrina*, occurs in the Indo-Pacific. This species commonly comes onto land to drink freshwater and for mating.

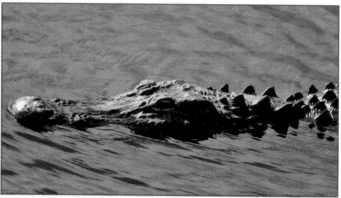

■ **25-22 American Alligator (Crocodilia)** ≈ The American alligator (*Alligator mississippiensis*) is one of two extant alligator species of alligators, and is endemic to the Gulf Coast of North America. It inhabits wetlands, principally freshwater, but does spend time in the brackish water of estuaries.

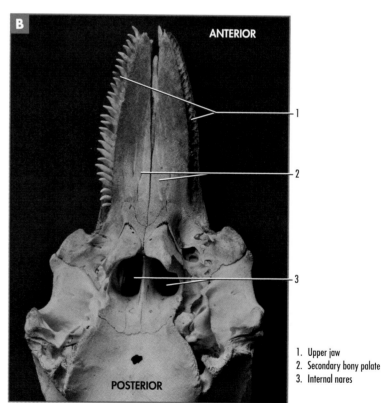

1. Upper jaw
2. Secondary bony palate
3. Internal nares

■ **25-23 Secondary Palate and Internal Nares** ≈ Amphibians have internal nares that open far forward in the oral cavity. The result is, when food is in the mouth there is no breathing; not an adaptive situation if food chewing is required. (**A**) In the crocodilians, such as this adult American alligator, the oral and nasal passages are separated by the presence of a palate and the internal nares are moved to the back of the mouth. With this structural arrangement, food can be chewed AND the organism can breathe. (**B**) This structural arrangement is particularly well developed in mammals as illustrated in this Pacific white-sided dolphin, *Lagenorhynchus obliquidens*. Although the blowholes have migrated posteriorly, the nasal cavity still extends anteriorly and there are two internal nares.

American bald eagle

Least tern

26 Aves

Birds are important components of virtually all surface marine habitats. Many are top predators and others are important food sources. They are one of the most visible marine groups and some would argue one of the most spectacular. The nearly 10,000 species of marine birds vary widely from the extremely small to impressively large. They lay a hard-shelled egg (Figure 25-5B) and show extensive parental care or utilize surrogates to care for their young. Birds maintain a constant body temperature using the heat produced by their internal metabolism (**endothermic homeotherms**, *endo*—within, *thermo*—heat, *homeo*—same). They have a four-chambered heart, an extremely efficient respiratory system, and exceptional vision and navigational skills.

As stated in Chapter 25, birds and crocodilians form a monophyletic group and are sister clades. They are both archosaurian diapsids (Chapter 25) with the apex of the triangular eye orbit at the bottom, heart ventricles fully divided into a four-chambered heart, and a gizzard. Their lower jaw is composed of a similar number of bones, their skull and vertebral column have a similar articulation, and in many other ways they are structurally, genetically, behaviorally, and physiologically similar or identical (Figure 26-1 and Table 26-1).

A group of dinosaurs known as theropods have a variety of shared derived characteristics with birds that include an S-shaped neck (Figure 26-2), fused clavicles (collar bones), wrist bones that allow for rotating motions (important in modern birds and in some theropod groups), and feathers (Figure 26-3).

As with most taxa, new fossil discoveries and molecular data, particularly as an increasing number of species' genomes are sequenced, leave traditional taxonomies and exact phylogenies in doubt. Currently, the Neornithes (living birds, *neo*—new, *ornith*—bird) are divided into two taxa: Paleognathae (*paleo*—ancient, *gnatho*—jaw) or ratites, and the Neognathae (*neo*—new) or carinate birds. Flightless birds occur in both groups, but all Paleognathae are flightless. They have a flat, but enlarged sternum and lack the large flight muscles that you consume if you eat chicken breasts (principally pectoral muscles).

Most extant birds are in the Neognathae, and include all of the flight birds plus some flightless ones. There are no known marine Paleognathae, but there are many marine Neognathae.

Although the distinction between flying and flightless birds is not important in determining taxonomy or phylogeny, contrasting flying and flightless birds reveals much

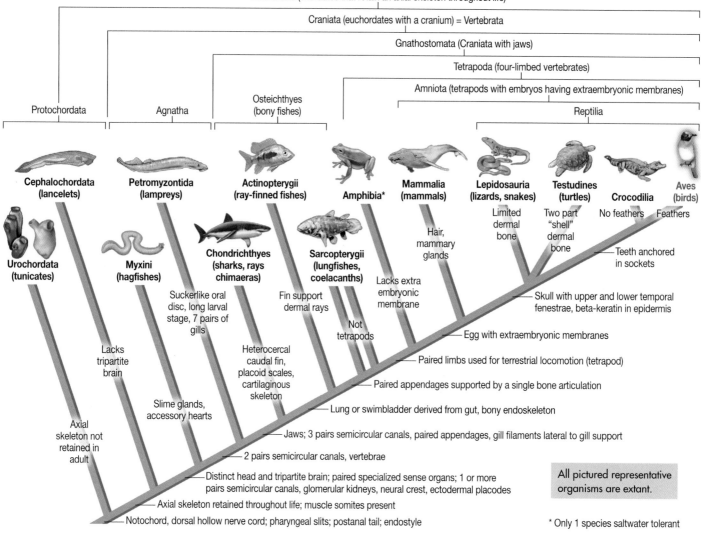

Euchordata (chordates that retain an axial skeleton throughout life)

Craniata (euchordates with a cranium) = Vertebrata

Gnathostomata (Craniata with jaws)

Tetrapoda (four-limbed vertebrates)

Amniota (tetrapods with embryos having extraembryonic membranes)

Reptilia

Protochordata   Agnatha   Osteichthyes (bony fishes)

Cephalochordata (lancelets)   **Petromyzontida (lampreys)**   **Actinopterygii (ray-finned fishes)**   **Amphibia***   **Mammalia (mammals)**   **Lepidosauria (lizards, snakes)**   **Testudines (turtles)**   **Crocodilia**   **Aves (birds)**

Urochordata (tunicates)   **Myxini (hagfishes)**   **Chondrichthyes (sharks, rays chimaeras)**   **Sarcopterygii (lungfishes, coelacanths)**

Limited dermal bone   Two part "shell" dermal bone   No feathers   Feathers

Hair, mammary glands

Teeth anchored in sockets

Suckerlike oral disc, long larval stage, 7 pairs of gills   Fin support dermal rays   Lacks extra embryonic membrane

Skull with upper and lower temporal fenestrae, beta-keratin in epidermis

Not tetrapods

Egg with extraembryonic membranes

Lacks tripartite brain   Heterocercal caudal fin, placoid scales, cartilaginous skeleton

Paired limbs used for terrestrial locomotion (tetrapod)

Paired appendages supported by a single bone articulation

Slime glands, accessory hearts

Lung or swimbladder derived from gut, bony endoskeleton

Axial skeleton not retained in adult

Jaws; 3 pairs semicircular canals, paired appendages, gill filaments lateral to gill support

2 pairs semicircular canals, vertebrae

Distinct head and tripartite brain; paired specialized sense organs; 1 or more pairs semicircular canals, glomerular kidneys, neural crest, ectodermal placodes

All pictured representative organisms are extant.

Axial skeleton retained throughout life; muscle somites present

Notochord, dorsal hollow nerve cord; pharyngeal slits; postanal tail; endostyle

* Only 1 species saltwater tolerant

■ **26-1 Chordate Cladogram** ≈ This cladogram shows that modern birds are extant, feathered reptiles most closely related to the Crocodilia. See Appendix C for definitions of terms.

about the physical constraints placed on organisms' anatomy, morphology, and physiology when flight is an important ecological factor influencing evolutionary history.

The physics of flight dictate a critical weight-to-power ratio. Bird adaptations are principally ones that decrease weight and increase power. Among those adaptations that decrease weight are hollow bones, absence of teeth, hollow and lightweight feathers, absence of a urinary bladder, small gonads except during breeding season, and small body size. The range is great, but there is no flying bird more than 18 kg, about 40 pounds, with the average flying bird weighing less than 0.5 kg. The African kori bustard (*Ardeotis kori*), at up to 19 kg, or 41.8 pounds, is a statistical outlier.

In contrast, flightless birds do not have hollow bones, some have a urinary bladder (rheas and ostriches) and some are quite large. Ostriches are the largest extant bird, weighing up to 155 kg, 343 pounds.

With regard to power, flight birds have huge keeled sternums (Figure 26-2) that provide a large surface area

for enormous flight muscles to attach. They have large anterior appendages forming wings, and to provide the necessary oxygen and nutrients to run these power plants, a high-pressure, high-heart-rate circulatory system and a respiratory system consisting of lungs and an extensive series of air sacs that maximize gas exchange.

Flightless birds generally lack a keeled sternum, have comparatively small muscles attached to their sternum, have small wings often difficult to see from a distance, and lack the extensive series of air sacs.

Flight provides birds a degree of mobility that allows them to move between terrestrial, salt water, and freshwater habitats. None are strictly marine, since all birds must return to land, or at least the coastal strip, to lay their eggs. Some birds, such as the light-footed clapper rail (Figure 26-4), lay eggs in a woven nest that floats up and down on the flood and ebb tides and may touch the benthos, but never touches the terrestrial environment.

Order	General Description	Examples	Approximate Number of Species	Etymology
Anseriformes (Figure 26-5)	Broad-billed and heavy-bodied birds	Geese, swans, and ducks	160+	*anser*—goose, *formes*—form
Sphenisciformes (Figure 26-6)	Hydrodynamic body; wings modified as flippers	Penguins	17	*sphen*—wedge, *formes*—form, for the short wings used for swimming
Gaviiformes (Figure 26-7)	Heavy-bodied, short-legged swimmers	Loons	5	*gavia*—bird, *formes*—form
Podicipediformes (Figure 26-8)	Similar in appearance to loons, but upper bill longer than lower	Grebes	20+	*podex*—rump, *pedis*—foot, *formes*—form
Phoenicopteriformes (Figure 26-9)	Large, pink or reddish, wading birds with down-curved, heavy beak	Flamingoes	6	*phoenico*—reddish-purple, *pteri*—wing, *formes*—form
Procellariiformes (Figure 26-10)	Hooked beak; large salt glands; gull-like in appearance	Shearwaters, petrels, fulmars, and albatrosses—pelagic birds	110+	*procella*—tempest, *formes*—form
Pelecaniformes (Figure 26-11)	Heavy-bodied birds; nostrils vestigial or absent; a throat pouch; all four toes involved in footweb	Pelicans, cormorants, boobies, gannets, and frigatebirds	65	*pelekan*—pelican, *formes*—form
Ciconiiformes (Figure 26-12)	Long-legged wading birds with long bill and neck	Storks, herons, ibises, egrets, spoonbills, vultures, and bitterns	115+	*ciconia*—stork, *formes*—form
Falconiformes (Figure 26-13)	Diurnal birds of prey; curved talons; large eyes	Falcons, hawks, eagles, ospreys, condors, and buzzards	300+	*falcon*—falcon, *formes*—form
Gruiformes (Figure 26-14)	Highly variable ranging from the chicken-like rails to the heron-like cranes; long-legged and long-necked	Coots, rails, and cranes	200+	*grus*—crane, *formes*—form
Charadriiformes (Figure 26-15)	Shorebirds	Gulls, auks, puffins, plovers, sandpipers, terns, curlews, godwits, dowitchers, avocets, turnstones, skuas, and others	360+	*charadri*—a curlew, *formes*—form
Coraciiformes (Figure 26-16)	Prominent bill; fused third and fourth toes	Kingfishers, hornbills, and others	200+	*cornic*—a crow, *formes*—form
Passeriformes (Figure 26-17)	Perching birds; few largely dependent upon the marine environment	Very large group of highly variable birds containing 60% of all bird species—crows, ravens, and several members of the genus Cinclodes use the marine shores as a habitat and food source	5,700+	*passer*—sparrow, *formes*—form
18 other orders with limited or no marine ties				

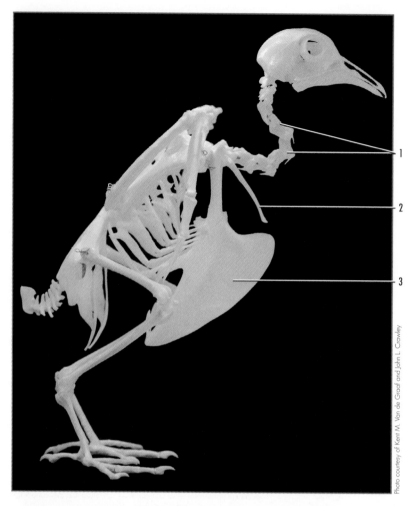

1. S-shaped neck
2. Fused clavicles (collar bones)
3. Breast bone (sternum).

■ 26-2 Skeleton of Bird ≈ This pigeon skeleton illustrates some of the skeletal elements of birds and theropods.

■ 26-3 Feathers ≈ The feathers of several bird species are shown, including a crow's (**1**), *Corvus branchyrhynchos*, and a red-tailed hawk's (**2**), *Buteo jamaicensis*. There are a number of different feather types on a single bird.

■ 26-4 Light-footed Clapper Rail (Order Gruiformes) ≈ The light-footed clapper rail, *Rallus longirostris levipes*, is a non-migratory resident of coastal marshes. Habitat destruction resulted in its being placed on the federal Endangered Species List in 1970. In the estuarine environments from Santa Barbara, California, to Bahia de San Quintin, Baja California, Mexico, they nest in the low-tide zones in cordgrass (Chapter 32 and 33) and higher tidal zones in pickleweed (Chapter 32 and 33). They are ground nesting birds.

Bird Orders

Marine birds' contact with water ranges from wading to extended submergence.

Order Anseriformes Anseriformes (*anser*—goose, *formes*—form) includes the swans, geese, and ducks. These waterfowl generally go where the food is and can be found in fresh and saltwater wetlands (Figure 26-5).

Canada goose

Brant goose

Male hooded merganser

Immature male red-breasted merganser

American wigeon

White-faced whistling duck

Northern pintail

Ruddy duck

■ **26-5 Ducks and Allies (Anseriformes)** ≈ (**A**) *Branta canadensis*, the Canada goose, occurs across most of North America in temperate and Arctic latitudes. It is a fairly large goose. Within parts of its range, individuals may stand up to 1.15 m. (**B**) The Brant goose, *Branta bernicla*, occurs on the East and West Coasts of North America in the winter, and on the Arctic Coast of North America in the summer. The East and West Coast individuals are recognized as subspecies. (**C**) The striking colors of this male hooded merganser, *Lophodytes cucullatus*, is typical in birds that demonstrate sexual dimorphism (*di*—two, *morpha*—form). Females lack this coloration and are usually quite drab in comparison. This merganser ranges across much of North America, but is predominantly an East Coast resident. It is a surface diving bird, pursuing fish, amphibians, and various invertebrates. (**D**) The red-breasted merganser male, *Mergus serrator*, occurs in coastal areas of North America and across northern Canada and the United States. It dives to pursue and eat fish and invertebrates. (**E**) The American wigeon, *Anas americana*, is widely spread across North America, feeding on vegetation. (**F**) *Dendrocygna viduata*, the white-faced whistling duck, occurs in much of South America and central Africa. Its diet consists of aquatic plant tubers and seeds, and aquatic invertebrates. (**G**) *Anas acuta*, the northern pintail, occurs across most of North America, where it feeds on aquatic plants and invertebrates. (**H**) The northern ruddy duck, *Oxyura jamaicensis*, ranges across North America. It is a diving duck that feeds on invertebrates. (*continued*)

Male   Mallard   Female

Ring-necked duck

Ferruginous duck

Wood duck

Common eider

King eider

■ **26-5 Ducks and Allies (Anseriformes)** ≈ *(continued)* The male and female mallard (I), *Anas platyrhynchos*, also illustrate sexual dimorphism. Ranging across most of North America, they are dabblers that feed on aquatic vegetation and on a limited quantity of invertebrates. (J) The ring-necked duck male, *Aythya collanis*, occurs across much of North America, where it feeds on submerged aquatic plant leaves, seeds, and roots. It will also eat some aquatic invertebrates. A portion of the faint, purplish namesake ring is visible to the bird's left and below its bill. (K) The ferruginous duck, *Aythya nyroca*, ranges from southern and eastern Europe and eastward to central Asia. Notice the webbing between the toes and the reduced number of toes as is typical of avian tetrapods. (L) The wood duck, *Aix sponsa*, occurs in parts of Canada, the United States, and Mexico. It feeds on aquatic plants, fish, amphibians, and invertebrates on the surface of water. (M) *Somateria mollissima*, the common eider, occurs in extreme coastal North America, where it feeds on invertebrates, including blue mussels. (N) *Somateria spectabilis*, the king eider, has a very limited range on parts of northern coastal North America. It feeds on aquatic plants and invertebrates at depths up to 60 m.

Order Sphenisciformes Sphenisciformes (*sphen*—wedge, *formes*—form, for the short wings used in swimming) includes only penguins, a group of some 17 species that may be one of the best-known marine birds (Figure 26-6). They vary widely in abundance, ranging from well over 20 million individuals of some species to as few as 3,500 individuals of others based upon current population estimates. Many penguin species spend the majority of their lives at sea, some for several months at a time. Barnacles on the tail feathers of some species indicate extended periods of times in the water. Diving depths and times are generally minor, but remote sensing techniques have revealed occasional impressive depths and times (more than 500 m and more than 20 minutes). Current populations are limited to the Southern Hemisphere across a range of climates from polar through temperate and tropical. As in most marine birds, penguins have salt glands. These secrete excess salt from the use of saltwater as their primary water source.

African penguin

Emperor penguin

Humboldt penguin

Gentoo penguin

Macaroni penguin

Magellanic penguin

■ **26-6 Penguins (Sphenisciformes)** ∼ (A) *Spheniscus demersus*, the African penguin, is the only penguin species breeding in Africa. It occurs along the southern African coast in both the Atlantic and Indian oceans, where it historically has depended upon fish as its primary food source. With fish stocks depleted from overfishing, they have also added invertebrates to their diets. (B) *Aptenodytes forsteri*, the emperor penguin, occurs in Antarctica and is the largest of all extant penguins. It feeds on fish and a number of invertebrates, diving to depths of more than 500 m. Unlike flight birds, the emperor has solid bones. This and other adaptations allow it to dive and stay submerged for nearly 20 minutes. (C) *Spheniscus humboldti*, the Humboldt penguin, lives along the coast of Peru and Chile, where it feeds predominantly on fish in the Humboldt Current. (D) The gentoo penguin, *Pygoscelis papua*, lives in a wide area of the Antarctic Ocean, including the Antarctic continent and surrounding islands. It ranges as far north as islands off South America and into the South Pacific, Atlantic, and Indian oceans. (E) *Eudyptes chrysolophus*, the macaroni penguin, inhabits the Antarctic Ocean from the west tip of South America to the east across the extreme Southern Atlantic and into the Southern Indian Ocean. It largely feeds on krill, but also eats other invertebrates and fish. (F) *Spheniscus magellanicus*, the Magellanic penguin, lives around the tip of South America on both the Atlantic and Pacific sides and into the northern edges of the Antarctic Ocean. It feeds on fish and invertebrates. Five-year-old Palu Peacock-Bouscaren, at 95 cm, is escorting this penguin back to its burrow.

Photo courtesy of Stephen J. Bouscaren, Ph.D.

Photo courtesy of Jennale Peacock

Order Gaviiformes

Gaviiformes (*gavia*—bird, *formes*— form) includes the loons (*loon*—diver). There are five known species (Figure 26-7).

Common loon

■ **26-7 Loons (Gaviiformes)** ≈ *Gavia immer*, the common loon, is a diving bird that feeds on fish and ranges across most of Canada, most coastal areas of the United States, and across northern Baja California.

Order Podicipediformes

Podicipediformes (*podex*—rump, *pedis*—foot, *formes*—form) includes the grebes (Figure 26-8). Worldwide there are 22 species, some largely marine, others most abundant in freshwater habitats.

Pied-billed grebe

Western grebe

■ **26-8 Grebes (Podicipediformes)** ≈ **(A)** The pied-billed grebe, *Podilymbus podiceps*, occurs across most of North America except to extreme northern latitudes. It is a diving bird that feeds on fish and invertebrates. **(B)** *Aechmophorus occidentalis*, the western grebe, has a range that is not well documented but occurs along most of the West Coast of North America and inland to western states and some Canadian provinces. Like other grebes, the western grebe is a diving bird.

Order Phoenicopteriformes

Phoenicopteriformes (*phoenico*—reddish-purple, *pteri*—wing, *formes*—form) comprises the five flamingo species (Figure 26-9). They are wading birds that live in lakes, tidal flats, mangrove swamps, and the sandy shores of islands. They filter feed by assuming a posture of lowered head while walking slowly with their bill along the surface of the water (Figure 26-9A, [upper right]). Finger-like projections from the bill remove suspended organisms from the water.

Caribbean flamingo

26-9 Flamingoes (Phoenicopteriformes) ≈

(A) The Caribbean flamingo, *Phoenicopterus ruber ruber*, occurs in South and Central America and the Caribbean, where it inhabits coastal lagoons and mudflats. (top, center) Like all flamingoes, the Caribbean flamingo is a filter feeder, using comb-like structures on its bill and a pumping motion to filter crustaceans and small invertebrates from the water. (top, right) A Caribbean flamingo shows the usual posture and position of the bill while feeding. (bottom, center) The striking color of a mature Caribbean flamingo results from plant pigments occurring naturally in its food—crustaceans. (B) *Phoeniconaias minor*, the lesser flamingo, is smaller than the Caribbean flamingo. It occurs in southern and eastern Africa, northwest India, and Madagascar, where it filters small food particles such as algae from the water.

Lesser flamingo

Order Procellariiformes Procellariiformes (*procella*—tempest, *formes*—form) contains more than 110 species, all of which are marine. They include the albatrosses, shearwaters, petrels, and fulmars (Figure 26-10).

Southern royal albatross

Southern giant petrel

Black-footed albatross

Laysan albatross

■ **26-10 Albatrosses and Allies (Procellariiformes)** ≈ (**A**) *Diomedea epomophora*, the southern royal albatross, lives in the Antarctic Ocean, but this oceanic bird generally does not approach the Antarctic continent. It occurs along the east and west nearshore areas of South America, New Zealand, and southeastern Australia. (**B**) *Macronectes giganteus*, the southern giant petrel, occurs from subtropical water to the Antarctic continent and is widespread in the Antarctic Ocean. It is a predator and opportunistic scavenger on carcasses, including penguins! The southern giant petrel is a predator of other birds, crustaceans, and other invertebrates. (**C**) *Diomedea nigripes*, the black-footed albatross, like other albatrosses, is an oceanic bird and one of three that occur in the Northern Hemisphere. It ranges from California and Alaska to Japan with the greatest occurrence in the Northeast Pacific, where it feeds on fish and some invertebrates. (**D**) The laysan albatross, *Phoebastria immutabilis*, is a second Northern Hemisphere albatross, ranging across the North Pacific from tropical waters to the Kamchatka Peninsula. It feeds predominantly on cephalopods.

Order Pelecaniformes Pelecaniformes (*pelekan*—pelican, *formes*—form) includes the pelicans, cormorants, gannets, frigatebirds, and others for a total of more than 60 species (Figure 26-11). Traditionally included in this group are species that molecular data indicate are more closely related to other species. This order is likely to be replaced by a number of other new orders in the near future, with several species included in other currently used orders.

Immature double-crested cormorant

Double-crested cormorant in breeding plumage

Double-crested cormorant feeding

Brandt's cormorant

White-breasted cormorant

Male   Brown booby

Female

Magnificent frigatebird female

■ 26-11 Pelicans and Allies (Pelecaniformes) ≈

(A) *Phalacrocorax auritus*, the double-crested cormorant, is distributed across North America from Florida and Mexico up to the Aleutian Islands. Like other cormorants, it dives from the surface of the water to secure its fish prey. (right) This double-crested cormorant is feeding on a large fish at the surface. The fish was large enough to require about 90 seconds of manipulation before it was swallowed. (B) Brandt's cormorant, *Phalacrocorax penicillatus*, is strictly marine, occurring from Alaska to Baja California in the Eastern Pacific. It dives to feed on fish from the surface to the bottom. In California, it particularly feeds on rockfish (*Sebastes*—Chapter 24). This specimen is in its breeding season plumage. (C) The white-breasted cormorant, *Phalacrocorax carbo lucidus*, is widely distributed from western and southern Africa to inland eastern Africa. It feeds on a wide variety of organisms, including fish and invertebrates. (D) These individuals are likely brown boobies, *Sula leucogaster*, based upon where they were photographed: Northeastern subtropical Pacific. Like other boobies, they dive in pursuit of prey, which includes squid and fish. (E) The magnificent frigatebird, *Fregata magnificens*, spends most of its life flying over the ocean, but seldom lands on the surface. It ranges along both coasts of North, Central and South America, but to higher latitudes along the east coast of South America and West Coast of North America. It also occurs in the Caribbean. This frigatebird feeds on fish, turtles, and some invertebrates, taking its prey from the surface and from other birds. *(continued)*

Brown pelican in breeding plumage | Brown pelican | Brown pelican in nonbreeding plumage

■ **26-11 Pelicans and Allies (Pelecaniformes)** ≈ *(continued)* (F) The brown pelican, *Pelicanus occidentalis*, occurs along the West Coast of the United States south to Chile, and the Gulf and Atlantic coasts of the southeastern United States south to the mouth of the Amazon River. It also is endemic to the Caribbean and the Galapagos Islands. It feeds by diving into the ocean and trapping fish in its throat pouch. The pelican on the left and in the center are the California subspecies in breeding plumage. There are five recognized subspecies.

Order Ciconiiformes Ciconiiformes (*ciconia*—stork, *formes*—form) includes more than 115 species of ibises, herons, spoonbills, bitterns, storks, and vultures (Figure 26-12).

Roseate spoonbill | African spoonbill | White ibis

Scarlet ibis | Immature | Black-crowned night heron | Adult

■ **26-12 Herons and Allies (Ciconiiformes)** ≈ (A) The roseate spoonbill, *Platalea ajaja*, is one of six extant spoonbill species. It is the only spoonbill occurring in the United States, but it also occurs in South and Central America, Mexico, and the Caribbean. It feeds by moving the spoon-shaped bill back and forth in the water, capturing invertebrates and vertebrates such as fish. (B) The African spoonbill, *Platalea alba*, occurs widely across southern Africa and Madagascar. Its habitats include marsh and swamp, where its food includes molluscs and crustaceans. (C) The white ibis, *Eudocimus albus*, lives along the west coast of Mexico and Central America, the Gulf Coast of the United States and Mexico, the Atlantic coast of Central America, and extreme northern South America. It probes for invertebrates in many habitats, including marine. (D) *Eudocimus ruber*, the scarlet ibis, has nostrils at the base of its bill (near its head), allowing it to breathe as it probes in mud and sand for food. Like flamingoes, it gets its color from the food it eats, and depending upon diet, may range from white to black, but is commonly a scarlet pink. It ranges from Venezuela to Brazil. (E) (left) This immature black-crowned night heron, *Nycticorax nycticorax*, as is common in many birds, looks significantly different than the adult (right). The black-crowned heron lives on every continent except Antarctica and Australia. It occurs across North America, except in extreme northern latitudes. It feeds principally at dusk and night consuming a variety of vertebrates, including the young of other birds, and occupies a variety of habitats. *(continued)*

Great blue heron

Tricolored heron

Yellow-crowned night heron

Cattle egret

Snowy egret

Common egret

■ **26-12 Herons and Allies (Ciconiiformes)** ≈ *(continued)* (F) The great blue heron, *Ardea herodias*, is a resident of North and Central America, the Caribbean, and the Galapagos Islands. It feeds on a range of vertebrates and invertebrates but its principal food is fish. (G) *Egretta tricolor*, the tricolored heron, feeds on fish and other vertebrates, and on crustaceans. It reportedly lives along the Gulf Coast of North America, through Central America, and as far south as Brazil. However, the authors photographed this individual in the lagoons of western Baja California. (H) The yellow-crowned night heron, *Nyctanassa violecea*, is reportedly present along the Pacific and Gulf Coasts of Baja California and mainland Mexico, through Central America and northern South America. However, this individual was photographed by the authors at the San Diego River Estuary. On the Atlantic coast, it ranges from Maine, along the Gulf Coast, to Central America and to southern Brazil. It feeds on a wide range of vertebrates and invertebrates. (I) *Bubulcus ibis*, the cattle egret, is widely distributed across a wide variety of habitats throughout Europe, parts of Asia, Africa, and North and South America. It typically feeds away from water in fields and along areas of cut grass, but it also feeds in wetlands, including estuarine habitats. (J) The snowy egret, *Egretta thula*, eats a variety of vertebrates and invertebrates. It occurs across parts of Canada, all of the United States, parts of Mexico and is abundant in Central and South America, and the Caribbean. It was nearly hunted to extinction in the 19th century for its feathers, clearly seen in the photo on the right. (K) *Ardea alba*, the common egret, is distributed across the United States, Mexico, and throughout tropical and warm temperate regions of the world, including the rainforest of South America, where it feeds on a variety of vertebrates and invertebrates.

Order Falconiformes Falconiformes (*falcon*—falcon, *formes*—form) contains birds of prey such as falcons, eagles, and hawks totaling more than 300 species. The osprey is also included in this order by some authors, but based upon differences between osprey and other diurnal birds of prey, other authors place it in a separate order.

This makes the placement of the osprey unresolved. The osprey is of interest for a number of reasons, not the least of which it is a single species with worldwide distribution that is not a consequence of introduction by humans (Figure 26-13).

■ **26-13 Falcons and Allies (Falconiformes)** ≈ The osprey, *Pandion haliaetus*, preys nearly exclusively on fish. It ranges worldwide, occurring on all continents except Antarctica. Another important marine falconiform is our National bird, the bald eagle (*Haliaeetus leucocephalus*). See the photo at the top left of page 207.

Order Gruiformes Gruiformes (*grus*—crane, *formes*—form) contains more than 200 species, including coots, rails, and cranes (Figure 26-14).

American coot

Light-footed clapper rail

Common moorhen

■ **26-14 Rails and Allies (Gruiformes)** ≈ (A) The American coot, *Fulica americana*, lives in North America. It is omnivorous and feeds on a wide range of plants and small aquatic animals, both vertebrates and invertebrates. It feeds at the surface and also dives. (B) The light-footed clapper rail, *Rallus longirostris levipes*, is one of 21 subspecies of *Rallus longirostris*. Its range is limited to a small part of Southern and Baja California, while the entire species range includes Northern California, the East Coast of North America, the Caribbean, and parts of South America. It feeds upon small aquatic animals. It is also shown in Figure 26-4. (C) *Gallinula chloropus*, the common moorhen, is distributed widely except in polar regions. It feeds on a wide range of plant material and small invertebrates.

Order Charadriiformes Charadriiformes (*charadri*—a curlew, *formes*—form) contains shorebirds, including gulls, auks, puffins, plovers, sandpipers, terns, willets, curlews, godwits, dowitchers, and others (Figure 26-15). This order contains more than 360 species. Like most of the taxa in this chapter, relationships within this order are largely unresolved for several groups. The order is generally considered to contain three primary groups: the shorebirds, which wade and probe the mud and sand for invertebrates; the gulls, which feed on vertebrates and invertebrates as the opportunities present themselves; and the auks, which fly underwater looking for fish prey.

Common murre

Tufted puffin

American avocet

Black oystercatcher

Black-necked stilt

■ **26-15 Gulls and Allies (Charadriiformes)** ≈ (**A**) *Uria aalge*, the common murre, feeds predominantly on fish, but also consumes some invertebrates. They flap their wings for propulsion and "fly" both in air and water. They are residents of Arctic and northern temperate waters of the North Pacific and Atlantic, spending most of its time at sea. Although controversial, there are generally seven subspecies recognized, including two that occur along coasts of the United States. (**B**) *Fratercula cirrhata*, the tufted puffin, occurs in the North Pacific, but ranges as far south as Southern California and along the coast of the Western Pacific. It is an oceanic bird that feeds on small fish and invertebrates. (**C**) The American avocet, *Recurvirostra americana*, feeds by sweepings its upcurved bill through the water. When the avocet contacts a small fish or invertebrate, the prey is captured and consumed. *R. americana* occurs in lower latitudes along all North American coasts as far south as Guatemala. (**D**) The black oystercatcher, *Haematopus bachmani*, occurs along the coast of North America from the Aleutian Island Archipelago through northern Baja California. The oystercatcher feeds upon a variety of mollusks, particularly mussels and limpets. (**E**) *Hymantopus mexicanus*, the black-necked stilt, occurs on the Pacific Coast of California, through inland areas of the Pacific Northwest, Baja California, and mainland Mexico, and through Central America, the southeastern United States, and parts of Brazil and Venezuela. It feeds on small fish and invertebrates. *(continued)*

Heermann's gull (winter plumage)

Heermann's gull (summer plumage)

Western gull

Laughing gull (winter plumage)

Ring-billed gull

Glaucous gull

■ **26-15 Gulls and Allies (Charadriiformes)** ≈ *(continued)* **(F)** *Larus heermanni*, Heermann's gull, consumes a wide variety of foods from small fish and carrion, to food it steals from other birds. Its range is similar to the western gull, but it also inhabits parts of the Mexican mainland as far south as the Tropic of Capricorn. **(G)** The western gull, *Larus occidentalis*, occurs along the West Coast of North America from British Columbia to the tip of Baja California. It is an opportunistic feeder, eating what is available by capturing live prey or stealing from other birds and marine mammals. It will consume everything from ochre sea stars, which it swallows whole, to french fries left on a picnic table. **(H)** The laughing gull, *Larus atricilla*, occurs in Baja California and mainland Mexico well south of the United States–Mexico border, and south along coastal South America to Chile on the west coast and northern Brazil on the east coast. It can be found in Florida and the Caribbean, and occasionally up to Maine. Like other gulls, it is omnivorous and opportunistic in its diet. **(I)** *Larus delawarensis*, the ring-billed gull, ranges across all of the United States, the southern half of Canada and most of Mexico. It is also found in the Caribbean. Its diet includes the foods listed for other gull species plus grains and even earthworms. **(J)** The glaucous gull, *Larus glaucescens*, ranges from Alaska to Washington, but during the nonbreeding season is found along the California coast. It is very similar in appearance to the western gull and often hybridizes with it. *(continued)*

Winter plumage

Summer plumage

Black-bellied plover

Long-billed curlew

Killdeer

Marbled godwit

■ 26-15 Gulls and Allies (Charadriiformes) ≈ *(continued)*

(K) The black-bellied plover, *Pluvialis squatarola*, is shown in winter plumage (left) and summer plumage (right). It feeds on invertebrates from insects through marine worms and mollusks. It is a coastal species occurring along the coast of North, Central, and South America, and the Caribbean. It does not occur along the extreme southern coast of South America. (L) The long-billed curlew, *Numenius americanus*, occurs along the West Coast of North America from British Columbia to the tip of Baja California, along the Gulf Coast, across most of mainland Mexico, along both coasts of northern Central America, and along the Atlantic coast of Florida and the Carolinas. It is seasonally present in Utah through North Dakota and into southwestern and central Canada. *N. americanus* probes mud and sand with its long bill looking for invertebrates. It also preys on various insects. (M) The killdeer, *Charadrius vociferous*, feeds on a wide range of invertebrates depending upon the habitat. Its habitats are more diverse than most shorebirds, ranging from mudflats to airports and rooftops, and although generally near water, it also occurs in areas where open water is in short supply. It ranges across the southern half of Canada, south through North and Central America, and the northern most portions of South America. It occurs coastally along northwestern South America. (N) *Limosa fedoa*, the marbled godwit, has a much more limited but similar range as the long-billed curlew. It occurs along the Northeastern Pacific from Washington to El Salvador, along the Western Atlantic from Pennsylvania south to the Yucatan Peninsula, seasonally in Montana through the Dakotas and north to central Canada. It probes in mud, sand, and marsh plants, feeding on invertebrates, including insects and crustaceans. *(continued)*

Ruddy turnstone (winter plumage)

Least sandpiper

Whimbrel

Willet

Caspian tern

■ **26-15 Gulls and Allies (Charadriiformes)** ≈ *(continued)* (**O**) *Arenaria interpres*, the ruddy turnstone, lives along the Arctic Coast of North America and the West Coast from southern Washington through South America. It is found along the Western Atlantic from New England to Argentina and through the Bahamas and the Caribbean. It is widely distributed in coastal regions throughout the rest of the world. (**P**) The least sandpiper, *Calidris minutilla*, feeds on a variety of invertebrates, including insects and crustaceans. It occurs in arctic and subarctic areas of North America as well as coastal Washington, Oregon, and Northern California. From coastal Southern California, it extends east across North America to the Carolinas and south through Mexico and northern South America. (**Q**) The whimbrel, *Numenius phaeopus*, lives across northern Alaska and Canada, including Hudson Bay, along the coasts of North America from central California through Mexico on the west, and the Carolinas south through Mexico on the East Coast. The whimbrel also is found in Africa, South America, Australasia, and north to Asia. It feeds by using its long bill to capture invertebrates, including fiddler crabs. (**R**) The willet, *Catoptrophorus semipalmatus*, ranges from Oregon through Mexico on the West Coast and Nova Scotia through Brazil on the East Coast of the Americas. The willet also can be found during the summer in prairie marshes from Oregon through North Dakota. It feeds on invertebrates using its long bill to locate prey. (**S**) The Caspian tern, *Sterna caspia*, preys on fish by diving aerially, but also may capture fish as the tern sweeps across the surface. It is distributed worldwide. *(continued)*

Royal tern

■ 26-15 Gulls and Allies (Charadriiformes) ≈ *(continued)*

(T) The royal tern, *Sterna maxima*, occurs in coastal areas of the Americas from mid-California to Peru, and New England to Argentina. It also occurs in the Caribbean and the Galapagos Islands. There is a subspecies that occurs along the west coast of Africa. Like other terns, it aerially dives for fish, but will feed on near surface invertebrates. (U) The least tern, *Sterna antillarum*, feeds on fish and a limited number of invertebrates. It hovers before plunging into the water from heights of 7 m or more and emerging with its prey (as shown in the photo sequence). Three subspecies are generally recognized whose range is from San Francisco to South America, Maine to Brazil, the Caribbean, and interior portions of the United States along major river systems. (V) *Larosterna inca*, the Inca tern, occurs on the coastal islands of Peru and Chile, where it feeds on anchovies in the Humboldt Current. Other fish species may be taken, but anchovies are the primary prey. (W) *Sterna elegans*, the elegant tern, resides along the West Coast of the Americas from British Columbia to Chile, where it feeds on fish and invertebrates. *(continued)*

Least tern . . .

. . . hovering, searching for food

. . . diving for food

. . . gotcha!

Inca tern

Elegant tern

Black skimmer

■ **26-15 Gulls and Allies (Charadriiformes)** ≈ *(continued)*
(X) *Rynchops niger*, the black skimmer, flies just above the water, extending its much longer lower bill into the water as it "skims" just below the surface catching small fish. It occurs only in coastal areas of North America and western South America, but ranges from the east coast of South America to the Andes Mountains.

Order Coraciiformes
Coraciiformes (*cornic*—a crow, *formes*—form) contains about 200 species, including the kingfishers (Figure 26-16).

Belted kingfisher

■ **26-16 Coraciiformes** ≈ The belted kingfisher, *Ceryle alcyon*, feeds on invertebrates, fish, and other vertebrates. In North America it occurs everywhere except the most extreme northern latitudes. It occurs through the Caribbean, Central America, and northern South America.

Order Passeriformes
Passeriformes (*passer*—sparrow, *formes*—form)— the single largest order, based on number of species. It comprises more than 5,700 species, none of which are marine, unless "marine" is defined as using the shore and intertidal areas as a food source in the absence of adaptations to the marine environment. If the latter definition is used, then crows (Figure 26-17), ravens, and several members of the genus *Cinclodes* may be considered marine. Where these species reside in a shore environment, they will opportunistically feed upon marine organisms.

■ **26-17 Passeriformes** ≈ **(A)** The American crow, *Corvus brachyrhynchos*, is omnivorous and feeds on a wide range of food, including carrion and refuse of any kind. It inhabits all southern provinces of Canada and all of the contiguous United States. Four subspecies are recognized. **(B)** Shown is a fledgling persisting in attempts to be fed by an indifferent parent on rocks along the coast of Southern California.

Pacific white-sided dolphin

Gray whale with heart-shaped spout

27 Mammalia

Marine mammals are among the most widely known and popular animals of the marine environment, even though there are relatively few mammal species compared to other vertebrates (Chapters 20–26). Of the 4,800 mammals, only about 120 are marine (Table 27-1). All but a few of these are predators, and of course the most famous of these is the killer whale, top predator of the sea. Predator, omnivore, or herbivore, all mammals are critical components of a marine environment.

Marine mammals show the exclusive characteristics of extant members of this clade, including hair and milk production. Generally, 26 orders of mammals are recognized. These are divided into three groups based upon reproductive pattern. The **monotremes** (*mono*—one, *trema*—hole) are oviparous (*ovi*—egg, *parous*—giving birth to), lack a nipple, and retain the cloaca (one hole) present in avian and non-avian reptiles. The other two groups are both viviparous (*vivi*—alive, *parous*—giving birth to). The **marsupials** (*marsupi*—a pouch) have a brief gestation period and the young are born at an extremely early developmental stage. Following birth, the young attach to a nipple in the pouch for the rest of their development. Adults have a nipple and the cloaca is present, but shallow. Placental mammals, or **eutherians** (*eu*—new, *therium*—wild beast), constitute the third group. Uterine

development is prolonged in this group and birth occurs when the young are more fully developed than in marsupials. The eutherians have a well-formed nipple and do not have a cloaca, but rather have separate urinary, reproductive, and digestive system openings. As currently classified, there is one monotreme order, seven marsupial orders, and 18 eutherian orders. All extant marine mammals are eutherians and all are in three orders: Sirenia, Carnivora, and Cetacea (Table 27-1 and Figure 27-1).

In addition to the characteristics listed above, mammals are endothermic homeotherms (Chapter 26) and have

≈ a variety of dermal glands, including scent, sweat, sebaceous, and mammary glands (exclusive to this clade).

≈ three middle ear bones (exclusive to this clade).

≈ teeth highly variable in size and shape in all but a few (exclusive to this clade).

≈ a four-chambered heart with high-pressure circulatory system.

≈ internal fertilization.

≈ a diaphragm, which separates abdominal and thoracic cavities and helps power air exchange (exclusive to this clade).

Order
  Suborder
    Superfamily
      Family
	General Description	Examples	Approximate Number of Species	Etymology

Sirenia (Figure 27-2)	Fusiform body, with large tail elongated laterally and used for propulsion; a relatively small head; two teats located under the flipper forelimbs; hind appendages absent	Dugong and manatees	4 (disputed)	*sirenia*—sea nymph
Carnivora	Highly variable, from fusiform body with flippers to bear shape	Seals, sea lions, walruses, sea otters, marine otters, and polar bears	37	*carni*—flesh, *ora*—mouth
Pinnipedia	Fusiform body with flippers; well-defined head; claws and tail	Seals, sea lions, and walruses	34	*pinna*—feather, *pedi*—foot
Phocidae (Figures 27-3, 27-4 and 27-5)	Earless (no external ear flap—pinna); generally little vocalization; do not rotate hind flippers under body so movement on land is limited	True seals: harbor seals, elephant seals, and others	19	*phoci*—seal
Otariidae (Figures 27-6 and 27-7)	External ear flap (pinna); very vocal; rotate hind flippers under body, making them fairly mobile on land	Sea lion: California sea lions, Guadalupe fur seals	15	*otarion*—little ear
Odobenidae (Figure 27-8)	Large, fusiform body compared to other pinnipeds except elephant seals; no external ear flaps; large pair of tusks; prominent "whiskers" (mustacial vibrissae)	Walrus	1	*odous*—tooth, *baino*—walk
Musteloidea	Variable but with similar body shape to that of a weasel; share dental and skull structural similarities	Red panda, raccoons, badgers, skunks, weasels, martens, otters	85	*mustela*—weasel
Mustelidae (Figure 27-9)	Elongated bodies and comparatively short legs; anal scent glands; loss of second upper molars	Otters (and non-marine forms)	2	*mustela*—weasel
Urosoidea	Only members of Carnivora that walk with soles of the hind feet flat on the ground	Bears	8	*ursa*—bear
Ursidae (Figure 27-10)	Heavy-bodied; long hair; an elongated snout; non-contractile claws	Bears (and other non-marine forms)	1	*ursa*—bear
Cetacea	Fusiform body, with large tail elongated laterally and used for propulsion (fluke); no hind limb; front limb modified into flippers; highly variable in size	Dolphins, porpoises, and whales	80+	*ceta*—whale
Mysticeti	Largest of the whales; plates of baleen; two blowholes	Gray whale, blue whale, and others	11+	*mystic*—moustache, *ceta*—whale
Eschrichtiidae (Figure 27-11)	No dorsal fin, but bumps or knuckles along the dorsal surface	Gray whale	1	Eschricht—Danish zoologist
Balaenopteridae (Figures 27-12 and 27-13)	Long folds of skin running from the mouth to the navel; dorsal fin near flukes; extremely large whales	Blue whale, humpback whale, and others	6	*balaena*—whale, *ptera*—wing
Balaenidae (Figure 27-14)	Extremely long baleen plates; very long heads in comparison to body size; narrow, curved upper jaw small compared to lower jaw	Right whales	4	*balaena*—whale
Odontoceti	Teeth present (no baleen); single blowhole	Dolphins, porpoises, sperm whale, beaked and bottlenose whales, beluga, narwhal, river dolphins	70+	*odonto*—tooth, *ceta*—whale

(continued)

Order Suborder Superfamily Family	General Description	Examples	Approximate Number of Species	Etymology
Delphinidae (Figures 27-15 through 27-19)	Diverse group, but generally with a well-defined snout, enlarged "forehead" or melon, and a pronounced, curved dorsal fin; most have a large number of conical teeth	Marine dolphins: bottlenose dolphin, common dolphin, Pacific white-sided dolphin, killer whale, pilot whale, and others	34+	*delphis*—dolphin
Phocoenidae	Relatively small; dorsal fin triangular in shape or absent; front limbs narrow; teeth flattened	Porpoises: Dall's porpoise, spectacled porpoise, and others	6	*phocaen*—porpoise
Physeteridae (Figure 27-20)	Small, thin lower jaw; blowhole to the left of midline; spermaceti organ present	Sperm whales: sperm whale, pygmy sperm whale, and dwarf sperm whale	3	*physteri*—blow hole on top of the head
Ziphiidae (Figure 27-21)	Elongated snout making them similar in appearance to dolphins; absence of notch in tail fluke	Beaked and bottlenose whales: Hubbs' beaked whale, Peruvian beaked whale	19+	*ziphus*—sword
Monodontidae (Figure 27-22)	Enlarged forehead like common dolphin, forming a melon; no dorsal fin; narwhal male with a single, long tusk; beluga white in color	Beluga whale and narwhal	2	*mono*—one, *odonto*—tooth

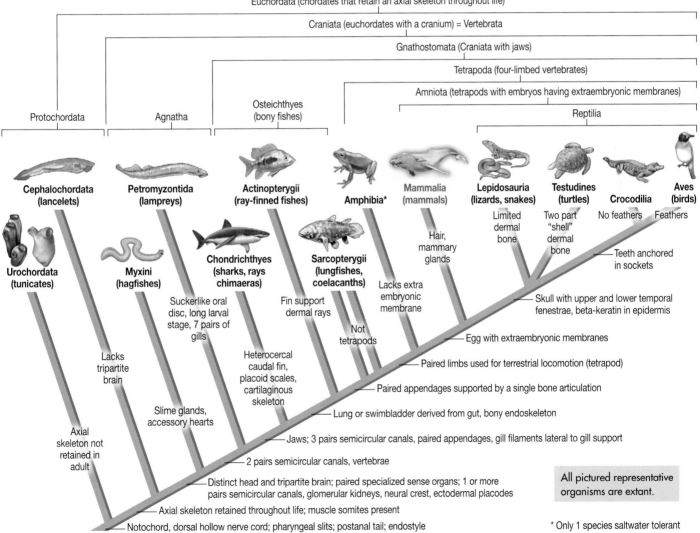

■ **27-1 Chordate Cladogram** ≈ The cladogram indicates the two defining characteristics of the Mammalia: hair and mammary glands, although hair is homologous to reptilian scales and feathers. See Appendix C for definitions of terms.

Marine mammals also show specific adaptations to the marine environment, and generally the degree of anatomical, morphological, and physiological adaptation is related to the length of time since ancestors entered the marine environment. Adaptations include

~ fusiform (*fusus*—spindle) body shape to reduce drag through water. Drag is also reduced by absence or reduction of the external ear (pinna), modification of limbs to flippers in most, and loss of hind limbs in many.

~ tail modified into a tail fin in Cetacea (whales) and Sirenia (sea cows).

~ presence of blubber/fat for thermoregulation in all but a few.

~ most with echolocation allowing navigation in murky and/or dark water.

~ ability to dive to depth in an environment where every 10 m increased depth results in one additional atmosphere of pressure. Adaptations include

  • increased oxygen binding proteins in muscles and blood.

  • mechanisms to tolerate high levels of carbon dioxide.

  • increased diving reflex (present in all mammals), which results in slower heart rate when diving and shunting of blood to critical organs such as the brain, heart, and lungs.

~ greater amount of blood in proportion to body size than other mammals.

~ nostrils or blowholes positioned to make breathing while swimming possible and with the musculature necessary to prevent water from entering between inhalations and exhalations.

~ most are voluntary breathers so breathing only occurs when organism consciously initiates it. (Compare with mammals like us: breathing occurs automatically, i.e., we do not have to think about breathing.)

Order Sirenia

The sea cows are fully aquatic animals, although not all are marine. They live in coastal marine waters, estuaries, swamps, and rivers. They are fully herbivorous, and marine species eat a variety of vegetation, including sea grass. There is one dugong species and three manatee species. The Florida manatee, *Trichechus manatus latirostris* (Figure 27-2) is one of two *Trichechus manatus* subspecies, and one of three *Trichechus* species.

1. Mangroves 2. Manatee

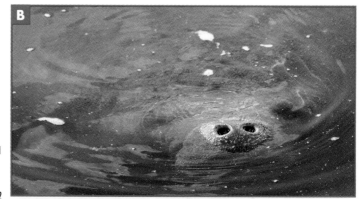

■ **27-2 Manatee (Order Sirenia)** ~ (A) The Florida manatee, *Trichechus manatus latirostris*, viewed from the surface in a Gulf Coast estuary in southwestern Florida, is visible as a large, slow-moving object. (B) Note that the manatee's nostrils are at the end of its snout. Compare with the position of the dolphin blowhole in Figure 17-16C. (C) Their head looks oddly small compared to their large, blubber-covered bodies. (D) Viewed from underwater, their aquatic characteristics are clearly visible. They have highly modified forelimbs used for steering, a large tail for propulsion, a fusiform body, and lack hindlimbs.

Order Carnivora

This order includes a great variety of organisms from dogs and cats to bears and seals. All members except the giant panda are predators with teeth for ripping the flesh of their prey, or in the case of **piscivores** (*pisci*—fish, *vore*—eat) like most seals and sea lions, with teeth that are small and numerous and that interlock. Carnivores also have a digestive system that is much shorter than herbivorous species (meat is easier to digest than plants).

Superfamily Pinnipedia

The seals, sea lions, fur seals, and walruses are semiaquatic marine mammals. They return to land to rest and sun themselves. Additionally, many return to land to breed and suckle their young. The seals, or earless seals, lack an external ear flap or pinna (plural—pinnae) (Figure 27-3A), and are the most diverse pinniped group. They are placed in the Family Phocidae. When seals come ashore, they tend to access sandy or gently sloped rocky shores. Unable to rotate their hind flippers forward and under their body, they move on shore using their anterior flippers and a caterpillar-like motion of their bodies, resulting in a noticeable rippling of their blubber-covered bodies. This somewhat limits their ability to move on uneven terrain, but don't challenge an elephant seal to a race, even across sand dunes. They can reach speeds of 19 km/h (12 mph)! The harbor seal, *Phoca vitulina* (Figure 27-3), is a small- to medium-size seal that occurs from the equator to Arctic waters in both the Atlantic and Pacific Oceans. It occurs in nearshore coastal areas such as estuaries, sandy beaches, coastal islands, and others. Note the relatively small size of their flippers in Figure 27-3 compared to body size.

"Flight" in water does not require the same power-to-weight ratio that so heavily influenced evolution in air, since water is much more viscous and dense than air. The small size of the pectoral fins in seals also reflects their functional role in steerage rather than propulsion. Seals are more anatomically and physiologically adapted to life in water than are other members of Order Carnivora, and what may appear to be maladaptive on land, is highly adaptive in an aquatic environment.

The elephant seal is the largest of the pinnipeds. The northern elephant seal, *Mirounga angustirostris* (Figure 27-4), occurs along the Aleutian Archipelago, southern Alaska, and across the Northeastern Pacific to Baja California. Males may be over 5 m and up to 2,700 kg, while females may be over 3 m and weigh 900 kg. In the 1880s the northern elephant seal was nearly hunted to extinction, but a few remained on the Guadalupe Islands off Baja California. These survivors repopulated the current range.

The southern elephant seal, *Mirounga leonina* (Figure 27-5), is the larger of the two elephant seal species. They live in Antarctic and sub-Antarctic waters. When ashore these seals are found on extreme southern islands, and on the shores of extreme southern Argentina, South Africa, and the coast of New Zealand. Males may be over 6 m long and weigh up to 4,000 kg. Females may be up to 4 m and weigh 1,000 kg. Southern elephant seals also were hunted to near extinction, but are recovering.

Elephant seals spend up to 90% of their life at sea, but are still semiaquatic since they are tied to beaches for mating and calving. While on shore, they do not feed and may lose up to one-third of their body weight. When at sea, they feed on squid, small sharks, rays, and skates, among others animals. Pursuing food, elephant seals may stay

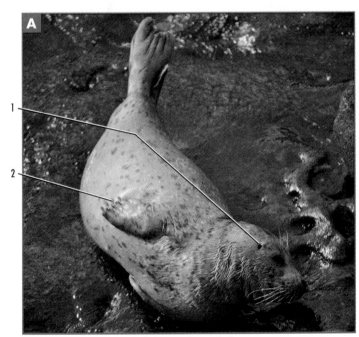

1. Auditory canal   2. Claws

■ **27-3 Harbor Seal (Order Carnivora, Family Phocidae)** ≈
(A) The harbor seal, *Phoca vitulina*, shows the hallmark characteristics of the seals: claws on forelimbs and no external ear flaps (pinnae). **(B)** Harbor seals tend to haul out on sandy beaches or low rocky surfaces, although resting areas may be rugged. While they may enter estuaries and large rivers, they typically stay within 100 km or less of their resting site. There are four to five subspecies of harbor seal (depending upon the authority consulted).

■ 27-4 Northern Elephant Seal (Order Carnivora, Family Phocidae)

≈ (A) Male northern elephant seals show the elongated snout that resulted in the name "elephant" seal. Weighing up to 2,700 kg (about three tons), the species was nearly hunted to extinction in the late 19th century. The northern elephant seal is making a comeback along the coast of North America and appeared on beaches near San Simeon, California, in 1991. (B) Females are significantly smaller, but both males and females throw sand over their bodies to protect their sensitive skin from sunlight. (C) Young seals have an interesting look and rate high on the oddly cute scale. (D) In July and August, males are on the beach molting. Elephant seal molts are said to be "catastrophic," meaning they lose all of their skin in a few weeks. (E) Even while on the beach molting, males make bellowing noises, raising their head and arching it toward their back and displaying their large snout. (F) Fights between males are common.

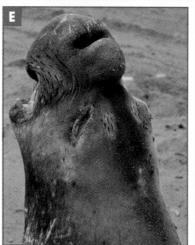

■ 27-5 Southern Elephant Seal (Order Carnivora, Family Phocidae)

≈ (A) The southern elephant seal is larger than its northern relative. It also can dive deeper and stay submerged longer. (B) Southern elephant seals have a particularly thick layer of blubber to protect them against the extreme cold of the Southern Ocean where they spend the majority of their time.

submerged for nearly two hours and dive as deep as 2,400 m, although their routine times are shorter, and they spend most of their underwater time at less than 700 m.

Sea lions and fur seals, the eared seals (Family Otariidae), have a much broader thorax and larger anterior flippers than do the earless seals. They are also able to rotate their hind flippers forward and under their body, and are much more adept at maneuvering uneven, rocky terrain. As a result, they occur along a wider range of shorelines than the seals. The California sea lion, *Zalophus californianus* (Figure 27-6), is probably the most familiar of all the pinnipeds and is the fastest pinniped swimmer. They occur from southwestern British Columbia to the southern tip of Baja California. Another member of the genus occurs on the Galapagos Islands.

■ 27-7 Steller Sea Lion (Order Carnivora, Family Otariidae) ≈ Female Steller sea lions (shown here) are typically much smaller than the males, weighing up to 300 kg while the males may attain weights over 1,000 kg. Note the "golden" chest typical of this species.

The Steller sea lion, *Eumetopias jubatus* (Figure 27-7), is the largest of the Otariidae and is the third largest pinniped after the walrus and elephant seals. They range across the Northern Pacific from Japan to central California, where they feed on a wide range of fish and cephalopods.

Family Odobenidae

The walrus, *Odobenus rosmarus* (Figure 27-8), is a large Arctic species with giant tusks. Males may be up to 3.5 m in length and weigh up to 2,000 kg. They show superficial characteristics intermediate between the seals and eared seals, having hind flippers that rotate forward and below the body, but are earless (no pinnae). Their preferred food is clams, but they do eat a variety of bottom invertebrates. They can be found in shallow ocean water along the continental shelf and on sea ice. Walruses live around the Arctic Ocean on eastern and western coasts of northern continents and islands, Greenland, and the North Atlantic and Pacific Oceans. Two subspecies are recognized and a third is disputed. The Pacific walrus (*Odobenus rosmarus divergens*) has the largest population numbers.

Family Mustelidae

Sea otters, *Enhydra lutris* (Figure 27-9), and marine otters are the sole extant marine members of this family. Sea otters occur in the Northwestern and Northeastern Pacific Ocean. They have been sighted as far south as San Diego, California, as recently as October 2011. The most southern known resident population in the Eastern Pacific is in northern Santa Barbara County. Sea otters inhabit nearshore marine environments, where they feed principally upon benthic invertebrates. Three subspecies are recognized.

Marine otters (*Lontra felina*) occur along the western coast of South America from central Peru to extreme

1. Pinna   2. Vibrissae

■ 27-6 California Sea Lion (Order Carnivora, Family Otariidae) ≈ Sea lions use their pectoral fins for propulsion as opposed to the seals, which use their pelvic fins for propulsion. Anatomically, this is reflected in the size of the pectoral muscles, scapula, and general structure of the seal lion's pectoral girdle. **(A)** Compare the length of the sea lion's pectoral fins to those of the harbor seal in Figure 27-3. **(B)** The pinnae on the California sea lion mark a familiar morphological character of the Otariidae.

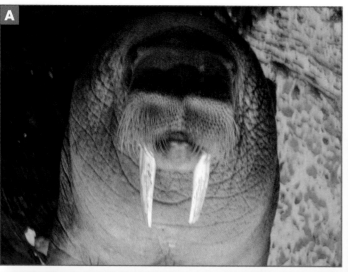

■ 27-8 Walrus (Order Carnivora, Family Odobenidae) ≈

Both male and female walruses have prominent tusks (**A**) and obvious whiskers (mustacial vibrissae) (**B**). (**C**) Hunted to extinction off Nova Scotia, there are currently two or three subspecies, depending upon the expert consulted. Their large, blubber-covered bodies are propelled predominantly by pelvic flippers.

1. Pectoral flippers
2. Pelvic flippers

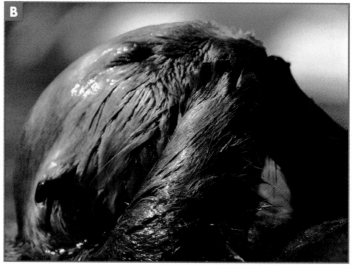

■ 27-9 Sea Otters (Order Carnivora, Family Mustelidae) ≈

Two subspecies of sea otter inhabit the Northeastern Pacific: the larger Alaskan sea otter (**A** and **B**) and the California otter (**C**) that occurs along the central California coast. Both subspecies inhabit the close inshore habitat with the Alaskan subspecies spending more time on land than its Californian counterpart.

southern Chile. (There used to be a population in the Western Atlantic Ocean, and there are unconfirmed reports that remnants of it may still occur in extreme southern Argentina). Marine otters inhabit littoral and nearshore sublittoral environments and are only distantly related to sea otters.

Both otters lack blubber, unlike the pinnipeds and cetaceans. They are able to maintain their body temperature in cold seas with the aid of their thick fur and behavioral thermoregulation. The sea otter has the densest fur of any mammal with approximately 650,000 hair follicles per square inch (compared with a few thousand per square inch in apes).

Family Ursidae

Polar bears, *Ursus maritimus* (Figure 27-10), live near and within the Arctic Circle. They are tied for largest extant bear with adult males reaching 700 kg and 3 m in length (The Kodiak bear is of equal size.). Polar bears prey on a variety of animals, particularly and typically seals. They are often found far at sea on ice floes or swimming in search of their primary prey. They also feed on carrion.

Order Cetacea

All marine mammals evolved from land-dwelling mammals and, therefore, represent mammalian ancestral lines that have entered the sea to feed and live. There have been several "mammalian invasions" of the sea. The cetaceans represent the earliest. Evidence supports the contention that cetaceans evolved from a primitive, hoofed mammal and molecular and fossil data indicate their closest, extant relative is the hippopotamus (*Hippopotamus amphibious*). Evidence for these relationships comes from the fossil record and from the anatomy, morphology, and molecular biology of living species.

Cetaceans are divided into two groups; baleen whales (Suborder Mysticeti) and toothed whales (Suborder Odontoceti).

Suborder Mysticeti

The family Eschrichtiidae is represented by a single extant species, the gray whale, *Eschrichtius robustus* (Figure 27-11), although their standing as the sole member of this family is disputed by molecular data. Named after John Edward Gray (not their color), they are a medium-size whale

■ **27-10 Polar Bears (Order Carnivora, Family Ursidae)** ~ Superficially, it may seem odd that pinnipeds are bears' most closely related extant group, but the evidence supports this conclusion. Polar bears are the largest extant carnivorous bears and are solitary, as are all bears. They depend upon polar sea ice for their range and feed almost exclusively on seals. As a result of global climate change, sea ice is melting and threatens their existence. Many experts predict extinction within 100 years.

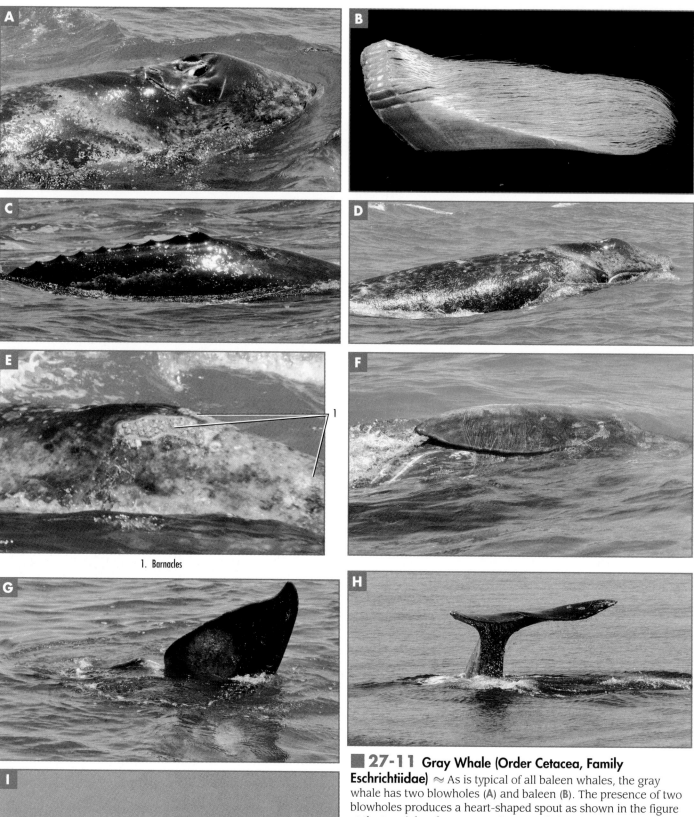

1. Barnacles

27-11 Gray Whale (Order Cetacea, Family Eschrichtiidae)

~ As is typical of all baleen whales, the gray whale has two blowholes (**A**) and baleen (**B**). The presence of two blowholes produces a heart-shaped spout as shown in the figure at the top right of page 227. (**C**) Gray whales lack a dorsal fin, but instead have a series of knuckles upon their dorsal surface. (**D**) The eye and curved mouth line is detailed on a young gray whale, with skin clear of barnacles, while the older mother of this calf (**E**) shows barnacles growing on her skin. (**F**) The pectoral fins are large and important in maneuverability, while the tail flukes (**G** and **H**) are the most important structure in propulsion. (**I**) As happens, the gray whale eventually succumbs to the rigors of life and is decomposed, providing food for beach or benthic organisms. *(continued)*

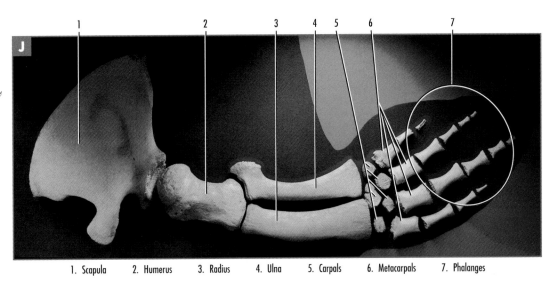

■ 27-11 Gray Whale ≈ *(continued)* The forelimb and shoulder blade (scapula) of a gray whale (J) are shown.

1. Scapula   2. Humerus   3. Radius   4. Ulna   5. Carpals   6. Metacarpals   7. Phalanges

reaching 14 m and a weight over 36,000 kg (36 Mg). They lack a dorsal fin but have distinct bumps or knuckles on their dorsal surface (Figure 27-11C). They occur in the Northwestern and Eastern Pacific Ocean. The migration route of the eastern population is well documented, moving from the Bering Sea along the coast of North America to the lagoons of central Baja California. Upon their return to the Bering Sea and Arctic Ocean, males take a more open ocean, direct route back, while females and their calves use a route similar to their southern migration.

Humpback whales, *Megaptera novaeangliae* (Figure 27-12), are placed in the Family Balaenopteridae. They may reach lengths of 16.5 m and weigh 36,000 kg or more. Humpbacks are fairly easy to recognize with their long pectoral fins, bump-like knobs on their head and mouth, dorsal fin set about two-thirds of the way back

■ 27-12 Humpback Whale (Order Cetacea, Family Balaenopteridae) ≈ Humpback whales are recognized by a small dorsal fin two-thirds of the way back along the body-line (A), frequent breaching (B), large, primarily white pectoral fins (C and D), *(continued)*

27-12 Humpback Whale (Order Cetacea, Family Balaenopteridae) ≈ *(continued)* bumps along the head (**E**), and two blowholes (**F**). As with all whales, even when the whale isn't seen, a "footprint" is left on the surface (**G**), or the flukes are seen as they submerge (**H**). (**I**) Here is a spyhoping humpback.

along the body, and frequent breaching. They occur in oceans around the world and travel distances in excess of 20,000 km during annual migrations.

The blue whale, *Balaenoptera musculus* (Figure 27-13), is the largest of the whales and is also a Balaenopteridae. It ranges throughout the world's oceans, including polar and tropical areas.

The Balaenidae includes the bowhead whale and three species of right whales. Each right whale species occurs in a different habitat. The southern right whale (Figure 27-14) occurs around the Antarctic Continent, around southern Australia, in the Southeastern Atlantic to Brazil, and the Southeastern Indian Ocean to Madagascar. The southern right whale, like the other right whales, lacks a dorsal fin, has rough patches of skin (callosities) on its head, and extremely long baleen plates set in a curved mouth.

Photo by John Calambokidis, Cascadia Research

27-13 Blue Whale (Order Cetacea, Family Balaenopteridae) ≈ Largest of the whales and perhaps the largest animal to have ever lived on Earth, the blue whale may grow to over 30 m in length.

Photos Stephen J. Bouscaren, Ph.D.

■ **27-14 Southern Right Whale (Order Cetacea, Family Balaenidae)** ∼ (A) The curved mouth line and large callosities are hallmarks of the right whale. (B) Shown are the particularly large lower jaw (arrow) and small upper jaw. The large, dorsal callosity is visible on the body midline. (C) One particular habit of the right whale is sailing, i.e., raising their flukes and allowing the wind to push them along.

Suborder Odontoceti

Delphinidae is the largest family of odontocetes. It includes a wide range of dolphins, from the familiar killer whale, *Orcinus orca* (Figures 27-15), bottlenose dolphin, *Tursiops truncates* (Figure 27-16), and Pacific white-sided dolphin, *Lagenorhynchus obliquidens* (Figure 27-17), to the less well-known Commerson's dolphin, *Cephalorhynchus commersonii* (Figure 24-18), and the Yangtze River dolphin, *Lipotes vexillifer*. The oceanic dolphins range across the world's oceans but occur principally in shallower waters along continental shelves. Some species are very limited in their distribution. For example, Commerson's dolphin is limited to the tip of South America, around the Falkland Islands (South Atlantic Ocean), and around the Kerguelen Islands (Southern Indian Ocean). This limited distribution is correlated with historically small population sizes. Other species are worldwide in their range; these include the killer whale and the short-finned pilot whale, *Globicephala macrorhynchus* (Figure 27-19).

Phocoenidae is the porpoise family. There are six species in three extant genera. Porpoises generally lack the melon so prominent in most dolphins, the dorsal fins do not have the sweeping posterior curve of most dolphins, and their teeth are not conical in shape as in the dolphins. Dall's porpoises are among the fastest of small cetaceans, reaching speeds of 55 km/h and they possess particularly small pectoral flippers located far forward on the body. There are two subspecies, and together they are common throughout the North Pacific.

Sperm whales, *Physeter macrocephalus* (Figure 27-20), are placed in the Family Physeteridae. The sperm whale is the largest of the Odontoceti and the deepest diver of the large whales, descending to depths over 1,000 m and remaining submerged for over one hour. At these depths, echolocation is their primary means of finding prey. Males may reach 18 m and weigh over 41,000 kg. They range throughout the world's oceans.

The Family Ziphiidae is second only to the Delphinidae in number of species. They are commonly known as beaked and bottlenose whales because of their snout's shape. They dive deeper than any other cetacean with depths recorded to 1,900 m for periods up to nearly 1½ hours. Few species in the Ziphiidae are well known. The 19 to 21 known species (disputed) vary in their range, but together occur throughout the world's oceans. Few occur along the continental shelf, but prefer deepwater areas. For the most part, they feed upon deepwater squid, other invertebrates, and fish near the sea floor. Blainville's beaked whale, *Mesoplodon densirostris* (Figure 27-21), occurs in deepwater of tropical and temperate oceans worldwide where it grows to 7 m.

The beluga whale, *Delphinapterus leucas* (Figure 27-22), is one of two species of Odontoceti in the Family Monodontidae. The beluga lives principally in the Arctic, and the absence of a dorsal fin is presumably adaptive to moving under ocean ice. Unlike most other whales, the beluga's neck vertebrae are not fused and it is able to freely move its small head from side to side and top to bottom. Their diet consists of a variety of invertebrates and fish. Males may reach 5 m and 1,500 kg.

Chapter 27 ∼ Mammalia

■ **27-15 Killer Whale (Order Cetacea, Family Delphinidae)** ≈
(**A**) The most famous of the Odontoceti, the killer whale, *Orcinus orca*, is a
member of the Family Delphinidae, meaning that killer whales are dolphins!
(**B**) Spyhoping is a common behavior seen in most cetaceans and used by
killer whales to spot potential prey out of water, such as seals on ice floes or
elephant seals on shore near enough to the water for "haul-out" capture (as
demonstrated in photo **A** during a killer whale show at Sea World San Diego).
(**C**) A portion of the 46–50 conical teeth of this top predator are visible in the
lower jaw and upper jaw. The upper and lower teeth interlock (Figure 27-16E).
(**D**) Note the characteristic disruptive coloration (predominantly black body,
broken by white spots) pattern and the gray "saddle" behind the dorsal fin.
It is thought that underwater, particularly in low visibility, this color pattern
breaks the body into visual pieces, which results in potential prey underesti-
mating the size of the approaching predator.

1. Melon   2. Rostrum

1. Rostrum   2. Blowhole

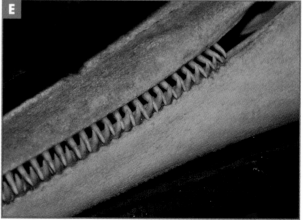

■ **27-16 Bottlenose Dolphin (Order Cetacea, Family Delphinidae)** ≈ (**A**) The 18-26 pairs of sharp, conical teeth of the bottlenose dolphin help it capture and consume up to 14 kg of food daily—principally fish, but may also include squid and pelagic crustaceans.
(**B**) The melon of the bottlenose dolphin is important in echolocation. (**C**) In contrast to the two blowholes in the Mysticetes, Odonticetes
like the bottlenose dolphin have a single blowhole. (**D**) This spyhoping bottlenose dolphin shows countershading, with darker coloration
on the dorsal and lateral surfaces and lighter shading ventrally. (**E**) A common dolphin, *Delphinus delphis*, skeleton shows how the teeth
of many Odontocetes overlap.

■ **27-17 Pacific White-sided Dolphin (Order Cetacea, Family Delphinidae)** ≈ A common behavior for the Pacific white-sided dolphin is leaping from the water at high rates of speed, often in groups of up to 100 individuals and with other species of dolphins.

■ **27-18 Commerson's Dolphin (Order Cetacea, Family Delphinidae)** ≈ Commerson's dolphins are among the smallest dolphins. Adults have a distinctive black and white color pattern with a small, rounded dorsal fin. Their range is limited to extreme southern South America and the Kerguelen Islands.

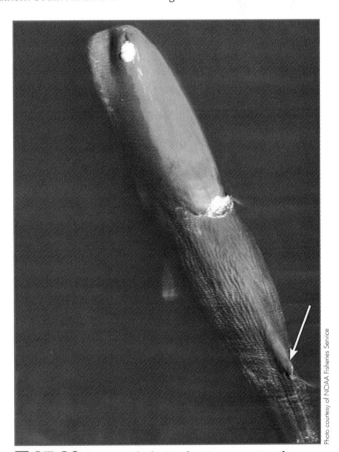

■ **27-19 Short-finned Pilot Whale (Order Cetacea, Family Delphinidae)** ≈ Second in size only to the killer whale in the Delphinidae, the pilot whale can grow up to 6.5 m in length and weigh up to 2,700 kg. It is easily recognized by its round head with only a slight beak and sickle-shaped pectoral fins.

■ **27-20 Sperm Whale (Order Cetacea, Family Physeteridae)** ≈ Adult male sperm whales may be up to 18 m in length. Their dorsal fin is little more than an elongated bump on the dorsal surface (arrow). They may weigh more than 40,000 kg, feeding on deepwater squid and a variety of fish. Whaling has reduced current populations to about one-third of what they were before whaling took its toll.

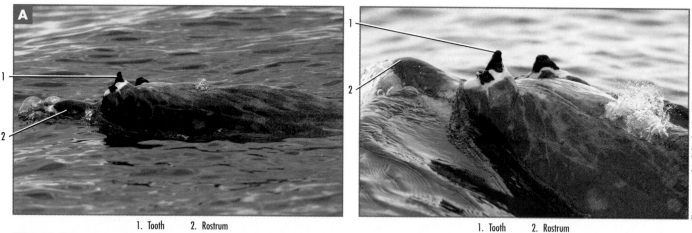

1. Tooth   2. Rostrum   1. Tooth   2. Rostrum

Photos courtesy of Ari S. Friedlaender, Ph.D.

■ **27-21 Blainville's Beaked Whale (Order Cetacea, Family Ziphiidae)** ≈ Blainville's beaked whales show a distinctive arching lower jawline that in males has an enlarged, tusk-like tooth erupting dorsoanteriorly. These teeth are clearly visible. In many males, the teeth are covered with barnacles. Blainville's beaked whales are a deep-diving species, with dives lasting up to 40 minutes.

■ **27-22 Beluga (Order Cetacea, Family Monodontidae)** ≈ Belugas can dive to 600 m and stay submerged up to 20 minutes. They are preyed upon by polar bears when they become trapped by sea ice, and by killer whales. They are highly social animals and may be seen in pods numbering in the 100s. Their head is distinctively different in appearance from other whales, and their dorsal fin is greatly reduced.

Coral leaf

Pachydictyon

28 Macroalgae

In this chapter, we introduce **macroalgae**; that is, those that can be seen with the naked eye. (Chapters 2 and 4 addressed simple, prokaryotic autotrophs—cyanobacteria and other autotrophic bacteria—and microscopic eukaryotic autotrophs, respectively. Macroalgae are all eukaryotic organisms and share many physiological features, but still constitute a very diverse group whose relatedness is being worked and reworked as new information comes in.

Traditionally, three main macroalgal groups have been recognized: the **rhodophytes** (red algae; *rhodo*—rose-colored, *phyte*—plant), the **chlorophytes** (green algae, *chloro*—green), and the **phaeophytes** (brown algae, *phaeo*—dusky), which are collectively known as seaweeds. The phylogeny in Figure 28-1 illustrates that the term "seaweed" is an informal one, as the three groups are classified in two distantly related major eukaryotic clades: the rhodophytes (Division Rhodophyta) and chlorophytes (Division Chlorophyta) in Archaeplastida, and phaeophytes (Division Heterokontophyta, which includes diatoms and "minor" microscopic marine groups) in Chromalveolata. Figure 28-2 shows representative specimens of each. Table 28-1 summarizes the major differences between these main groups.

Plastid origin has proven to be useful in identifying relationships between phyla of simple eukaryotes. It was first suggested in 1905 by Konstantin Mereschkowsky that plastids might be symbiotic cyanobacteria, a fact that has been thoroughly substantiated by cellular, biochemical, and nucleic acid evidence accumulated over the last 100+ years, most notably by Lynn Margulis. This process, now known as **endosymbiosis** (*endo*—within, *sym*—with, *bios*—life), occurred when a eukaryotic cell engulfed (by endocytosis) a free-living cyanobacterium but didn't digest it. Rather, the engulfed cyanobacterium and the host cell established a mutually beneficial relationship where the host received sugars (photosynthate) produced by the cyanobacterium, and the cyanobacterium had "adopted" a home with a stable environment and a steady supply of CO_2. This describes primary endosymbiosis, and accounts for the origin of chlorophyte and rhodophyte plastids. The electron microscope reveals two membranes (the chloroplast envelope) around these plastids: the original cyanobacterial cell membrane and around that, the membrane derived from the host's cytoplasmic membrane during endocytosis. Plastids of phaeophytes were produced by secondary endosymbiosis, in which a eukaryotic cell engulfed a *red alga*, resulting in four membranes around the plastid, two from primary endosymbiosis (the chloroplast envelope), one from the cell membrane of the red alga, and one from the cell membrane of the phagocytic cell.

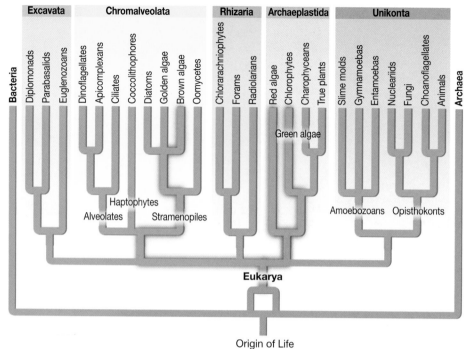

■ **28-1** **Phylogeny of the Three Domains of Life** ≈ This phylogeny shows the relationship of the three major macroalgae groups commonly referred to as "seaweeds." The red and green algae are in the Archaeplastida, whereas the brown algae are in an entirely different lineage, the Chromalveolata. See Appendix A for definitions of terms, clades, and taxa in this figure.

Sea comb

Dead man's fingers

Feather boa kelp

■ **28-2** **Three Groups of Macroalgae** ≈ Shown are examples of red, green, and brown algae. (A) *Plocamium* (sea comb) is a red, (B) *Codium* (dead man's fingers) is a green, and (C) *Egregia* (feather boa kelp) is a brown.

Table 28-1 ≈ Marine Macroalgae Divisions and Classes

Division / Class	Estimated Number of Species	Plastid Origin	Photosynthetic Pigments	Flagella	Storage Materials	Etymology
Rhodophyta / Rhodophyceae	4,000 species (majority are marine)	Primary endosymbiosis	Chlorophyll *a*; phycocyanin; phycoerythrin	Absent	Floridean starch (in cytoplasm)	*rhodo*—rose-colored, *phyte*—plant
Chlorophyta / Ulvophyceae	17,000 species (minority are marine)	Primary endosymbiosis	Chlorophylls *a* and *b*; lutein; β-carotene	Present (usually paired)	Starch (in chloroplast)	*chloro*—green, *phyte*—plant
Heterokontophyta / Phaeophyceae	1,500 species (majority are marine)	Secondary endosymbiosis	Chlorophylls *a*, c_1, and c_2; fucoxanthin	Present only on reproductive cells; anterior is a "tinsel" flagellum and posterior is a "whiplash" flagellum	Laminarin and/or D-mannitol (outside of chloroplast)	*phaeo*—dusky *phyte*—plant

As is always the case, each biological discipline has its own terminology, and seaweed biology is no different—even if the informal term *seaweed* might suggest otherwise! As appealing as it is to apply the terms root, stem, and leaves to seaweeds, these terms are only applied to true plants with vascular (conducting) tissues (Chapter 32). In fact, we should not even refer to a seaweed as a plant, though it is often done informally. Refer to Figure 28-3 as you read the following descriptions. The "body" of a seaweed is called the **thallus** (*thallos*—twig), which is a general botanical term for a simple "plant" body that has little differentiation into specialized structures. In some cases, algal thalli are as simple as chains of cells (filaments) or patches of cells adhering to a surface (crusts). At the other

extreme, some algae have structures resembling roots, stems, and leaves. These are called, in order: **haptera** (*haptein*—to grasp), **stipes** (*stipes*—stalk), and **blades**. Haptera comprise a kind of **holdfast**, a structure that anchors the alga to the substrate. Some holdfasts have haptera (Figure 28-3), but others are simple discs (Figure 28-4A) or are not differentiated from the thallus (Figure 28-4B). A final structure is a gas-filled bladder found in some brown algae called a **pneumatocyst** (*pneuma*—breath, wind; *cystis*–bag) (Figure 28-5).

Branching patterns are also useful in identification (Figure 28-6). Branching patterns range from no branching, through organized branching, to random branching. Each seaweed species generally exhibits a consistent branching pattern.

Regardless of the group, all intertidal seaweeds are confronted with harsh conditions, such as mechanical force from wave action and exposure during low tides. Solutions to these are illustrated in Figures 28-7 and 28-8. In addition, seaweeds must contend with changes in salinity and temperature during times of exposure.

Seaweed life cycles are highly variable and reproductive structures are quite useful in identification. Specifics of sample life cycles will be covered in each chapter, but some terminology will be introduced here. (You may find it useful to refer to Figure 1-6 as you read on.) A typical, **biphasic** (*bi*—two, *phasis*—appearance) life cycle involves **alternation of generations**, in which there are two separate multicellular generations: one is haploid (*haplos*—single) where the cells have one complete set of chromosomes (designated as **n**) and the other is diploid (*di*—two), where the cells have two complete sets of chromosomes (designated as *2n*). The diploid generation is called the **sporophyte** (*sporo*—seed, *phyte*—plant). It produces **spores** by meiosis. Spores are reproductive cells that have the capacity to advance the life cycle without assistance from another reproductive cell. They do so by undergoing mitosis to produce the other multicellular generation—the **gametophyte**

Split kelp

1. Stipe   2. Blade   3. Holdfast with haptera

■ 28-3 Thallus Structures ≈ This young specimen of *Laminaria* illustrates the basic parts of a seaweed: a holdfast made of haptera, the stipe, and the blade. This photo was taken shortly after a storm. Notice how tattered the blade is.

Rockweed

Sinuous seaweed

■ 28-4 Holdfast Diversity ≈

Not all holdfasts have haptera. In many cases, the holdfast is a disc (arrow), as in *Fucus* (A). In other algae (B), there is no distinct holdfast; the entire low-growing seaweed is attached to the surface, as illustrated by *Colpomenia*.

■ 28-5 Pneumatocyst ≈

Many brown algae have air bladders for buoyancy. *Nereocystis* (bull kelp) has a single, large pneumatocyst (arrow) located between the stipe and its several blades.

Bull kelp

(*gamos*—marriage, *phyte*—plant). The gametophyte is haploid and produces gametes by mitosis. Gametes advance the life cycle through fertilization and produce a diploid sporophyte zygote, which develops into the multicellular sporophyte by repeated mitotic divisions, thus completing the life cycle. In some cases, the gametes look alike (**isogamous;** *iso*—equal, *gamos*—marriage); in others they are distinguishable as egg and sperm (**anisogamous;** *aniso*—unequal). Likewise, sporophyte and gametophyte may look alike and can only be differentiated through microscopic examination of the reproductive cells each produces. Such life cycles exhibit **isomorphic** (*morph*—form) alternation of generations. When the sporophyte and gametophyte are obviously different, the species exhibits **heteromorphic** (*hetero*—other) alternation of generations. An interesting side note to this is that studies have often shown that what were once thought to be different algal species are in fact the gametophyte and sporophyte generations of the same species!

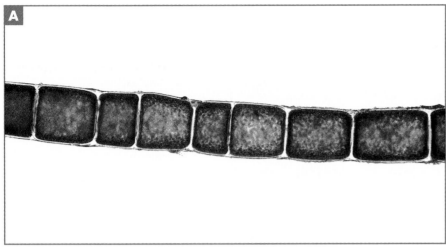

Green hair weed

Rockweed

Tidepool coralline algae

Gel weed

■ **28-6 Branching Patterns** ≈ (A) *Chaetomorpha* is an unbranched, filamentous green alga. (B) Dichotomous (*dichoto*—in two); *tome*—to cut) branching is illustrated by *Fucus*. Notice that at each branch point two equal branches are produced, forming a "Y." (C) *Corallina* illustrates pinnate (*pinna*—feather) branching, where there is a main axis that gives off lateral branches to produce a feather-like appearance. (D) *Gelidium* demonstrates irregular branching, which is just that—irregular!

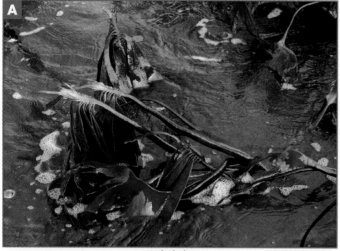

Split kelp

Rockweed

Cylindrocarpus

Rockweed

Nail brush seaweed

■ **28-7 Adaptations to Wave Action** ≈ Waves constantly pound the rocky intertidal habitat. Three adaptations to this force are illustrated here. (**A**) *Pterygophora* has a flexible stipe and just bends with the waves. (**B**) *Cylindrocarpus* grows low and close to the rocks. (**C**) Other intertidal algae, such as *Endocladia*, simply grow on parts of rocks protected from the wave force. Or, put another way, they are *incapable* of surviving on the parts receiving wave force directly. Of course, all these adaptations would be fairly useless were it not for the tenacity with which the holdfast keeps the alga attached to the substrate.

■ **28-8 Adaptation to Exposure** ≈ In roughly each 24-hour period, tide levels go through one or two cycles of highs and lows in the intertidal zone, depending on geographic location. In addition, there are seasonal differences in the magnitude of the highs and the lows. This manifests itself in vertical zonation of intertidal organisms. One adaptation to periodic exposure to air is illustrated by *Fucus*, which forms mats (**A**). This arrangement results in only the surface layer drying while the underlying layers remain wet. (**B**) In this photo, the golden-brown part of the thallus has been turned over. Notice the difference in hydration between it and the dried thalli at its right. (**Note:** the part that was turned over was returned to its original position after the photo was taken.)

Coralline alga

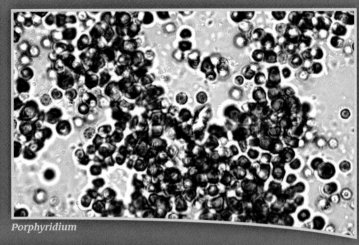

Porphyridium

29 Rhodophyta

The Division Rhodophyta (red algae) comprises a single class, Rhodophyceae. The majority of seaweeds belong to this group. In fact, there are more red algal species (4,000–6,000) than all other seaweeds combined. Most rhodophytes are found in temperate or tropical seas, though freshwater forms occur. The rhodophytes and chlorophytes (Chapter 30) belong to the major eukaryotic clade Archaeplastida, along with the true plants (Figures 28-1 and 29-1).

Fossil, cytological, and biochemical evidence places this group as among the oldest photosynthetic eukaryotic organisms. Based on molecular comparisons, red algae appear to be monophyletic; that is, they all trace their ancestry to a common "red algal" species. The oldest rhodophyte fossils, found in Canadian arctic deposits, are 1.2 billion years old. These were filamentous organisms and resemble the modern genus *Bangia* in internal structure (Figure 29-2).

Formerly, the Rhodophyceae was divided into two subclasses: the Bangiophycidae (named after Niels Bang, a Danish botanist) and the Florideophycidae (*florid—* reddish). Subsequently, evidence has led to the splitting of these subclasses into a dozen or more orders. It is beyond the scope of this book to formally detail each of these,

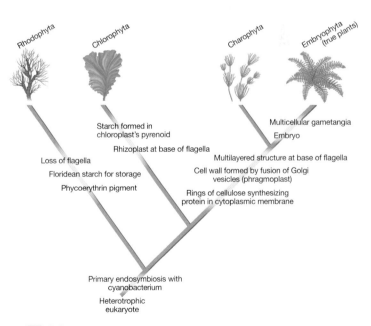

29-1 Archaeplastid Cladogram ~ Rhodophyta, Chlorophyta, Charophyta, and Embryophyta form a monophyletic group. Over a billion years ago, an endosymbiotic event occurred between a eukaryotic heterotroph and a cyanobacterium, with the descendants of the latter eventually evolving into chloroplasts.

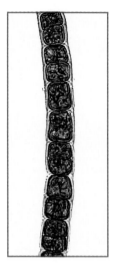

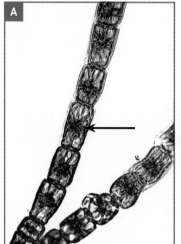

■ **29-2** *Bangia* **(Bangiophycidae)**
≈ The oldest known rhodophyte fossil (1.2 billion years ago) strongly resembles extant species of *Bangia*, especially in internal organization. Notice the simple, unbranched filament. This is considered to be an ancestral condition. Filaments range from 50 to 150 μm in diameter.

■ **29-3** **Rhodophyte Stellate and Discoid Chloroplasts** ≈
(**A**) *Bangia* species are filamentous and have the stellate chloroplasts typical of bangiophytes (**arrow**). (**B**) *Plocamium* demonstrates the florideophyte derived condition of peripheral, discoid chloroplasts (**arrow**).

so we will informally retain the two subclasses (which comprise the majority of red algae). Their characteristics are given in Table 29-1.

Evidence suggests that rhodophyte plastids (organelles that house photosynthetic pigments) are the product of primary endosymbiosis. Structurally, they may be **stellate** (*stella*—star) as in most bangiophytes or **discoid** (*discus*—disc) as in most florideophytes (Figure 29-3). The pigment chlorophyll a[1] is present, as are the unique accessory pigments phycoerythrin (*phyco*—seaweed, *erythro*—red) and phycocyanin (*cyan*—deep blue). The relative proportions of these pigments account for the black, brown, golden, greenish, and violet color differences between species and within species (Figure 29-4). It also is responsible for much frustration on the part of beginning phycologists in identifying these as "red" algae! But in general, shaded and

---

[1] It has long been held that chlorophyll d is also present in the rhodophytes, but new evidence shows this is not the case. The earlier reports were the result of contamination by a cyanobacterium.

subtidal species unequivocally are reddish. The storage material is **floridean starch**, a highly branched polysaccharide resembling glycogen, the animal storage material. It is stored in the cytoplasm.

With rare exception (see *Porphyridium purpureum*, shown on page 249, top right), marine rhodophytes are multicellular. During mitosis, the nuclear envelope remains intact. Centrioles are absent, but the **nuclear associated organelle**, possibly associated with microtubular (mitotic spindle) organization during cell division, is present at each spindle pole. In the ancestral condition (exhibited by most bangiophytes), growth occurs throughout the thallus, a process known as **diffuse growth**. In the derived condition (found mostly in florideophytes) the thallus is formed from filaments of cells and growth occurs at their tips as **apical cells** divide (Figure 29-5). In some cases, as in *Acrochaetium*,

■ **Table 29-1** ≈ Rhodophyte Classes

Subclass	Characteristics	Life Cycle	Examples	Approximate Number of Species	Etymology
Bangiophycidae	Nonfilamentous thallus; diffuse growth in most; stellate chloroplasts	Biphasic alternation of generations; asexual spores produce diploid, microscopic stage (once thought to be the species *Conchocelis rosea*) that occupies greater depths than gametophytes and are thus not competing with them (noncompeting developmental stages is a common strategy among animals, too).	*Porphyra, Bangia*	100+	Niels Bang—a Danish botanist
Florideophycidae	Filamentous thallus in most; growth from one or more apical cells; discoid chloroplasts	Triphasic alternation of generations; carposporophyte produces diploid spores	*Palmaria, Halosaccion,* all coralline algae, *Mastocarpus, Gelidium, Polysiphonia, Ceramium,* and many others	6,000	*florid*—reddish

A Pterocladia

C Turkish towel

D Laver

Rubber threads

E Corallines

■ 29-4 Red Algae Aren't Always Red ≈ All eukaryotic phototrophs possess the green pigment chlorophyll *a*. Other pigments also are present, sometimes in high enough quantities to obscure the green color of chlorophyll *a*. This is the case with red algae. The pigment phycoerythrin provides the red color and is especially abundant in subtidal species because it absorbs blue light, which penetrates water farther than other wavelengths of visible light. Exposed species are the ones with the greatest variety of colors due to the destruction of phycoerythrin by sunlight and to the presence of additional protective pigments. Further, some species are capable of adjusting relative amounts of their pigments based on the duration of solar exposure as a consequence of their vertical location in the intertidal zone. The following represent some of the variety seen in red algae: (**A**) *Pterocladia*, (**B**) *Nemalion* (arrow), (**C**) *Mastocarpus*, (**D**) *Porphyra*, and (**E**) various corallines. With the exception of *Porphyra*, all are florideophytes.

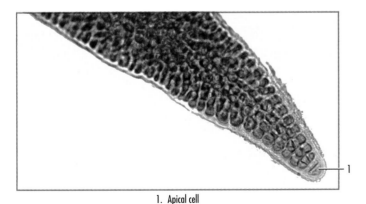

1. Apical cell

■ 29-5 Apical Cell ≈ Elongation of filaments often involves mitosis of a single apical cell at the end of the filament. The division plane is transverse to the axis of growth. If the thallus is composed of multiple filaments, these derived cells subsequently divide in two or three planes.

the filament is **uniseriate;** that is, a single column of cells is derived from the apical cell (Figure 29-6). Because there is only a single apical cell, the thallus is referred to as **uniaxial.** In some uniaxial rhodophytes the apical cell derivatives divide again in more than one plane, producing branches and/or an interior of compacted filaments of similar appearance to form **pseudoparenchyma.** In more complex forms, multiple apical cells produce a **multiaxial thallus.** In many instances, a compact, pigmented surface layer, the **cortex** (*cortex*—bark), surrounds a colorless interior, the **medulla** (*medulla*—pith or marrow) (Figure 29-7). These variations on filamentous growth produce a variety of morphologies among the red algae, as shown in Figure 29-8.

The cell wall (Figure 29-9) consists of a cellulose matrix (as in plants), but usually is less rigid because cellulose is not as abundant. Much of the wall is composed of

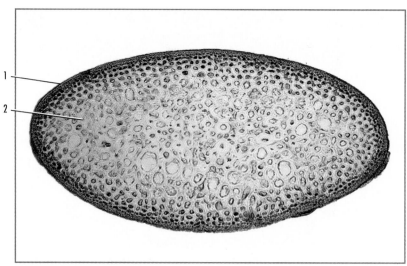

1. Cortex   2. Medulla

■ 29-6 Uniseriate Filamentous Growth ≈
Acrochaetium (Florideophycidae) is a microscopic alga
with filaments only a single cell wide (about 10 μm
across). Each cell holds a single, large chloroplast.
Most species grow attached to plants or animals.

■ 29-7 Cortex and Medulla ≈ This cross section of *Gelidium* (Florideophycidae) demonstrates the difference between the pigmented surface cells
(with chloroplasts) of the cortex and the larger, unpigmented cells of the
medulla.

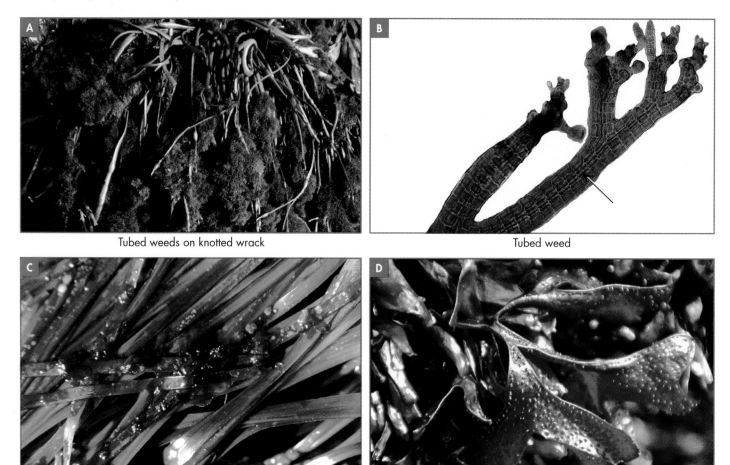

Tubed weeds on knotted wrack

Tubed weed

Red fringe

Papillate seaweed

■ 29-8 Florideophyte Morphologies Based on Filamentous Growth ≈ (A) Shown are whole plants of *Polysiphonia (Vertebrata)*
lanosum growing as epiphytes on the brown alga knotted wrack (*Ascophyllum nodosum*). (B) This is a micrograph of a small portion of
Polysiphonia. Note the filaments forming the thallus and the compressed pseudoparenchyma (arrow) in the interior. (C) *Smithora naiadum*
is a small, membranous epiphyte of the surfgrass *Phyllospadix*. The blades of *Phyllospadix* are less than 1 cm wide. (D) *Mastocarpus stellatus*
has multiaxial growth that results in thick, curled blades with distinctive bumps (papillae) on the surface that are associated with reproductive structures.

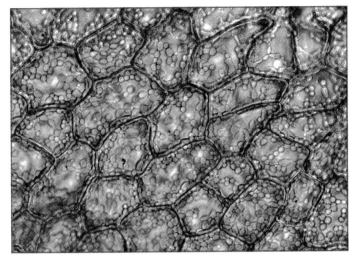

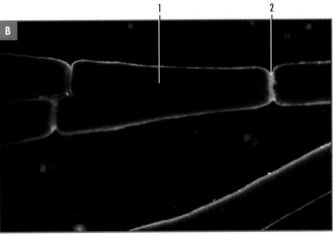

■ **29-9 Rhodophyte Cell Walls** ≈ Thick cell walls separating adjacent cells are clear in this micrograph of an unidentified membranous red alga. Note also the discoid chloroplasts mostly located at the periphery of each cell.

1. Intergeniculum   2. Geniculum

■ **29-10 Jointed Coralline Thallus (Florideophycidae)** ≈ Most coralline algae have segmented thalli, with segments (intergenicula) separated by flexible joints (genicula). (A) Shown is the dichotomously branched coralline *Jania crassa.* (B) With magnification, the intergenicula and the genicula of *Jania* are obvious. In this specimen, intergenicula are approximately 200–300 μm in width.

complex polysaccharides that fall into two main categories: **carrageenan** and **agar**, both of which are economically important as gelling agents. They are used in paints, cosmetics, foods, and pharmaceuticals as stabilizing agents. A major use of agar is as a solidifying agent in bacteriological media.

In the corallines, calcium carbonate ($CaCO_3$) impregnates the organic matrix of the wall (Figure 29-10). Desiccation is a particular problem for corallines and they usually are found in tide pools where they are least affected by tidal changes. Some corallines have jointed segments called **intergenicula** (*inter*—between, *genu*—knee, *ula*—diminutive suffix) joined by flexible joints (**genicula**). Other corallines form crusts on rocks or other surfaces (Figure 29-11).

In a certain few rhodophytes, the wall is deposited in such a way that reflected light produces **iridescence** (*irid*—rainbow, *escence*—to be or show). This has been attributed to thin, alternating layers of cell wall material with different refractive indices in some (Figure 29-12A) and to iridescent bodies in others (Figure 29-12B).

Rhodophyte life cycles exhibit either a **biphasic alternation of generations** (one spore producing generation) or a **triphasic alternation of generations** (two spore producing generations). The biphasic cycle has been covered previously (Chapter 28), so the more unusual triphasic cycle will be covered here. It will be useful to follow Figure 29-13 as you read. It also may be useful to review terminology in Figure 1-6.

As with all life cycles involving alternation of generations, there is a haploid gamete-producing (gametophyte) generation and a diploid spore-producing (sporophyte) generation. The difference is that in the triphasic life cycle, there are *two* spore-producing generations: the **carposporophyte** (*carpo*—fruit) and the **tetrasporophyte** (*tetra*—four).

■ **29-11 Crustose Coralline Thallus (Florideophycidae)** ≈ Some corallines form crusts on rocks and other substrates. This specimen is *Lithothamnium.* Reproductive structures are located in the knobby protuberances.

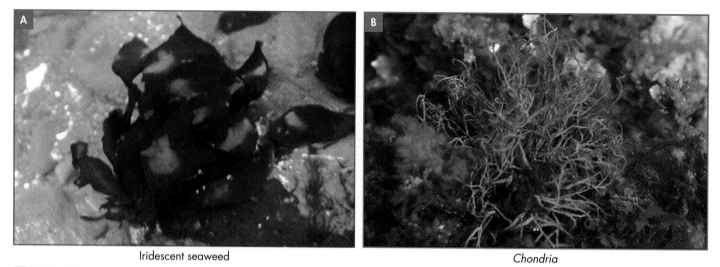

Iridescent seaweed

Chondria

■ **29-12** **Iridescence** ≈ (**A**) Several species of *Mazzaella* (formerly known as *Iridaea*) are iridescent when submerged. In these species, iridescence is due to cell wall deposition. (**B**) *Chondria californica* is an epiphytic rhodophyte that demonstrates iridescence due to cellular components rather than wall composition. Both species are florideophytes.

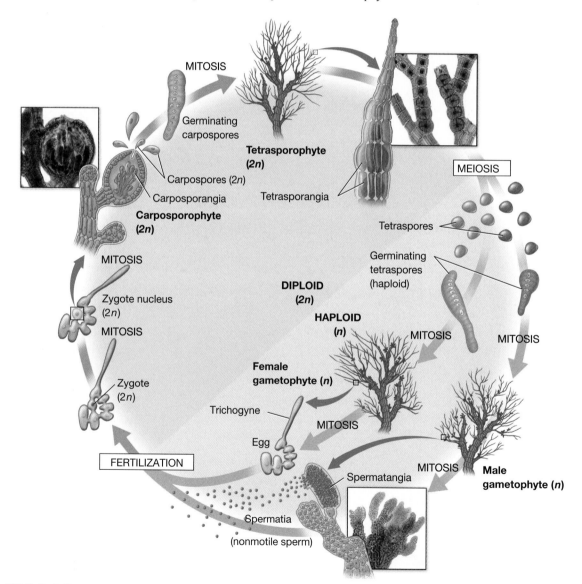

MITOSIS

Germinating
carpospores

**Tetrasporophyte
(2n)**

Carpospores (2n)

Carposporangia

Tetrasporangia

**Carposporophyte
(2n)**

MEIOSIS

Tetraspores

Germinating
tetraspores
(haploid)

MITOSIS

Zygote nucleus
(2n)

**DIPLOID
(2n)**

**HAPLOID
(n)**

MITOSIS

MITOSIS

MITOSIS

Zygote
(2n)

**Female
gametophyte (n)**

Trichogyne

MITOSIS

Egg

MITOSIS

**Male
gametophyte (n)**

FERTILIZATION

Spermatangia

Spermatia
(nonmotile sperm)

■ **29-13** **Triphasic Life Cycle of *Polysiphonia* (Florideophycidae)** ≈ Many red algae have a triphasic life cycle in which there is one gamete-producing generation and two diploid, spore-producing generations: the carposporophyte and the tetrasporophyte. See text for details.

We will begin with the familiar gametophyte generation, using *Polysiphonia* as the representative organism. *Polysiphonia* has separate male and female gametophytes. The male gametophyte has special branches that produce haploid, nonmotile **spermatia**. The female gametophyte has specialized branches containing a **carpogonium** (oogonium), from which extends an elongated **trichogyne**. Fertilization occurs when the spermatium contacts the trichogyne. Nuclear fusion produces a diploid zygote, which undergoes division to produce diploid **carposporangia** within a globular, diploid carposporophyte. This is the carposporophyte generation and it remains attached to the female gametophyte. Diploid **carpospores** are released, and these develop into diploid tetrasporophytes, which are identical to the gametophytes in appearance. Certain cells in the tetrasporophyte undergo meiosis to produce four haploid **tetraspores**, which are formed in a tetrahedral (*tetra*—four, *hedron*—denoting flat sides of a solid shape) arrangement. Release of the tetraspores followed by mitosis results in a new gametophyte generation.

Some unicellular rhodophytes exhibit a gliding motility, but centrioles and flagella are absent in all stages of the life cycle. The occurrence of the complex (triphasic) life cycle of most rhodophytes has been proposed as an adaptation to the lack of motility.

Some rhodophytes float freely in the water, others grow on plants (**epiphytic**; *epi*—upon, *phyte*—plants) or animals (**epizoic**; *zoite*—animal), and still others are **parasitic** (*parasitos*—eating at another's table). The majority, however, grow attached to a hard substrate like rock. Often, corallines are important in building and maintaining coral reefs. Rhodophytes are able to grow at greater depths than other seaweeds because their photosynthetic pigments absorb blue and green light, which penetrate to greater depths than other colors of white light. Their global distribution and diversity is greatest in the tropics, which suggests water temperature is a primary influence.

Figures 29-14 through 29-29 illustrate common red algae.

■ 29-14 *Corallina* **(Florideophycidae)** ≈ *Corallina* is a widely distributed and common coralline alga. It is characterized by its pinnate (*penna*—feather) branching; that is, lateral branches come off the main axis as in a feather. Its common name is coral seaweed.

■ 29-15 *Bossiella* **(Florideophycidae)** ≈ *Bossiella*, commonly known as coral leaf, is a North American Pacific Coast alga characterized by "wing nut" shaped intergenicula. Reproductive conceptacles (the bumps in this photo) are located on the faces of the intergenicula. Intergenicula are approximately 5 mm wide.

Seagrass crust

■ 29-16 *Melobesia mediocris* **(Florideophycidae)** ≈ *Melobesia* is a crustose coralline epiphyte of *Phyllospadix* (as shown here) and other thallose algae. Its species are distributed worldwide. Its common name is seagrass crust.

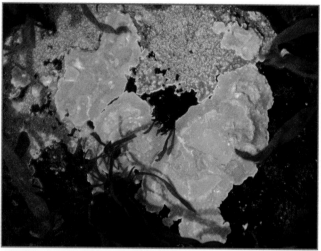

■ 29-17 *Clathromorphum* **(Florideophycidae)** ≈
Species of this crustose coralline are found along the northern latitudes of both North American coasts. Older plants become layered in the same manner as roof shingles, as in this New Hampshire specimen.

■ 29-18 *Cumagloia andersonii* **(Florideophycidae)** ≈
Commonly known as hairy seaweed, *Cumagloia* is characterized by tough cord-like thalli with lateral hairs. It grows in the high intertidal zone of rocky shores along both North American coasts and is an annual plant. This specimen was photographed in Oregon.

■ 29-19 *Halosaccion* **(Florideophycidae)** ≈ *Halosaccion glandiformis*, commonly known as sea sacs, is a red alga of the middle intertidal zone. It is found on the Pacific Coast of North America. These specimens were photographed in Oregon. The color varies from golden green (**A**) to violet red (**B**). The common name is sea sacs or salt sacs because the enlarged part of the thallus stores water, an adaptation to desiccation and temperature extremes.

■ 29-20 *Chondrus crispus* **(Florideophycidae)** ≈
Chondrus crispus (Irish moss) is a mid-intertidal red alga with dichotomous branching. Found on both sides of the Northern Atlantic Ocean, it is a source of carrageen used as an emulsifying or thickening agent in ice cream and other foods, toothpaste, cosmetics, shoe polish, and pharmaceuticals. This specimen was photographed in Massachusetts.

29-21 *Ahnfeltiopsis linearis* (Florideophycidae) ≈
Ahnfeltiopsis has a flattened, dichotomously branched thallus. It is frequently found buried in sand and lives on the West Coast of North America.

29-22 *Constantinea simplex* (Florideophycidae) ≈ This species resembles a mushroom, with a flattened round blade at the top of a short stipe (hidden by shadow in this photograph but highlighted by the arrow). Each year the blade dies leaving a scar on the stipe, and a new blade is grown. Because of this, it is possible to estimate the age of individuals. This species grows along the West Coast of North America from Alaska to Northern California.

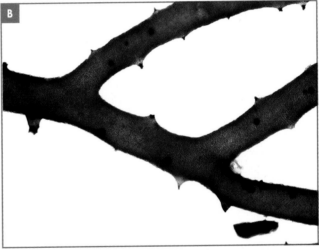

29-23 *Endocladia muricata* (Florideophycidae) ≈ (A) This rhodophyte, also known as nail brush seaweed, grows in tufts and often looks more dark brown than red; but red it is! It grows high in the rocky intertidal zone and can withstand long periods out of water. (B) Its thallus is covered by conical projections, as shown in this micrograph.

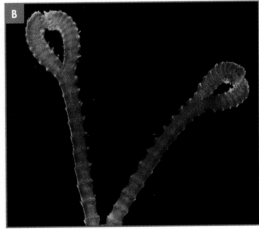

29-24 *Centroceras clavulatum* (Florideophycidae) ≈ (A) The red-purple thalli of *Centroceras clavulatum* grow in dense tufts up to 5 cm in height. (B) This dark field micrograph illustrates the dichotomous branching with distinctive in-curved branchlets at the apex of each branch. Spines (composed of two or three cells) are also visible at the junctions of thallus segments.

29-25 *Plocamium pacificum* (Florideophycidae) ≈ One of the most beautifully and delicately branched rhodophytes of the Pacific is *Plocamium pacificum.* It deserves its common name: sea comb. Another specimen is shown in Figure 28-2A.

29-26 *Cryptopleura ruprechtiana* (*Botryoglossum farlowiana*) (Florideophycidae) ≈ This species was recently moved from the genus *Botryoglossum* to *Cryptopleura.* Its blades are flat with ruffled margins and lack a midrib except at the base, accounting for its common name: fringed hidden rib. It is a low intertidal species of western North American rocky coasts. Other species are distributed in parts of South America, Europe, and Africa.

29-27 *Prionitis lanceolata* (Florideophycidae) ≈ Short branches along the edges of the blade characterize members of the genus. Its common name is bleach weed.

29-28 *Hildenbrandia* (Florideophycidae) ≈ *Hildenbrandia* grows on rocks in the mid-intertidal zone as bright red crusts made of microscopic vertical filaments. Sexual stages are unknown. Also known by the common name red rock crust, this specimen was photographed in Massachusetts. Some *Hildenbrandia* species grow in freshwater.

29-29 Miscellaneous Rhodophytes ≈ Shown are young rhodophytes growing as epizoites on a living black turban snail shell.

Sea lettuce

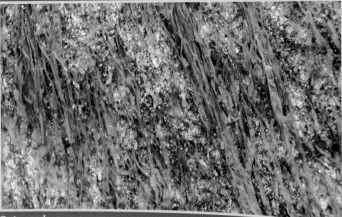
Gut weed

30 Chlorophyta

This chapter covers green algae that are visible to the naked eye. Chapter 4 covers the microscopic greens.

A variety of evidence has led to the conclusion that green algae are closely related to red algae and to terrestrial plants in the major eukaryotic clade Archaeplastida. (Figures 28-1 and 29-1). Fossils resembling extant green algae are known from the early Cambrian, some 500 million years ago.

All chlorophyte cells have at least one plastid, though it may not be pigmented. If pigmented, it is known as a **chloroplast** (*chloro*—green, *plastos*—formed). Chlorophyll *a* is the primary pigment, but accessory pigments **chlorophyll *b*, lutein**, and β-carotene are also present. The two chlorophylls are abundant and are responsible for the green color of the group. The plastid is the product of primary endosymbiosis (Chapter 28). Starch is stored within the plastid, in a space between membranes known as the **stroma** (*stroma*—coverlet).

Green algae range from unicellular, to filamentous, to thallose, but most marine species are microscopic. Of the macroalgae, the majority are made of **uninucleated** cells, but some species are **multinucleated** whereas others are **coenocytic**, (*koinos*—common, *kutos*—vessel) in which no cell walls or membranes separate the nuclei; the entire thallus

is one, large, multinucleated cell! In most instances, the cell walls are cellulose or modified cellulose, but some tropical species have calcified ($CaCO_3$) walls. If present, flagella are in pairs (or multiples of pairs) and are of equal length.

Marine greens illustrate three types of life cycle. The **diplontic** life cycle is dominated by the multicellular diploid sporophyte, with gametes being the only haploid cells. Some exhibit a **haplontic** life cycle, which is dominated by the multicellular gametophyte and the only diploid stage is the zygote. Still others have multicellular diploid sporophytes *and* multicellular haploid sporophytes (as described in Chapter 28). In some instances, both multicellular generations look the same and the life cycle is said to be **isomorphic** (*iso*—equal, *morphe*—form). Others have a **heteromorphic** (*hetero*—other) life cycle, in which the sporophytes and gametophytes differ in appearance. Figure 30-1 illustrates the former life cycle in *Ulva*.

Only 10% of the nearly 17,000 green algal species are marine, with the majority of marine macroalgae belonging to seven orders within the class Ulvophyceae (Table 30-1). It has yet to be established if Ulvophyceae represents a monophyletic clade. Only six orders with marine representatives will be covered here: Ulvales, Ulotrichales, Acrosiphonales (included in Ulotrichales by some authors), Dasycladales, Caulerpales, and Cladophorales. Within

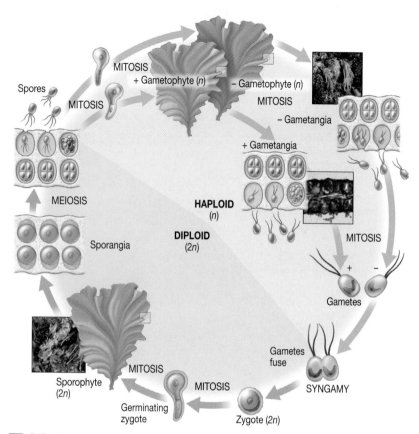

30-1 *Ulva* **Life Cycle** ≈ The *Ulva* life cycle is isomorphic, that is, the gametophyte and the sporophyte look alike. It is also isogamous because the gametes, too, look alike. This is why the sexes are designated as "+" and "–" rather than "male" and "female." Notice that the haploid gametes each have two flagella and the haploid spores have four.

Ulvophyceae, Ulotrichales and Ulvales appear to be in the same clade and were the earliest to split off from the others. Dasycladales and Caulerpales are sister clades. Cladophorales are in the same clade as the Siphonocladales, which is not covered here. Their relationship is an area of ongoing research.

30-2 *Ulva* **(Ulvales)** ≈ Commonly known as "sea lettuce," *Ulva* earns its name as it grows in sheets that are two cells thick. It is an unmistakable green alga of the mid- to high intertidal zones of rocky shore as well as marine and estuarine mudflats worldwide.

Table 30-1 ≈ Ulvophyceae Orders

Order	Characteristics	Life Cycle	Examples	Approximate Number of Species	Etymology
Ulvales (Figures 30-2 and 30-3)	Thallus tubular or a sheet one or two cells thick; uninucleate; chloroplasts at cell's periphery	Isomorphic alternation of generations	*Ulva, Enteromorpha* (now *Ulva*), *Monostroma*	50	From Greek "sedge"
Ulotrichales (Figure 30-4)	Mostly unbranched, haploid filaments; cup- or band-shaped parietal chloroplast with numerous pyrenoids	Haplontic (zygotes are the only diploid stage)	*Ulothrix*	480	*Ulo*—wooly, *thrix*—hair
Acrosiphonales (Figure 30-5)	Branched or unbranched filaments; most multinucleate; single perforate chloroplast	Multitude of complex, unresolved heteromorphic life histories	*Acrosiphonia*	Unknown	*acro*—apex, *siphon*—tube
Caulerpales (Figures 30-6 to 30-8)	Thallus coenocytic, except where reproductive cells are produced; numerous discoid chloroplasts	Poorly understood; gametes anisogamous	*Codium, Bryopsis, Caulerpa, Udotea Halimeda, Penicillus*	350	*caulo*—stem, *herpo*—to creep
Dasycladales (Figures 30-9 and 30-10)	Radially symmetrical thallus calcified in most; unicellular until gametes are formed; nucleus found in holdfast until migration to reproductive upper parts to form gametes within cysts	Diplontic (gametes are the only haploid stage)	*Acetabularia, Batophora*	38	*dasy*—dense, *clad*—branch
Cladophorales (Figures 30-11 and 30-12)	Filamentous thallus; multinucleate cells until maturity, then cytokinesis occurs; reticulate (networked) or numerous small discoid chloroplasts	Isomorphic alternation of generations	*Cladophora, Chaetomorpha*	425	*clad*—branch, *phor*—bearing

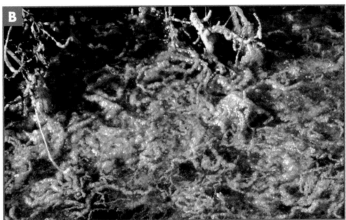

■ **30-3** *Ulva intestinalis* **(formerly** *Enteromorpha intestinalis***) (Ulvales)** ≈ **(A)** *Ulva (Enteromorpha) intestinalis* is so named because of its tubular construction. Commonly known as gut weed, it is often found in association with flat-blade species of *Ulva*, and was recently placed into that genus. It is often seen floating in mats with air bubbles trapped in the tubular thallus. This specimen was photographed in a New Hampshire rocky intertidal habitat. **(B)** This one is from a Southern California estuary. Another specimen living on rocks off the Oregon coast is shown at the top right of page 259.

Members of the Ulvales have uninucleate cells with flattened chloroplasts. Most are marine or estuarine, with the genera *Ulva* (Figure 30-2) and *Enteromorpha* (Figure 30-3) being the best known. After long recognizing similarities between the two, *Enteromorpha* was moved into the genus *Ulva* in 2003.

Ulotrichales are generally unbranched filaments with **parietal chloroplasts** (located at the edge of the cytoplasm near the cell wall) that either completely or incompletely encircle a large **central vacuole** (Figure 30-4). Both freshwater and marine species are known. Meiosis occurs in the zygote after a resting period, making the life cycle haplontic.

Acrosiphonales are branched or unbranched filamentous forms found in cold water. The heteromorphic life cycle alternates between a multicellular gametophyte and a unicellular sporophyte. *Acrosiphonia* is an example (Figure 30-5).

Caulerpales includes the coenocytic genera *Caulerpa*, *Derbesia*, *Bryopsis*, *Codium* (Figure 30-6), *Penicillus* (Figure 30-7) and *Halimeda* (Figure 30-8).

The Dasycladales are tropical. Morphologically, they have branches in rings (whorls) and calcified walls. The life cycle is diplontic, in which gametes are the only haploid cells. *Acetabularia* (Figure 30-9) and *Batophora* (Figure 30-10) are examples.

In the Cladophorales, all cells are multinucleate with parietal chloroplasts. Typically, they exhibit isomorphic alternation of generations. Examples include filamentous genera *Chaetomorpha* (Figure 30-11) and *Cladophora* (Figure 30-12).

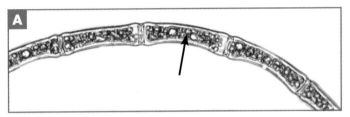

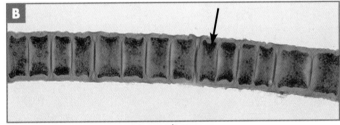

Mermaid's tresses

■ **30-4** *Ulothrix* **(Ulotrichales)** ≈ **(A)** *Ulothrix* species are represented in both freshwater and marine habitats. The filaments are unbranched and contain a single parietal chloroplast (arrows). **(B)** In this stained specimen, the cup-shaped chloroplasts are apparent. Note the darker edges of each chloroplast. This is a clue that it is thicker than the center. Imagine looking straight down on the letter "C" positioned this way: ∩. The top and bottom of the "C" would be "thicker" than the middle.

■ **30-5** *Acrosiphonia* **(Order Acrosiphonales)** ≈
Acrosiphonia looks like frayed green rope. In fact, its common name is green rope. It grows on rocks in the low intertidal zone. This specimen was photographed in Northern California.

■ 30-6 *Codium fragile* (Caulerpales)

≈ (**A**) Some species of *Codium* are low growing on rock surfaces, but *Codium fragile* is not one of them. Its dark green color and dichotomous branching make it easy to recognize. In this specimen, the brown patches are gametangia. *Codium* often grows in a mutualistic symbiosis with the cyanobacterium *Azotobacter,* supplying the cyanobacterium with glucose and receiving fixed nitrogen in return. (**B**) The thallus is formed from colorless, intertwined multi-nucleate filaments that form the central medulla (*medulla*—pith). These periodically branch and differentiate into **utricles** (*uter*—leather bag) on the surface. These utricles are approximately 150–350 µm in diameter.

Dead man's fingers

Neptune's shaving brush

■ 30-7 *Penicillus* (Order Caulerpales)

≈ (**A**) This Florida *Penicillus* species lives up to its name, because it looks like a small brush. In fact, its common name is Neptune's shaving brush. It grows in calm, tropical waters with sandy or muddy bottoms. It reaches a height of about 10 cm and is composed of a calcified stalk and a cap of dichotomously branched filaments (**B**).

Watercress

■ 30-8 *Halimeda* (Caulerpales) ≈

The thallus of *Halimeda* species (arrow) is made of somewhat flexible nodes joining calcified segments. The segments are coenocytic and initially contain only starch-storing amyloplasts (*amylo*—starch; *plast*—formed); chloroplasts develop later. Under ideal conditions, *Halimeda* can add a segment per day! *Halimeda* and related fossil species are found worldwide and form beds 50 m thick in the continental shelf region near the Great Barrier Reef in Australia. These specimens were photographed off St. Thomas Island in a sea grass bed.

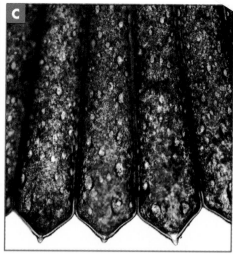

Mermaid's wine glass

■ **30-9** *Acetabularia* **(Dasycladales)** ∼ **(A)** The mermaid's wine glass is a delicate, unicellular green alga that can reach several centimeters in height! It attaches to surfaces by "holdfast" branches, which house the single nucleus. The **cap** at the top is formed of gamete-producing branches (**rays**). The single nucleus undergoes meiosis, which is followed by multiple mitotic divisions to produce numerous haploid secondary nuclei. These nuclei migrate from the base, enter the cap rays, and become **encysted** (enclosed within a wall). Cysts are released and subsequently release their gametes, which undergo fertilization to produce a zygote and complete the life cycle. This specimen was photographed on Grand Cayman. **(B)** In this close-up of the cap, the secondary nuclei have entered the darker rays. The caps are approximately 1 cm in diameter. **(C)** This micrograph shows the multiple cysts (the white spots) in each cap ray.

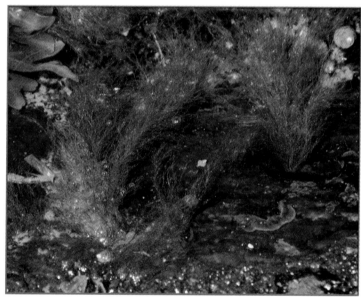

Spaghetti algae

■ **30-11** *Chaetomorpha* **(Cladophorales)** ∼ Unbranched filaments characterize this genus. Its name means "bristle shaped." Although some species grow in fresh water, most are found in brackish or marine environments.

■ **30-10** *Batophora* **(Dasycladales)** ∼ *Batophora* is found growing near mangroves and in brackish water. Each main branch has densely whorled, delicately forked branchlets.

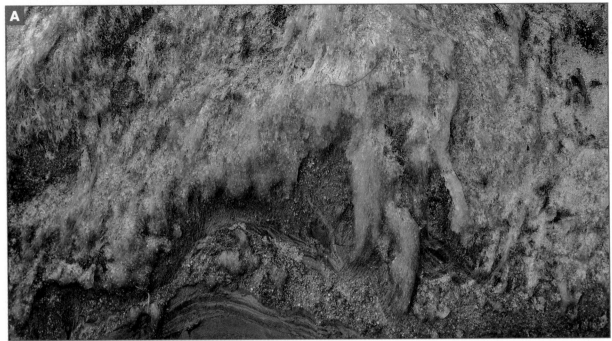

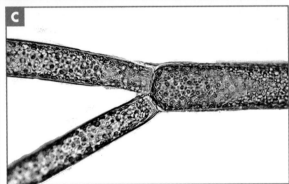

■ 30-12 *Cladophora* (Cladophorales) ≈

(A) The generic name Cladophora is assigned to any branched green alga with multinucleate cells. It is not a monophyletic group and will undergo revision as more data become available. This specimen was found growing fairly high in the rocky intertidal zone. (B) Note the branched filaments. These range from 100 to 200 µm in diameter. Also note the epiphytic diatoms growing on it (arrow). (C) This higher magnification shows one branch, the cell walls, and numerous chloroplasts.

Banded tidepool fan

Convoluted sea fungus

31 Phaeophyceae

The Class Phaeophyceae is placed in the Stramenopile clade within the major eukaryotic clade Chromalveolata and comprises all of the brown algae (Figures 28-1 and 31-1). Characteristic of stramenopiles, motile phaeophycean cells possess two flagella—a longer anterior one and a shorter one at the posterior. The anterior flagellum has numerous **tripartite** (*tri*—three, *partitus*—divided) hairs and is referred to as a **tinsel flagellum**. The posterior flagellum is the more typical eukaryotic **whiplash type**. Phaeophyceans range from microscopic filamentous forms to the giant kelps (Figure 31-2). They typically are the most obvious members of the rocky intertidal and littoral flora north of the Tropic of Cancer.

Phaeophycean fossils from between 150 and 200 million years ago have been recovered from this monophyletic and predominantly marine group. Currently, over 250 genera encompassing more than 1,500 species are recognized, though these numbers will undoubtedly change as more information becomes available.

The chloroplast is the product of secondary endosymbiosis (Chapter 28). Photosynthetic pigments include chlorophylls a, c_1, and c_2, and fucoxanthin, which accounts for their brown coloration (Figure 31-3). The polysaccharide **laminarin** is the primary storage material and it accumulates in a membrane-bound vesicle outside of the chloroplast.

The cell wall consists of a cellulose framework with varying amounts of the polysaccharides **alginic acid** and **fucoidin** filling the intervening spaces. Alginic acid is responsible for thallus flexibility, minimizing desiccation, and other functions. Fucoidins may be involved in anchoring the young sporophyte thallus to its intertidal substrate.

Thalli can be single filaments, aggregates of filaments without tissue differentiation (**pseudoparenchymatous**), or differentiated into stipes, holdfasts, and blades (**parenchymatous**). Mitotic activity for growth can occur in an apical cell (Figure 31-4), all over the thallus (diffuse growth), or be organized into definite regions (**meristems**). In some, the meristem is located beneath filamentous projections (hairs). As the meristematic cells divide, daughter cells formed toward the thallus produce thallus growth, whereas those on the other side form the hairs in a mechanism known as **trichothallic growth**.

Most phaeophytes demonstrate a typical biphasic life cycle (Chapter 28), with alternation between a multicellular gamete-producing (gametophyte) generation and a multicellular spore-producing (sporophyte) generation. The two generations may either look alike (isomorphic) or look different (heteromorphic). *Laminaria* provides an example (Figure 31-5).

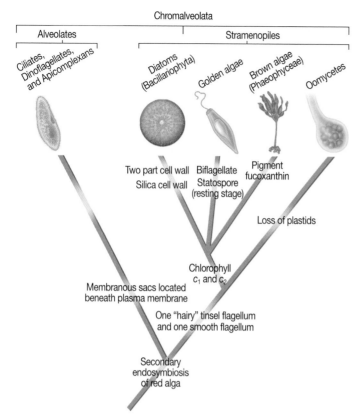

Chromalveolata

Alveolates | Stramenopiles

Ciliates, Dinoflagellates, and Apicomplexans

Diatoms (Bacillariophyta)

Golden algae

Brown algae (Phaeophyceae)

Oomycetes

Two part cell wall
Silica cell wall

Biflagellate
Statospore (resting stage)

Pigment fucoxanthin

Loss of plastids

Chlorophyll c_1 and c_2

Membranous sacs located beneath plasma membrane

One "hairy" tinsel flagellum and one smooth flagellum

Secondary endosymbiosis of red alga

■ **31-1 Stramenopile Cladogram** ≈ Stramenopiles are one major clade within the larger eukaryotic clade Chromalveolata. They are characterized by the presence of two flagella—a longer anterior one and a shorter one at the posterior. The anterior flagellum is a tinsel flagellum with numerous tripartite hairs (Figure 31-5). The posterior flagellum is a typical eukaryotic whiplash type.

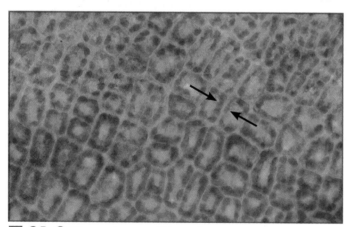

■ **31-3 Phaeophytean Chloroplasts** ≈ Phaeophycean chloroplasts are brown because of the abundance of the accessory pigment fucoxanthin. In addition, plastids contain chlorophyll a, c_1, c_2, and other pigments. These discoid chloroplasts of *Dictyopteris* lack pyrenoids and are found at the cells' periphery (arrows).

The brown algae are an economically important group. Alginic acid extracted from brown algal cell walls has many commercial applications. It is found in pastry fillings, frozen desserts, salad dressings, ice cream, paper, polishes, lotions, pharmaceuticals, and many other products. Detached brown algae that have washed ashore ("drift") are used as cattle fodder (Figure 33-9C).

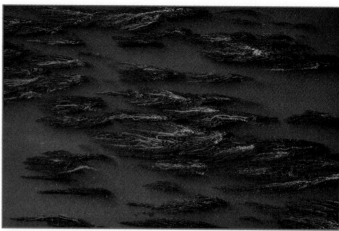

■ **31-2 A Kelp Forest** ≈ This aerial view off the coast of Southern California shows the canopy of a *Macrocystis* forest (giant perennial kelp). Remarkably, these marine giants can grow at a rate of up to 0.6 m per day and reach lengths up to 60 m, with much of that length forming the canopy, shown here. Kelps are harvested for their alginic acid, which is used in a variety of products as a thickening or emulsifying agent.

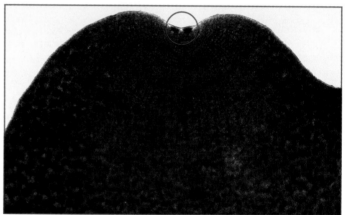

■ **31-4 Apical Cell Growth** ≈ Some phaeophytes grow through the mitotic activity of an apical cell. Shown here are two apical cells (circled), indicating that the axis is dividing into two branches (and also suggested by the two "lumps" of cells formed at this apex). Other phaeophytes demonstrate diffuse growth, where cells throughout the thallus divide. In other cases, specific regions of dividing cells called "meristems" are responsible for growth.

Five major orders of brown algae will be covered (Table 31-1): Dictyotales, Sphacelariales, Fucales, Ecto-carpales, and Laminariales. See Chapter 28 for life cycle terminology.

The Dictyotales are largely a tropical and subtropical group. One or more apical cells are responsible for growth and alternation of generations is isomorphic. Their spores lack flagella. Major genera include *Dictyota* (Figure 31-6), *Dictyopteris* (Figure 31-6), *Padina* (Figure 31-7), and *Zonaria* (Figures 31-8, 31-9, and upper left on page 265). Dictyotales (along with Sphacelariales) are the two most ancient orders in the Class.

Thalli of Sphacelariales grow from an apical cell (Figure 31-10), and then the derivatives may undergo further division in a transverse or longitudinal plane to

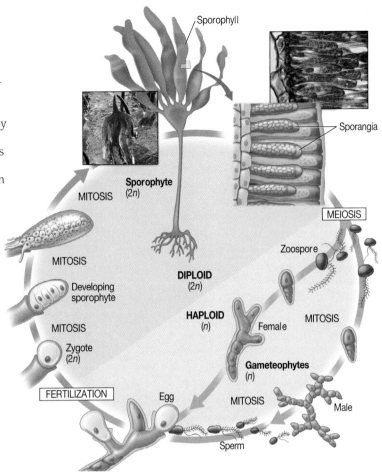

■ **31-5** *Laminaria* **Life Cycle** ≈

The life cycle of *Laminaria* is representative of most phaeophytes. There is alternation between multicellular gametophytes that produce gametes by mitosis and multicellular sporophytes that produce spores by meiosis. Blades bearing sporangia are called "**sporophylls**." Note the two flagellar types on the zoospores and sperm.

Sporophyll

Sporangia

Sporophyte (2n)

MITOSIS

MITOSIS

Developing sporophyte

MITOSIS

Zygote (2n)

FERTILIZATION

Egg

MITOSIS

Sperm

MEIOSIS

DIPLOID (2n)

Zoospore

HAPLOID (n)

Female

MITOSIS

Gameteophytes (n)

Male

■ **Table 31-1** ≈ Class Phaeophycean Classes

Order	Characteristics	Life Cycle	Examples	Approximate Number of Species	Etymology
Dictyotales (Figures 31-6 to 31-9)	Growth from an apical cell; numerous discoid chloroplasts per cell	Isomorphic alternation of generations; spores nonmotile (*aplanospores*); sperm uniflagellate	*Dictyota*, *Dictyopteris*, *Padina*, *Zonaria*	200+	*dictyota*—netlike
Sphacelariales (Figure 31-10)	Growth from a large apical cell producing a multiseriate and branched filamentous thallus; numerous discoid chloroplasts per cell	Isomorphic alternation of generations; isogamous, anisogamous, and oogamous species known	*Sphacelaria*	80	*sphacelaria*—gangrene (species turn black when treated with bleach)
Fucales (Figures 31-11 to 31-18)	Macroscopic with dichotomous or radial branching; growth from an apical cell	Diplontic; male and female gametangia may be on the same plant or on separate plants; fertilization is oogamous (large nonmotile egg and small motile sperm)	*Fucus*, *Silvetia*, *Pelvetiopsis*, *Ascophyllum*, *Sargassum*	500+	*phykos*—seaweed
Ectocarpales (Figures 31-19 to 31-23)	Filamentous or thallus of compacted filaments; chloroplasts band-shaped; diffuse growth	Isomorphic alternation of generations; gametes may be isogamous or anisogamous	*Ectocarpus*, *Colpomenia*, *Ralfsia*, *Scytosiphon*	600	*ecto*—external, *carp*—fruit
Laminariales Figures 31-24 to 31-33)	Large sporophytes, with differentiation into a holdfast, stipe, and blade(s); pneumatocysts in many; specialized conducting tissue in many; intercalary meristem located between stipe and blade(s); circumferential growth by meristematic cells (meristoderm) at the surface	Heteromorphic alternation of generations with microscopic gametophyte; fertilization is oogamous (large nonmotile egg and small motile sperm)	*Macrocystis*, *Laminaria*, *Saccharina*, *Pelagophycus*, *Nereocystis*	120+	*lamina*—blade

■ 31-7 *Padina pavonica* **(Dictyotales)** ≈ *Padina* is found in shallow tropical waters. Its surface is calcified (it is the only calcified phaeophyte genus) and presents concentric rings. These specimens are from the St. Thomas Island in the U.S. Virgin Islands. The common name is peacock's tail.

■ 31-6 *Dictyota flabellata* **(above) and** *Dictyopteris undulata* **(below) (Dictyotales)** ≈ *Dictyota* (mermaid's gloves) is mostly dichotomously branched with the branches lying in a single plane. A single layer of small, photosynthetic cortical cells surround a single layer of large, colorless medullary cells. This Southern California *Dictyopteris* species grows in the lower and subtidal levels. It is easily recognizable because of its bushy appearance, midrib, and bluish iridescence when under water.

■ 31-8 *Zonaria farlowii* **(Dictyotales)** ≈ *Zonaria* is found in the lower intertidal to subtidal zone of rocky Southern California shores. It is characterized by divided, fan-shaped blades with lighter coloration at their apices. Frequently, concentric rings of hairs are evident. (A portion of one ring is shown within the circle.) Patchy regions of sporangia and gametangia (arrow) can be seen on these specimens.

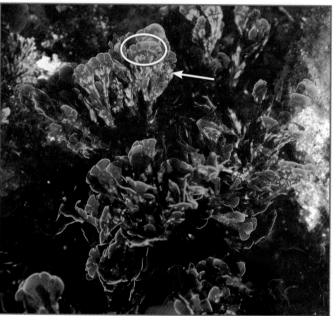

Banded tidepool fan

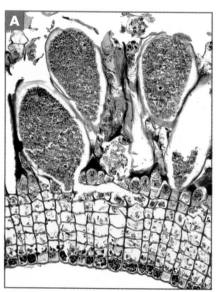

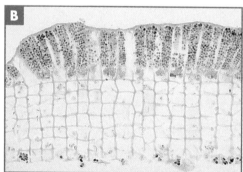

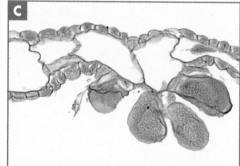

■ 31-9 *Zonaria* **Sporangia and Gametangia** ≈ Microscopic cross sections through blade. **(A)** Nonmotile spores are produced from sporangia emerging from the thallus, as shown here. In this cross section, notice how each **unilocular** (*uni*—one; *locus*—place or compartment) **sporangium** is derived from a single cell. Notice also, the distinctive brick-like arrangement of medullary cells and the single layer of cortical cells containing chloroplasts along the bottom and top of the blade. **(B) Plurilocular** (*pluri*—several) **antheridia** (the male gametangia) are shown here. Each sperm (the black dots) has a single flagellum, which is not visible at this magnification. **(C)** Each **oogonium** (the female gametangium) produces a single, large egg. Oogonia and antheridia are on separate individuals.

produce branched filaments more than one cell in width. Discoid chloroplasts and isomorphic alternation of generations also characterize the order. Isogamous, anisogamous, and **oogamous** (large nonmotile egg and small motile sperm) species are known.

Fucales are macroscopic with dichotomous or radial branching (Figure 31-11), with each branch growing from its own apical cell. Their life cycle resembles that of most animals in that diploid multicellular individuals develop gametangia that produce gametes by meiosis. Therefore, the only haploid cells are the gametes and the life cycle is diplontic. In some species, male and female gametangia are found on the same individual; in others, sexes are separate. A representative life cycle is shown in Figure 31-12. Genera include *Fucus* (Figures 31-11 and 31-13), *Silvetia* (Figure

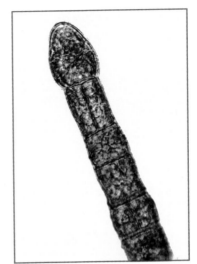

■ **31-10** *Sphacelaria* **(Sphacelariales)** ≈ Shown in this micrograph is the prominent apical cell of brown rock fuzz. Note that the cells immediately behind the apical cell have divided transversely and the filament has become multiseriate; that is, multiple rows of cells.

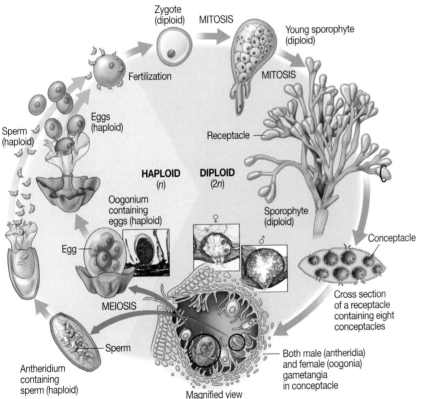

■ **31-11** *Fucus spiralis* **(Fucales)** ≈ *Fucus* is the type genus for the Order Fucales. Notice the dichotomous branching, prominent midrib in the stipe, and the swollen regions (**receptacles**) terminating the branches. These house microscopic pits (**conceptacles**) containing gametangia. The conceptacles are visible as spots on the receptacles in this photo. The common name for this species is spiral rockweed.

■ **31-12** *Fucus* **Life Cycle** ≈ The *Fucus* life cycle has no alternation of generations. The multicellular generation is diploid and produces gametes by meiosis. Male gametangia (antheridia) and female gametangia (oogonia) are found inside conceptacles (microscopic pits). Some species are unisexual, whereas others are bisexual. (Note: the artwork illustrates a conceptacle with both antheridia and oogonia, whereas the micrographs show unisexual conceptacles.) Gametes from a local population are released in synchrony with tides to improve chances of fertilization.

■ **31-13** *Fucus vesiculosus* **(Fucales)** ≈ *Fucus vesiculosus* (bladder wrack) is common on the shores of the Atlantic Ocean and Baltic Sea. Notice the paired pneumatocysts on the stipes (arrows), the dichotomous branching, the midrib, and the receptacles at the ends of branches.

31-14), *Pelvetiopsis* (Figure 31-15), *Cystoseira*, *Halidrys* (Figure 31-16), *Ascophyllum* (Figure 31-17), and *Sargassum* (Figure 31-18).

As defined now, the Order Ectocarpales includes members of the previously recognized Orders Chordariales, Dictyosiphonales, and Scytosiphonales. Thalli of Ectocarpales are made of branched filaments organized into a prostrate portion, which acts as the holdfast, and an erect filamentous portion, though in individual species they may not be equally evident. The life cycle is isomorphic and growth is diffuse. Gametangia are plurilocular (*plurel*—more, *locus*—place) and sporangia are both unilocular

(*uni*—one) and plurilocular. Genera include *Ectocarpus* (Figure 31-19), *Ralfsia* (Figure 31-20), *Endarachne* (Figure 31-21), *Colpomenia* (Figure 31-22), *Scytosiphon* (Figure 31-23), and *Petrospongium* (upper right photo on page 265).

The Laminariales include all seaweeds known as "kelps." All demonstrate alternation of generations (Figure 31-5). The gametophyte thallus is microscopic and filamentous, but the macroscopic sporophyte thallus is differentiated into a holdfast with haptera, a stipe, and one or more blades (Chapter 28). Sporophytes are generally perennial (*perennis*—"lasting the year through"); that is, they live for several years. Pneumatocysts are often present (Figure 31-24). Tissue differentiation produces an outer **epidermis** whose cells contain chloroplasts (Figure 31-25). Internal to the epidermis are several layers of colorless cells that

■ **31-14** *Silvetia compressa* (Fucales) ≈ *Silvetia compressa* resembles *Fucus*, but lacks the midrib and pneumatocysts. It also shares the common name rockweed. It is primarily found on the Pacific Coast of North America, south of San Francisco Bay.

■ **31-15** *Pelvetiopsis limitata* (Fucales) ≈ Another member of the Fucales is *Pelvetiopsis*, which looks like a miniature *Fucus* or *Silvetia* (hence the name dwarf rockweed). It tends to grow higher in the rocky intertidal zone than these other genera. This young specimen was found growing at eye level on a sea wall. It has yet to develop receptacles at the ends of its branches.

■ **31-16** *Halidrys dioica* (Fucales) ≈ Flattened, tapering pods of pneumatocysts are a distinctive characteristic of *Halidrys dioica*. It is found in the littoral or sublittoral regions of rocky coasts along Southern and Baja California.

■ **31-17** *Ascophyllum nodosum* (Fucales) ≈ *Ascophyllum nodosum* (knotted wrack) is the only species of the genus and is characterized by elongated pneumatocysts spaced evenly along its long, narrow stipes. It is found on North Atlantic rocky shores.

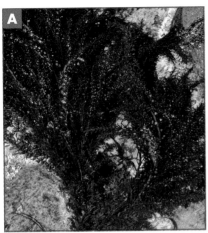

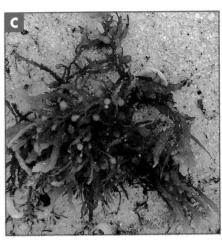

■ **31-18** *Sargassum* **spp. (Fucales) Habit** ≈ (A) Also known as wireweed, *Sargassum muticum* is native to Japan, but was introduced to Washington State in the 1940s. By the 1970s it had spread to Southern California. It has also been introduced into parts of Europe. *S. muticum* is found in calm waters at the low intertidal or subtidal levels, where it grows to two or more meters in length. The Sargasso Sea (just north of the Atlantic Tropic of Cancer) was named for the large, floating rafts of *Sargassum* found there. (B) This single branch shows the wiry stipe, narrow blades, and small pneumatocysts (a few millimeters in diameter) occurring singly at the base of the blades. Gametangia also are found at the bases of the blades, but are not seen here. Note the air bubbles in the water produced from photosynthesis. (C) This *S. fluitans* was found in the drift along the Florida Gulf Coast. It is one of the floating *Sargassum* species.

■ **31-19** *Ectocarpus* **(Ectocarpales) Habit and Microscopic Anatomy** ≈ (A) *Ectocarpus* is a major component of the algal turf in this Southern California rocky littoral habitat. It is composed of erect branches (1–3 cm in height) emerging from a prostrate, filamentous base. The green alga is *Ulva*. (B) Shown is a micrograph of a plurilocular sporangium. Spores are produced by meiosis. Note the band-shaped chloroplasts in the filament at the top (arrow).

■ **31-20** *Ralfsia* **spp. (Ectocarpales)** ≈ It is hard to imagine something that looks like a tar spot (its common name) being alive, but alive it is! A basal layer several cells thick gives rise to relatively short and firmly attached erect filaments. Reproductive structures are produced among these filaments. Each patch is several centimeters in diameter.

■ **31-21** *Endarachne binghamiae* **(Ectocarpales)**
≈ *E. binghamiae* is a common inhabitant of the midtidal zone in temperate and tropical waters. The blades are approximately 3 cm wide and it is held to the rocks by a single discoid holdfast. Extracts from it have been found to stimulate division of immune cells *in vitro* (literally, "within glass," meaning "in a test tube [lab]").

■ **31-22** *Colpomenia sinuosa* (Ectocarpales) ≈ *Colpomenia* has a globular, hollow thallus (measuring a few centimeters across) and is found growing on rocks or other algae as an epiphyte (*epi*—upon, *phyte*—plant). It is also called sinuous seaweed.

■ **31-23** *Scytosiphon lomentaria* (Ectocarpales) ≈ *Scytosiphon lomentaria* (soda straws) is an inhabitant of the low intertidal zone on both sides of the Pacific and parts of Europe. Its thallus is composed of numerous, unbranched tubes up to 30 cm long and 0.5 cm wide with constrictions at regular intervals.

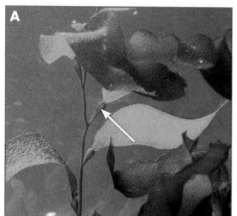

■ **31-24** *Macrocystis* (Laminariales) ≈ *Macrocystis* (giant perennial kelp) is the poster child for kelp! It grows in large forests off the coast of California (Figure 31-2) and reaches heights of 60 m. It is a perennial. (**A**) Each blade has a pneumatocyst (arrow) at its base. (**B**) A giant kelp requires a giant holdfast. This holdfast washed ashore with a portion of its rocky substrate still attached—a true testimony to the strength of the holdfast's ability to, er, hold fast! (**C**) Blades with pneumatocysts are produced sequentially out of a broad blade (arrow) as the stipe elongates.

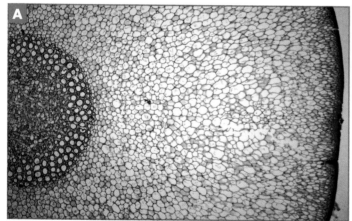

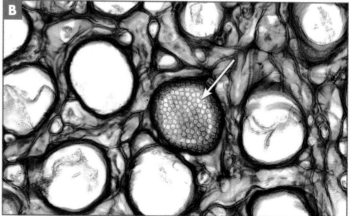

■ **31-25** *Macrocystis* Stipe Anatomy ≈ (**A**) Note the tissue differentiation in this stipe cross section. The outermost cellular layer is involved in photosynthesis. These cells are also capable of division (comprising the meristoderm) and enable circumferential growth of the stipe. The colorless cortical layer is composed of storage cells and surrounds the medulla, which is composed of conducting cells. Conducting cells are aligned end-to-end throughout the kelp's stipe and extend into the blades. They transport photosynthate (mostly the sugar alcohol mannitol, but also amino acids and ions) from the photosynthetic cells to the kelp's nonphotosynthetic parts. One study revealed a transport rate in *Macrocystis* of 50 cm per day. (**B**) End walls of conducting cells are perforated (arrow), not unlike conducting cells in flowering plants.

constitute the **cortex** (*cortex*—bark). Located internal to the cortex is the **medulla** (*medulla*—pith, marrow). Specialized medullary cells have simple **sieve plates** (analogous to transport cells in many vascular plants) on their end walls and transport the products of photosynthesis (**photosynthate**) from the blades to the haptera. Growth in thallus length is achieved by **intercalary** (loosely translated: "inserted between") meristems. Surface cells constituting **meristoderm** (*meristos*—divisible, *derm*—skin) divide to produce growth in diameter. Important genera include *Macrocystis* (Figures 31-2 and 31-24), *Laminaria* (Figure 31-26), *Saccharina* (Figure 31-27), *Egregia* (Figure 31-28), *Alaria* (Figure 31-29), *Pterygophora* (Figure 31-30), *Pelagophycus* (Figure 31-31), *Nereocystis* (Figures 28-5 and 31-32), and *Postelsia* (Figure 31-33).

■ **31-26** *Laminaria setchellii* **(Laminariales)** ≈ There are 20+ species of *Laminaria* worldwide, and they all share a particular feature: they are flat (*lamina*—plate). In this species (split kelp), a single stipe gives rise to half a dozen or so belt-like blades and reaches a height of 1 m. The blades are resting on blades of the sea grass *Phyllospadix*.

■ **31-27** *Saccharina latissima* **(formerly *Laminaria saccharina*) (Laminariales)** ≈ The sporophyte of this Atlantic species grows as an **annual**; that is, each year a new generation is produced. In the winter, the blade is thick, but smooth. By summer it has developed its "tire-tracks" and ruffled edges. Its common name is sugar kelp because of the high concentration of the sugar alcohol mannitol. It reaches a height of 3 m.

■ **31-28** *Egregia* **(Laminariales)** ≈ *Egregia's* long (up to 15 m), belt-like stipe with short blades and pneumatocysts emerging from both sides earn the common name, feather boa kelp. It is found on the West Coast of North America in the low intertidal zone. This is probably several individuals growing alongside one another, but individual holdfasts (arrows) can be 25 cm in diameter. For better detail of blades and pneumatocysts, see Figure 28-2C.

■ **31-29** *Alaria marginata* **(Laminariales)** ≈ The winged kelp is found in lower rocky intertidal and subtidal zones from Alaska to California. The dozen or so species of *Alaria* are found in arctic and temperate regions of the Northern Hemisphere. Note the prominent midrib in each blade.

■ 31-30 *Pterygophora californica* (Laminariales) ≈ This
perennial kelp has a woody stipe that ends with a single blade.
Lateral blades below the terminal blade are sporophylls; that is,
they bear sporangia, and these are what you see in these specimens.
Blades are shed after spores are produced and are replaced by a
new set higher up the stipe the next year. Age of *Pterygophora*
can be determined by growth rings in the woody stipe. It has been
determined that individuals can live up to 20 years. Its common
name is old growth kelp

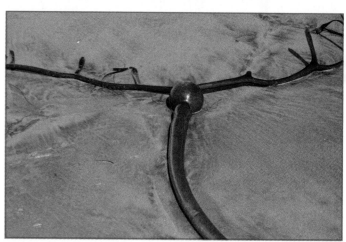

■ 31-31 *Pelagophycus porra* (Laminariales) ≈ This is a
deepwater kelp that may occasionally (as seen here) be found in
the drift. The stipe can grow to 27 m and is topped by a large,
single pneumatocyst. Emerging from the pneumatocyst are two
dichotomous branches, with each branch terminating in a blade
up to 20 m in length. This specimen was washed ashore after a
storm and much of it is missing, but when complete the common
name, elk kelp, is certainly apt. It avoids competition with *Macrocystis* by growing in deeper water.

■ 31-32 *Nereocystis lutkeana* (Laminariales) ≈ *Nereocystis
lutkeana* (bull kelp) can reach a total height of 40 m, 90% of which
is the stipe. The single pneumatocyst has a volume of 3 L and
contains 10% carbon monoxide (CO). Clusters of blades arise from
short branches emerging from the pneumatocyst. It is capable of
growing 10 cm per day. This specimen was found in the drift of an
Oregon beach.

■ 31-33 *Postelsia palmaeformis* (Laminariales) ≈ Its
short, stumpy haptera in the holdfast and up to 100 blades in
a tuft at the top of the stipe give this alga its common name: sea
palm. It is a resident in the low to midtidal zone of rocky areas
exposed to surf from central California northward to Canada. Its
height (0.5 m), flexibility, and tenacity of the holdfast combine to
permit *Postelsia* to survive the pounding of surf in exposed coasts.

Saltwort

Hottentot fig

32 Marine Anthophyta

Vascular plants, unlike the algae, have a high degree of tissue and organ differentiation, and this begins with the presence of **vascular** (*vas*—vessel) **tissue**, which is responsible for the transport of materials between different parts of the plant. A transport system relieved the necessity of all plant cells being in contact with a water source and made possible the invasion of land. Paradoxically, the topic of this chapter is vascular plants that have subsequently evolved an aquatic or semiaquatic life style.

"True" plants belong to the division Embryophyta, a clade within the Archaeplastida (Figure 29-1). Based on fossil evidence, the earliest embryophytes evolved about 470 million years ago (mya). In turn came the development of vascular tissue (410 mya), **seeds** (370 mya), and **flowers** (130 mya). Seeds enclose the new sporophyte **embryo** (*embruon*—fetus) and are a means of delaying its development until conditions are conducive to survival. They house nutritive material for the embryo's early, pre-photosynthetic development. (Formation of an embryo is a major synapomorphy of Embryophyta.) Flowers are reproductive structures that produce fruit to house the seeds. Fruits are a means of dispersing seeds from the parent plant.

The vascular plant life cycle illustrates typical alternation of generations with the sporophyte being the dominant, independent generation. Gametophytes are greatly reduced in size and are frequently dependent on the sporophyte for sustenance.

While we may informally (and incorrectly!) apply the terms *roots*, *stems*, and *leaves* to nonvascular plants, only vascular plants have these organs. In general, **roots** anchor the plant and absorb water and minerals from the soil. **Leaves** are the primary photosynthetic organs and grow from the stems. **Stems** are responsible for growth of the plant in length, allowing it to become taller, spread out, or both. This allows production of more leaves and in dense areas of growth, the opportunity to seek sunlight. Leaves develop from certain places on the stem called **nodes** (*nodus*—knot). If a node produces only a single leaf and the leaves emerge in different directions from the stem, the leaf arrangement is said to be **alternate**. If the node produces two leaves and they emerge 180° from one another (as measured around the stem), they are said to be **opposite**. If many leaves emerge from a node, the leaves are in a **whorled** arrangement.

Vascular tissue (Figure 32-1) is of two types—**xylem** (*xulon*—wood) and **phloem** (*phloos*—bark)—and both are composed of multiple cell types. It is beyond the scope of this book to describe these tissues in detail, but here are some salient features of both. Both tissues are involved in conducting materials from one part of the plant to another. Xylem is responsible for transporting water and minerals from roots to stems to leaves. The elongated conducting cells (tracheary elements) are dead at maturity with only the cell wall remaining and are aligned end-to-end, forming tubes through which water and minerals are carried. Phloem (Figure 32-1) is responsible for transporting the products of photosynthesis (photosynthate) from leaves to other parts of the plant, though it also transports materials in the opposite direction as well. The elongated conducting cells at maturity have lost many organelles, including the nucleus, but retain others.

Three main groups comprise vascular plants (Figure 32-2): the **ferns** (seedless vascular plants), the **gymnosperms**, (cone producing plants) and the **angiosperms** (flowering plants). Of these three main groups, only the angiosperms

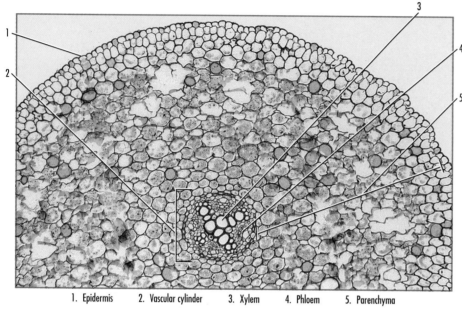

1. Epidermis   2. Vascular cylinder   3. Xylem   4. Phloem   5. Parenchyma

■ **32-1 Vascular Plant Tissue Organization** ≈ This micrograph of a vascular plant (eudicot) root cut in cross section illustrates simple tissue organization. On the surface, the single layer of cells is the epidermis. The circular region in the root's center is the vascular cylinder, which is composed of xylem (the large, thick-walled cells forming an "X") and phloem (the green, thin-walled cells filling in between the xylem). Between the epidermis and the vascular cylinder is parenchyma, made of large, thin-walled cells that perform a variety of functions. In a root, it frequently is used to store starch, which is visible as pink granules. In stems and leaves, chloroplasts are found in the parenchyma.

Torrey pine

Female cone

Male cones

■ **32-2 Gymnosperms and Angiosperms** ≈ (A) Gymnosperms reproduce with cones and produce seeds. While not well represented in the marine environment, some species grow in coastal regions and are under the influence of a marine climate. This photograph is of a Torrey pine (*Pinus torreyana*). These are a relict population, restricted only to cliffs in La Jolla, CA, and the Channel Islands off California. It is an endangered species. Notice that this individual does not have the usual conical pine tree shape. On-shore winds result in these pines growing lower to the ground and having a "blown over" shape. Those individuals that grow in more protected areas (some less than 100 yards from this specimen) grow more erect. (B) The gymnosperm reproductive structure is a cone. Shown is a female Torrey pine cone. The cone scales carry the female gametophyte, which houses the egg. These will develop within a structure that becomes the seed. Also visible are the leaves (needles). Notice that they grow in bundles. The number of needles in a bundle is characteristic for each pine species. The Torrey pine has five needles in each bundle. (C) Male cones produce pollen, which is the male gametophyte and houses the sperm. (D) Flowers are the angiosperm's reproductive organs, and they come in a wide variety of shapes, sizes, and arrangements. It might be difficult to believe, but every plant in this sand dune community is an angiosperm and most are in bloom.

Dune angiosperms

(*angio*—a small vessel, *sperma*—seed, referring to seeds carried inside a fruit) are well represented in the littoral and sublittoral environments (though ferns are found in the understory of mangrove forests). The flower is the angiosperm reproductive organ (Figure 32-3). At its most complex, the flower consists of four types of modified leaves arranged around a compressed stem. That is, there is little space between the modified leaves so they all appear to emerge from the same place. The first flower structures (and lowest on the stem) to be produced are the **sepals** (*sépale*—covering). These typically appear green and leaf-like. They enclose the developing flower bud. **Petals** (*petalon*—leaf) are the next series of leaves. These typically are leaf shaped, but pigmented to attract **pollinators** (animals that disperse pollen for the angiosperm). The next series is made of highly modified leaves—so much so that they no longer resemble leaves. These are the **stamens**, which consist of **anthers** (*anthera*—flowery) that produce **pollen** (the male gametophyte), and **filaments** that hold the anthers aloft. The final part of the flower is made of one or more in-folded leaves to form the **pistil**. The pistil consists of an **ovary** that houses one or more **ovules**, each of which contains the female gametophyte, a **stigma** (where pollen lands), and a **style** that connects the stigma with the ovary. The portion of the stem to which the flower is attached is called the receptacle. If the ovary is positioned above the receptacle, it is **superior**. If during development the ovary becomes buried in the receptacle, it is **inferior**.

Other flower terminology is necessary. Flowers can be bisexual (monoecious), that is, with both stamens and pistil, or unisexual (dioecious), in which only stamens or pistil are found. Flowers can be **complete** and have all four parts, or **incomplete** and be missing one or another of the structures (e.g., no petals). Flowers can also show **radial symmetry** (**regular flower**) or **bilateral symmetry** (**irregular flower**). Flowers can be solitary on a stem, or can be found in characteristic groupings called **inflorescences** (*inflorescere*—come into flower).

There are three major angiosperm clades: the **magnoliids** (named after French botanist Pierre Magnol), the **monocotyledons** (*mono*—one, *cotyledon*—cup-shaped cavity), and the **eudicots** (*eu*—true, *di*—two), with the monocotyledons and eudicots comprising the majority of angiosperms (22% and 75%, respectively). The magnoliids and other, smaller deep-branching clades don't have marine representatives and are not treated here. It is unclear when and in what order these clades separated.

The majority of flowering plants (estimated at 190,000 species) belong to the monophyletic eudicot clade. All have two cotyledons and pollen grains with three openings, or pollen grains derived from that condition. Eudicots can produce true wood via a **vascular cambium**, though many are **herbaceous**, and most have flower parts in multiples of four or five. **Petioles** (*petiolus*—little stalk) attach dicot leaves to the stem and leaf veins form a branched network (Figure 32-4A). Stem vascular tissue is either cylindrical or separate vascular bundles in rings (Figure 32-4B). In addition, there are many biochemical and nucleic acid unifying features. Important estuarine, sand dune, and marine families are outlined in Table 32-1.

The monocots are a monophyletic group with the following apomorphies: the seed has a single cotyledon (seed leaf), they do not produce wood (they are herbaceous), their leaves wrap around the stem and have parallel veins (Figure 32-5A), and their stems have a "scattered" (actually, quite complex) organization of vascular tissue (Figure 32-5B).

■ **32-3 Basic Flower Structure** ≈

(A) Most flower parts are visible in this *Hibiscus* photo. At the left are the green sepals that extend over the yellow petals. In *Hibiscus,* there are additional, nonflower leaves below the sepals. These are called bracts and are the narrow, inwardly curved leaves to the left of (below) the sepals. Numerous stamens with their anthers are also visible. *Hibiscus* is unusual in that the stamen filaments are fused to form a tube around the style,

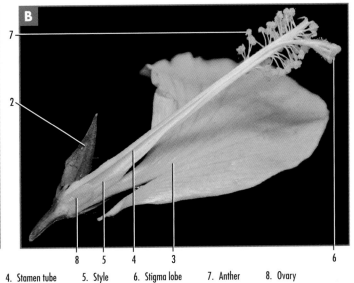

1. Bract   2. Sepal   3. Petal   4. Stamen tube   5. Style   6. Stigma lobe   7. Anther   8. Ovary

which can be seen emerging at the right end of the flower (it is narrower than the stamen tube). The five stalks with rounded heads are the stigma lobes where pollen lands. The ovary is not visible in this view. (B) This dissected *Hibiscus* has most of the petals and sepals removed, and the ovary and stamen tube have been cut open. The ovary is the oval object at the left. Faintly visible within the ovary are the bead-like ovules, each of which houses a female gametophyte and will be become the seed after fertilization. You can also see the style emerging from the ovary and passing within the stamen tube.

■ 32-4 Basic Eudicot Features ≈

The primary eudicot feature is two cotyledons. However, other features are fairly consistently seen in eudicots that allow their identification without the seed. (A) Leaf veins form an interconnected network, as shown in this leaf. Also note the distinct petiole (arrow) attaching each leaf to the stem. (B) Eudicot stem vascular bundles (arrows) are organized into a ring. In woody eudicots (or any woody plant for that matter), the bundles fuse to form a complete ring. Where the xylem and phloem join, a growth region (vascular cambium) develops and produces wood and other tissues.

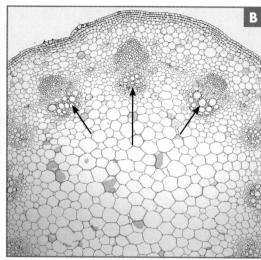

■ Table 32-1 ≈ Eudicot Orders and Families

Order Family	Characteristics	Marine/Estuarine/ Sand Dune Examples	Approximate Number of Species	Etymology
Apiales **Apiaceace (Umbelliferae)** Carrot Family (Figure 32-11)	Usually herbaceous; leaf petioles often sheathing the stem; inflorescence a simple or compound umbel; flowers complete with inferior ovary	Angelica	3,500	apium—celery, aceae—standard botanical suffix denoting a family
Asterales **Asteraceae (Compositae)** Sunflower Family (Figure 32-12)	Mostly herbaceous; inflorescence a head composed of one or both disc flowers and ray flowers, all attached to the receptacle; ovary inferior.	Ambylopappus, Ambrosia, Baccharis, Cotula, Jaumea	23,000	aster—star, aceae—family suffix
Brassicales **Batacea (Batidaceae)** Saltwort Family (Figure 32-13)	Low, bushy shrubs; marine; leaves opposite and fleshy; flowers unisexual; ovary superior	Batis	2	batis—seashore plant, aceae—family suffix
Caryophyllales **Aizoaceae** Carpetweed Family (Figure 32-14)	Annual or perennial herbs; leaves usually opposite; flowers solitary and bisexual; flower parts numerous; "petals" are not true petals	Mesemryanthemum, Carpobrotus	2,500	aei—always, zoon—animal, aceae—family suffix
Amaranthaceae (Including Chenopodiaceae) Amaranth Family (Figure 32-15)	Diverse group united by technical features	Atriplex, Chenopodium, Salicornia, Arthrocnemum, Suaeda	2,200	amaranthus—unfading, aceae—family suffix
Frankeniaceae Frankenia Family (Figure 32-16)	Shrubs; grow from rhizome; leaves opposite with salt secreting glands; flowers bisexual, regular, and complete with superior ovary	Frankenia	90	Named either for naturalists J. Franke (Swedish botanist) or Johann Frankenius (colleague of Linnaeus)
Nyctaginaceae Four o'clock Family (Figure 32-17)	Perennials; leaves opposite, usually unequal in size; flowers bisexual; sepals petalloid, forming a tube; ovary superior	Abronia	300	nyct—night, aceae—family suffix
Plumbaginaceae Leadwort Family (Figure 32-18)	Leaves typically surrounding stem at base; flowers bisexual, regular, small, and sometimes tubular; flower parts in 5s	Limonium	400	plumbum—lead, aceae—family suffix

(continued)

Order Family	Characteristics	Marine/Estuarine/ Sand Dune Examples	Approximate Number of Species	Etymology

Lamiales
  Acanthaceae
  Acanthus Family
  (Figure 33-5E)
	Trees and shrubs of mangroves; leaves opposite; flowers small, regular, complete, and bisexual; (pneumatophores grow above water to aerate underwater/underground parts in *Avicennia*)	*Avicennia*	10	*akanthos*—bear's foot, *aceae*—family suffix

Plantaginaceae
  Plantain Family
  (Figure 32-19)
	Mostly herbs; leaves basal; inflorescence a spike; flowers unisexual or bisexual	*Plantago*	300	*planta*—sole of foot, *aceae*—family suffix

Orobanchaceae
  Broomrape Family
  (Figure 32-20)
	Root parasites; stems mostly underground; flowers complete	*Cordylanthus*	200	*orobanch*—"legume strangler," *aceae*—family suffix

Myrtales
  Onagraceae
  Evening Primrose Family
  (Figure 32-21)
	Herbs and shrubs; flower parts usually in 4s; ovary inferior	*Oenothera.*
		Camissonia
			650	*onagra*—oleander, *aceae*—family suffix

Rhizophorales
  Rhizophoraceae
  Mangrove Family
  (Figure 32-22)
	Tropical and subtropical plants; stems woody; stilt roots frequently produced; flowers regular; petals often fleshy and shorter than sepals	*Rhizophora*	150	*rhizo*—root, *phoros*—to bear, *aceae*—family suffix

Solanales
  Convolvulaceae
  Morning Glory Family
  (Figure 32-23)
	Perennial or annual; usually herbaceous vines; flowers bisexual, regular, and complete with 5 sepals, 5 fused petals, stamens fused to the petals, and a superior ovary; petals often pleated	*Convolvulus,*
		Cressa
			1,600	*convolvere*—to twist, *aceae*—family suffix

Cuscutaceae
  Dodder Family
  (Figure 32-24)
	Annual, parasitic vines; roots live only long enough for parasite to tap into host; flowers small with parts in 5s and ovary superior; sometimes included with Convolvulaceae	*Cuscuta*	150	*cuscuta*—ancient Arabic name, *aceae*—family suffix

Unplaced, but near Lamiales and Solanales
  Boraginaceae
  Borage Family
  (Figure 32-25)
	Variety in growth habits; stems and leaves often hairy; basal leaves in addition to stem leaves; flowers often in coiled (like a scorpion's tail) inflorescence; flowers bisexual, radial, tubular with parts in 5s and a superior ovary.	*Heliotropium,*
		Amsinckia
			2,000	*burage*—hair stuffing, *aceae*—family suffix

Flower parts in multiples of three (for example, 3 sepals, 3 petals, 6 stamens, and a 3-parted ovary) has long been used as a unifying monocot feature, but the evidence now suggests that this is the ancestral condition and not an apomorphy. It is estimated that there are 56,000 monocot species. Important estuarine, marine, and dune monocot families are outlined in Table 32-2.

As we have seen in Chapters 28 through 31, the littoral and sublittoral zones of coastlines are dominated by macro-algae. What vascular plants there are generally grow in the littoral zone, though some are sublittoral and others are adapted to sandy regions that rarely, if ever, get submerged with water. The main environmental factors that must be dealt with, then, are salinity (including the drying effects of salt), periodic submergence, substrate stability, and aeration of underground parts. Each will be considered independently.

Marine vascular plants are **halophytes** (*halo*—salt) and are able to tolerate environmental salinities higher than **glycophytes** that grow in low-salt substrates (like "typical" soil). However, halophytes are confronted with a challenge not faced by glycophytes, and that is getting water into the plant via the roots. Water moves passively into plant roots by **osmosis** (*osmose*—a push), the process of water diffusing from a region of higher concentration to a region of lower concentration across the selectively permeable[1] cytoplasmic membrane. This requires a higher concentration of dissolved substances in the roots than in the soil, a condition not found

---

The cytoplasmic membrane is said to be selectively permeable (*permabilis*—pass through) because some materials can pass through it and others cannot. As a rule, water passes freely through the membrane. The ability of dissolved substances (solutes) to pass through the membrane depends on their size and other physical properties.

32-5 Basic Monocot Features ~

The primary monocot feature is the presence of a single seed leaf (cotyledon). However, as with eudicots, other features are consistently seen that allow identification of a plant as a monocot without having to view the seed. **(A)** Monocot leaves typically have a parallel venation, as illustrated in this close-up of two *Spartina* leaves. Figure 32-32B shows how the leaf base wraps around the stem (instead of having a distinct petiole), another typical monocot feature. **(B)** This cross section of a monocot stem illustrates another monocot feature—vascular tissue arrangement in the stem. For a long time, the bundles were considered "scattered," which implied lack of organization. Three-dimensional studies revealed a quite complex vascular bundle arrangement as they course their way through the stem. While this is not a useful feature in the field, you may be observing microscopic specimens in your class.

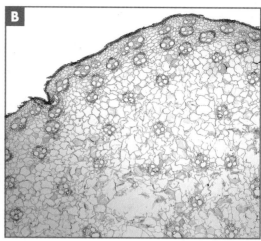

Table 32-2 ~ Monocot Orders and Families

Order Family	Characteristics	Marine/ Estuarine/Sand Dune Examples	Approximate Number of Species	Etymology
Alismatales **Hydrocharitaceae** Waterweed Family (Figure 32-26)	Diverse aquatic herbs; flowers usually complete and regular; ovary inferior; plants rooted or floating	*Thalassia,* *Halophila*	80–100	*hydro*—water, *charit*—grace, beauty, *aceae*—standard botanical suffix denoting a family
Juncaginaceae Arrowgrass Family (Figure 32-27)	Leaves linear and often rounded in cross section; grow from rhizome; flowers not showy	*Triglochin*	15	*juncus*—rush, *aceae*—family suffix
Zosteraceae Eelgrass Family (Figure 32-28)	Perennial grass-like herbs; flowers unisexual and not showy, lacking petals and sepals	*Phyllospadix,* *Zostera*	14–18	*zoster*—belt or girdle, *aceae*—family suffix
Poales **Cyperaceae** Sedge Family (Figure 32-30)	Herbs and shrubs; grow from rhizomes; aerial stems triangular in cross section; flowers lack petals	*Scirpus*	5,000	*cyperus*—sedge, *aceae*—family suffix
Juncaceae Rush Family (Figure 32-31)	Rhizomes; leaves usually basal and round in cross section; flowers bisexual and complete	*Juncus*	400	*junct*—to join, *aceae*—family suffix
Cymodoceaceae Manatee grass Family (Figure 32-29)	Perennial herbs; grow from rhizomes; flowers unisexual, lacking petals and sepals	*Syringodium*	16	*cymo*—wave, *aceae*—family suffix
Poaceae (Gramineae) Grass Family (Figure 32-32)	Annual and perennial herbs; flowers reduced to stamens and/or pistils associated with a variety of bracts; wind pollinated; hollow stems	*Distichlis,* *Monanthochloe,* *Spartina*	10,000	*poa*—grass, *aceae*—family suffix

in marine and estuarine environments. Halophytes have several physiological mechanisms to produce osmotically favorable conditions. One is to accumulate salts in the root so there is a higher concentration than in the environment (thus making the root's water content lower, so water diffuses in). Because there is a limit to how much salt even a halophile can tolerate, some are able to synthesize organic solutes in excess of the environmental salt concentration and accomplish the same thing. Other physiological mechanisms are also employed, but are beyond the scope of this book.

Once in the plant, high salinity must be dealt with. Adaptations include dilution of salts through growth (increasing plant mass) or by **succulence** (*succus*—juice) (Figure 32-6A). Another adaptation is transporting salts to older plant parts and then shedding them (Figure 32-6B). These plants are known as salt accumulaters. A third is salt excreters that remove it via epidermal salt glands (Figures 32-6C and 32-6D).

Another related issue is the ability of halophytes to retain water once they have it. Plants adapted to drying conditions are called **xerophytes** (*xeros*—dry) and many salt marsh and mangrove plants show xerophytic adaptations. In addition to diluting salts, succulence is also a mechanism for retaining water. Another is to have a thickened waxy **cuticle** over exposed parts to reduce evaporation (Figure 32-7A). **Bundle sheath cells** surround leaf veins, and in xerophytes the bundle sheaths are well developed with waxy walls, which minimize water loss (Figure 32-7B). Finally, many xerophytes have a reduced surface area, especially in the leaves (Figure 32-7C). With a smaller surface area, water loss is reduced.

Anchorage to a soft, shifting substrate requires a mechanism for good anchorage. Plants of salt marshes and sandy regions frequently grow from underground stems called **rhizomes** (Figure 32-8A). These may be located up to 1 m below the surface. For perennial plants, rhizomes also act as storage organs when the plant goes through dormancy. The roots may be of two types. Thicker roots serve the primary function of anchorage, whereas finer ones are responsible for absorption. In some cases, trees produce **prop**, or **stilt**, **roots** from stems for stabilization (Figures 32-8B and 33-5B).

Supplying oxygen to underground and submerged plant parts is another challenge faced by many marine and estuarine plants. Many have specialized **aerenchyma** tissue (Figure 32-9) in which the normal parenchyma cells separate and form internal air channels throughout the plant. This tissue is present (up to 40% of the volume!) in the stilt roots and other specialized structures of mangrove trees (*Rhizophora* and *Avicennia*) (Figures 32-8B and 33-5E). It also has been shown that roots of some salt marsh plants

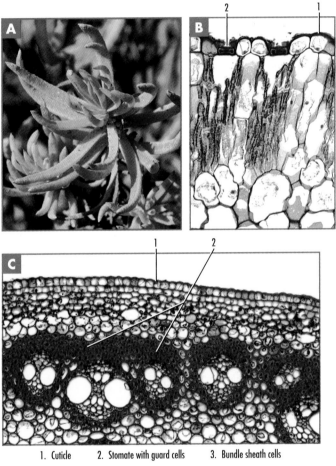

1. Cuticle   2. Stomate with guard cells   3. Bundle sheath cells

■ **32-7 Xerophyte Adaptations** ≈ It might seem strange that plants growing around water would have adaptations to drying, but drying in marine and estuarine plants comes from salt in the water (resulting in osmosis out of the plant), not the absence of water. (**A**) Vascular plants have tiny pores called stomates in stems and leaves that allow air for photosynthesis inside, but they also let water out. Reducing the surface area concurrently reduces the number of stomates through which water can evaporate. These *Suaeda* leaves show a small surface area and also illustrate some degree of succulence. The *Frankenia* leaves in Figure 32-6C also show reduced surface area. (**B**) The aerial parts of land plants are covered with a waxy cuticle that minimizes water loss. A xerophyte adaptation is to have a thicker cuticle. This is a cross section of a *Salicornia* petiole (leaf base). The cuticle is the irregular red material on the epidermis. (**C**) Bundle sheath cells surround vascular bundles. Xerophytes have well-developed bundle sheath cells, many of which have waxy walls (stained red) that restrict water passage.

■ **32-6 Halophyte Adaptations** ≈ (**A**) Succulence (water storage) permits dilution of salts within cells. It also is a xerophytic adaptation to the drying environmental conditions faced by many estuarine plants. These are leaves of *Batis*. (**B**) This *Salicornia* species illustrates shedding, in which salts are concentrated in older parts of the plant (turning them red) that are subsequently lost. The narrower brown regions of the stem (arrow) are where parts have already been shed. Note that *Salicornia* also illustrates succulence. Compare this specimen with the ones in Figures 32-15A and 32-15C. (**C**) Some halophytes handle excess salt by secreting it onto the surfaces of their leaves. Salt grains are visible on these *Frankenia* leaves. (**D**) *Limonium* is also a salt-excreter.

actually aerate the anaerobic surroundings by releasing oxygen.

An adaptation to submergence is location of the leaf **stomates** (*stoma*—mouth), the openings that allow air, which carries carbon dioxide for photosynthesis, into the plant. In terrestrial plants, stomates are typically on the "under" surface of leaves. Many low-lying halophytes and other plants that float on water (called hypcophytes) have their stomates on the "upper" surface, as the "under" surface is likely to be under water or lying on damp mud (Figure 32-10).

Figures 32-11 through 32-25 illustrate eudicot diversity in marine, estuarine, and sandy habitats. Figures 32-26 through 32-32 do the same for monocots.

■ 32-8 Adaptations to Substrate Instability

≈ The sandy and muddy substrates in estuaries and mangrove thickets are not firm, so anchorage of the plant is an issue faced by plants growing there. (**A**) One adaptation is to grow from an underground stem (rhizome) that is not easily dislodged by the shifting substrate. Shown is a short *Zostera* rhizome segment (it's been broken) from which roots and leaves emerge. (The dark green, leafy specimen in the upper right is *Ulva*—a green alga.) (**B**) The red mangrove (*Rhizophora*) produces stilt roots from stems that add support to the tree. They also have specialized tissue that conducts air to the underground roots that live in anaerobic mud (See Figure 32-9).

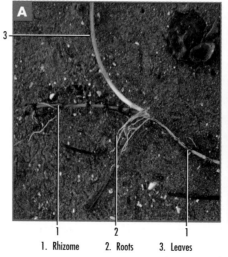

1. Rhizome   2. Roots   3. Leaves

■ 32-9 Aerenchyma

≈ Marine and estuarine plants live in water-saturated mud, which displaces air and the oxygen that it contains. A typical adaptation seen in any plant growing in these conditions (including freshwater) is the production of a tissue called aerenchyma in the roots. Parenchyma cells separate, producing spaces through which air can pass, as seen in this micrograph. Compare this micrograph with the root in Figure 32-1.

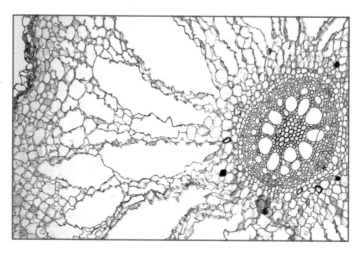

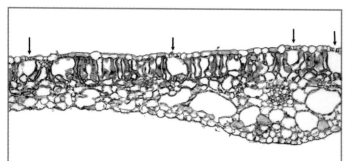

■ 32-10 Hydrophyte Leaf

≈ The pores (stomates) that allow air into the leaves of land plants are most abundant on the leaf's lower surface. But, the lower leaf surface of plants living in water or on muddy substrates will be covered and won't be exposed to air. Stomates (arrows) on the upper surface, as shown in this hydrophyte leaf, is an adaptation shown by most hydrophytes. Note also the absence of a significant cuticle and bundle sheath (compare with Figures 32-7B and 32-7C).

■ 32-11 Carrots (Apiaceae or Umbelliferae)

≈ This is the carrot family, and members are usually perennial herbs with complexly shaped leaves. Shown is *Angelica hendersonii*, which grows on coastal bluffs and coastal strands in the northwestern United States. The typical carrot inflorescence of flowers in an inverted umbrella (called an **umbel**) is visible. Flowers are white, flattened, and bisexual with an inferior ovary. *Angelica* species are common in northern latitudes and are not restricted to marine environments.

Beach bur

Marsh jaumea

32-12 Sunflowers (Asteraceae or Compositae)

≈ The sunflower family is the largest of the eudicots and demonstrates great diversity. At first glance, many sunflower inflorescences give the appearance of being a single flower, but such is not the case. The inflorescence, called a **head**, consists of a single receptacle to which multiple flowers are attached and which has bracts (leaves) underneath. Flowers may be bisexual or unisexual, and are of two (for our purposes—some authors recognize five) morphological types. **Disc flowers** have their petals fused into a tube. **Ray flowers** have their petals fused into an elongated extension with three to five teeth at the end. Inflorescences may contain only disc flowers, only ray flowers, or may have both. (A) Beach bur (*Ambrosia chamissonis*—the common name for the genus is ragweed, the one of allergy fame) inhabits coastal strands of western North America. It is a spreading, herbaceous plant with silvery leaves. (B) *Ambrosia* heads, which are oriented downward, contain either staminate disc flowers (above) or pistillate disc flowers (below) on the same plant. These pistillate flowers have already produced the bur fruit, visible at the bottom of the flowering stem (arrow). (C) *Jaumea carnosa* is an inhabitant of salt marshes and mudflats along the West Coast of North America, and clearly tolerates submergence. (D) This photo shows seven ray and multiple disc flowers in *J. carnosa*. It is a perennial herb that shows some succulence. (E) Yarrow (*Achillea*) is a widely distributed herbaceous plant characterized by finely dissected leaves and heads composed of both disc and ray flowers. This specimen was growing in coastal sand dunes in Northern California, but *Achillea* species are widespread and capable of growing in a variety of habitats.

Yarrow

32-13 Saltworts (Bataceae or Batidaceae)

≈ Saltwort (*Batis maritima*) is an inhabitant of tropical and subtropical coastal salt marshes in the Western Hemisphere. It has succulent leaves, and the staminate and pistillate flowers are on different plants. Pistillate flowers are shown in the upper left photo on page 275.

Ice plant

Hottentot fig

Sea fig

32-14 Carpetweeds (Aizoaceae)

≈ The ice plant (carpetweed) family is characterized by succulent leaves in an opposite arrangement on the stem. (A) True ice plant (*Mesembryanthemum crystallinum*) has become naturalized in coastal strands, but is native to Africa. It also is planted as an ornamental but has been classified in California as a moderately invasive species. In spite of its invasiveness, it is a beautiful plant with complete and bisexual flowers and leaves with large water vesicles that give it the appearance of being frost-covered. (B) *Carpobrotus* is another member of the family that has become naturalized in sand dune communities of California and Baja California. (C) Sea fig (*C. chilense*) has pinkish purple flowers and originally came from South America. Notice the numerous "petals," stamens, and stigma lobes. Shown in the right-hand photo on page 275 is the closely related Hottentot fig (*C. edulis*) with light yellow flowers. It is native to South Africa and actually is considered an invasive species in California, even though it has been intentionally planted along highways for erosion control. A flower that has gone to fruit is shown at the right.

Pickleweed

Pickleweed

Saltbush

Seablite

■ **32-15 Amaranths (Amaranthaceae Including Chenopodiaceae)** ≈ The amaranth family is well represented in salt marsh communities and species are found worldwide. The following organisms were at one time placed in the Chenopodiaceae, but have been moved to the Amaranthaceae. (**A**) Pickleweed (*Salicornia* spp.) is probably the signature species of salt marshes. Species are either perennial or annual, and have "jointed," succulent stems (actually the leaf petioles—see below) with no obvious leaves. The "woody" portions below (arrow) are where segments that have concentrated salt have been shed (Also see Figure 32-6B). This specimen was photographed in Baja California. (**B**) What appear to be *Salicornia* stems are actually succulent leaf petioles (the stalks of eudicot leaf bases), which wrap around the stem and give it the jointed appearance. This is a micrograph of a *Salicornia* cut in cross section. The circular region in the center of the specimen is actually the stem, with the outer portion being the petiole. Notice the typical eudicot circular arrangement of vascular bundles within the stem. Vascular bundles in the petiole are cut in various ways, indicating a variety of paths through the petiole (network venation typical of eudicots). When salt-laden petioles are shed, what remains is the true stem. (**C**) *Salicornia* flowers are usually bisexual, but greatly reduced in size, and are mostly covered by the succulent petiole. The white objects are stigma lobes set to trap pollen grains that might blow by. (**D**) Saltbush (*Atriplex*) is found in marshy areas of all sorts. This species was found growing at the edge of a salt marsh. (**E**) Saltbush flowers have no petals or sepals, as shown in this photo. (**F**) Seablite (*Suaeda*) is found in salt marshes and mud flats. Its succulent leaves are thin and long, and its flowers are bisexual, but lack petals.

■ **32-16 Frankenias (Frankeniaceae)** ≈
Members of the Frankenia family are shrubby with regular, complete flowers with a superior ovary. Alkali heath (*Frankenia grandifolia*—quite a prideful name for a plant whose flower is less than 1 cm in length!) grows in sandy areas on the margins of coastal salt marshes. The leaves are opposite and curled under, an adaptation to reduce water loss by deflecting evaporative air currents from the stomata.

■ **32-17 Four O'Clocks (Nyctaginaceae)** ≈ The four o'clock family is composed of herbs and shrubs with bisexual and regular flowers. Petals are absent, but the sepals are colored and form a tube of varying shapes. The sand verbenas (*Abronia*) are not related to true verbenas (*Verbena*; Verbenaceae). (**A**) Shown is *A. umbellata*. Its stems grow across the sandy surface and its leaves are opposite. Notice the fine hairs on the tubular flowers. (**B**) *A. maritima* has deeper reddish-pink flowers. Below the flowered inflorescence in this photo is an inflorescence whose flowers have gone to fruit (arrow).

■ **32-18 Leadworts (Plumbaginaceae)** ≈ The leadwort family is made of perennial herbs with complete, regular flowers. Shown is a sand dune community species of sea lavender (*Limonium*). Note the flowering stalk at the left (arrow). These are easy to overlook when plants are crowded. The leaves of a different *Limonium* species are shown in Figure 32-6D.

■ **32-19 Plantains (Plantaginaceae)** ≈ Plantains are annual or perennial herbs with basal leaves and spike-like inflorescences. Flowers are regular and usually bisexual. **(A)** This species of *Plantago* is growing on the virtually vertical face of a tall (several meters high) rock in the intertidal zone on the southern Oregon coast. Life is opportunistic and tenacious! **(B)** This is *P. maritima* and is growing in a coastal strand of Northern California. Note the flowers emerging from the spikes.

■ **32-20 Broomrapes (Orobanchaceae)** ≈ Members of the broomrape family are root parasites. Salt marsh bird's beak (*Cordylanthus maritimus*) is found in coastal salt marshes of the southwestern United States and Baja California. It gets its common name from the shape of its white flowers and is an endangered species.

■ **32-21 Evening Primroses (Onagraceae)** ≈ Evening primroses show wide variety in form from herbs to shrubs and trees. Unifying characters include complete flowers, generally with 4 sepals, 4 petals, 4 or 8 stamens, and a 2- or 4-parted inferior ovary. Beach evening primrose (*Camissonia cheiranthifolia*) is a coastal strand species of California and Oregon with spreading stems and whose flowers, in spite of the family name, often open in the morning.

■ **32-23 Morning Glories (Convolvulaceae)** ≈ Alkali weed (*Cressa truxillensis*) is an unusual member of the morning glory family because it isn't vine-like, but its flower structure is consistent with that placement. Note the two style lobes terminating in white, rounded expansions and the five purple anthers.

■ **32-22 Mangroves (Rhizophoraceae)** ≈ Mangroves are trees of tropical and subtropical regions. The red mangrove, *Rhizophora mangal*, is an intertidal species characterized by its stilt roots with aerenchyma (also seen in Figures 32-8B and 32-9) and seedling development while still on the parent tree. These are the "pods" you see in this photo.

■ **32-24 Dodders (Cuscutaceae)** ≈ Dodders have thin, twining, yellow to orange stems. All are parasitic and tap into their host's phloem through structures called **haustoria** (*haus*—to draw). (**A**) *Cuscuta salina* has almost completely covered its salt marsh host, *Frankenia*. Amazingly, dodders don't seem to kill their hosts, though they are obviously a drain on the host's health and productivity. (**B**) This *C. salina* has found a *Salicornia* host. The white, regular flowers with five petals belong to the dodder.

■ **32-25 Borages (Boraginaceae)** ≈ This is a family that as yet has not been placed into an order. Borages show a wide variety of growth habits, from herbs to shrubs and trees. Flowers are regular, tubular, and complete, with parts usually in 5s, and with a superior ovary. (**A**) Salt heliotrope (*Heliotropium curassavicum*) grows in the western United States in sandy, saline, or alkaline soils. It is moderately succulent. (**B**) Frequently, borage flowers are in a coiled ("scorpioid") inflorescence, as shown here. Young *H. curassavicum* flowers have yellow spots on the petals. With age, these become purple as seen in this photo.

■ **32-26 Turtle Grasses (Hydrocharitaceae)** ≈ In spite of the name, turtle grass (*Thalassia testudinum*) is not a true grass. It is found in the Caribbean, along the shores of the Gulf states, and many other locations worldwide, and grows from an underground rhizome. It can withstand some amount of exposure to air, but is generally submerged. It also requires high salinity and protection from heavy wave action. Pollen grains are released in chains, not singly.

■ **32-27 Arrowgrasses (Juncaginaceae)** ≈ Sea arrowgrass (*Triglochin maritima*) also is not a grass. Its leaves are elongate and somewhat rounded in cross section (reducing surface area). Their expanded bases form a sheath around the short rhizome. It is widely distributed in salt and other marshes throughout North America and parts of Europe. (**A**) Shown is *T. maritima* growing in a salt marsh. (**B**) On the left is a flowering stalk with the sepals/petals (they are indistinguishable) still attached as the ovaries are developing into fruit. The stalk on the right is further along in development; the sepals/petals have dropped off, leaving just the fruit.

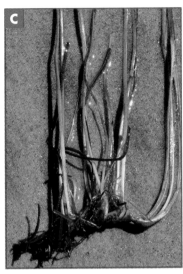

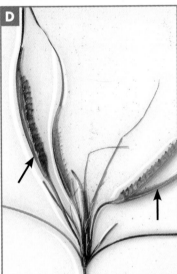

■ **32-28** **Eelgrasses (Zosteraceae)** ≈ Members of this family are grass-like (but not grasses) and have leaves arranged in two rows along the rhizome. Like grasses, the flowers do not produce petals. (**A**) Eelgrass *(Zostera marina)* is found in shallow waters of bays on both coasts of North America. It is usually submerged. Flowers are bisexual. (**B**) Surfgrass *(Phyllospadix)* is found in rocky intertidal areas subjected to surf. Notice the long leaves, which frequently attain a length of over 1 m. (**C**) Shown are *Phyllospadix* leaves emerging from a rhizome, which is entangled in older leaves and algae. (**D**) Flowers are unisexual and the inflorescences are enclosed in an expanded portion of the leaf called a spathe *(spathe—broad blade)*, indicated by the arrows. Shown are three pistillate inflorescences whose flowers have already gone to fruit. The stigma lobes are still visible as light brown hairs on the pistils of the middle inflorescence.

■ **32-29** **Manatee Grasses (Cymodoceaceae)** ≈ Manatee grass *(Syringodium filiforme)* is yet another grass-like plant that isn't a grass. Its leaves are long, narrow, round and grass-like, and they grow from rhizomes buried in the muddy or sandy substrate. Flowers are unisexual, with staminate and pistillate flowers on separate individuals. They are sublittoral and are found in tropical and subtropical oceans worldwide.

■ **32-30** **Sedges (Cyperaceae)** ≈ Sedges *(Scirpus* spp.) are perennial plants characterized by erect, triangular stems. The inflorescences are located above one or more leaves called bracts and are composed of bisexual flowers with sepals and petals reduced to bristles. (**A**) The majority of *Scirpus* species are freshwater, but a few species grow in salt marshes. These individuals are growing at the mouth of the Russian River in Northern California and so come under the influence of tidal fluctuations. The inflorescences are the brown patches. (**B**) Shown is an inflorescence from the plants in (**A**). The inflorescence structure is complex, with a series of bracts enclosing each apetalous *(a—without, petalon—leaf)* flower. Such flowers are typically wind pollinated and so the stamens (visible here) usually extend beyond the limits of the flower to catch the wind.

■ 32-31 Rushes (Juncaceae) ≈ Rushes (*Juncus* spp.) are perennial plants of moist places, including salt marshes. Stiff, grass-like leaves that are round in cross section characterize rushes. Flowers are bisexual, but the petals and sepals are reduced. (A) This ambitious *J. acutus* var. *sphaerocarpus* is growing in the middle of halophytes at the edge of coastal sand dunes. (B) Seen here are *J. acutus* var. *sphaerocarpus* inflorescences. And, if you look carefully, you'll see a little green insect among them.

■ 32-32 Grasses (Poaceae or Gramineae) ≈ The grasses belong to one of the largest monocot families. They have representatives in marine, estuarine, and dune communities. Flowers are reduced to stamens and pistil(s) surrounded by a variety of bracts to form complex inflorescences. The leaves are long and form a sheath around the hollow stem. (A) California cordgrass (*Spartina foliosa*) is frequently found in salt marshes and stands above most other plants, reaching heights of over 1 m. (B) Shown is a *Spartina* inflorescence. Note the salt on the leaf and how its base forms a sheath around the stem. (C) Saltgrass (*Distichlis staminate*) is a perennial with separate sexes. The plant's flat appearance is because the leaves are in two ranks along the stem. It grows in salt marshes. (D) Shown is a detail of a *Distichlis* staminate inflorescence with its emergent stamens. (E) Shore grass (*Monanthochloe littoralis*) is a salt marsh and mudflat species found in latitudes less than about 35° N. The overall appearance is that of a wiry plant with leaves in clusters along the stem. It spreads by a surface rhizome. (F) American dunegrass (*Leymus mollis*) is a tall perennial of coastal strands on both coasts of the northern United States and the Great Lakes. Note that growth in this Northern California stand is restricted to the dune sand; it isn't growing in the coarser wet sand of the beach. It has a deep rhizome that anchors it to the shifting substrate. (G) Shown is a clump of *L. mollis* leaves arising from the underground rhizome. The light brown structures at the top are the inflorescences.

Agate Beach, OR—high tide

Agate Beach, OR—low tide

33 Marine Habitats

Marine environments are extremely diverse and the physical conditions present at different geographical locations vary widely. As a consequence, extensive terminology has been developed to help scientists communicate these conditions.

This chapter will limit coverage to nearshore sublittoral, littoral, and supralittoral environments commonly encountered and use vernacular descriptive terms common to North America. The focus is on representative organisms, but major physical conditions are listed. However, it must be realized that habitats are a mosaic of subhabitats, each with its own physical conditions and characteristic organisms.

Reefs

Common marine reefs include coral (Figure 33-1) and rocky (Figure 33-2) reefs. Increasingly, artificial reefs (Figure 33-3) are built by sinking ships or building specialized structures that are placed in the ocean. These increase recreational opportunities and substrate supporting increased biological diversity.

Coral reefs occur around the world.

■ **33-1 Coral Reefs** ≈ (A) Typically, coral reefs are not long continuous structures, but instead, have a complex structure broken by rocky outcroppings and fingers of sandy bottoms. The dark areas in this photograph are the reef and scattered rock. The light green is a sandy bottom running from left to right, and the wave line is the seaward edge of the shallow reef. (B) A coral column reaches toward the surface as an array of fish swim overhead. *(continued)*

■ 33-1 Coral Reefs ≈ *(continued)* (C) The reef's edge is covered with a diversity of reef organisms: bacteria, coral, gorgonians, sponges, and organisms representing virtually every animal phylum and autotrophic division.

1. Rocky reef   2. Sandy bottom

■ 33-2 Rocky Reef ≈ Seaward from a sea cliff covered with homes is a gray line abruptly ending at the drop-off onto a sandy bottom covered with blue-green water. This gray, blue-green line marks the location of a rocky reef.

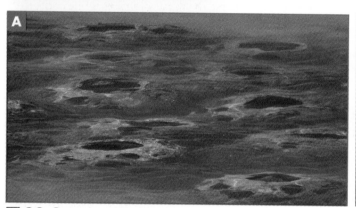

■ 33-3 Artificial Reef ≈ (A) Large, hollow concrete structures looking like giant Nerf® balls sit just offshore along Seven Mile Beach on Grand Cayman. They were placed in the water to provide an artificial reef habitat for local marine species like this blue tang, *Acanthurus coeruleus* (B).

The best-known reefs are tropical and shallow water. However, they also occur in deep, temperate waters. Coral reefs cover less than 1% of the ocean's surface, but contain a large portion of the earth's total biological diversity and as much as 25% of the earth's marine species. (This last statement is made recognizing that recent discoveries in the largely unexplored deep ocean show that an equal if not greater biological diversity may remain undiscovered.) Coral reefs are among the most biologically productive habitats on Earth per unit of surface area.

Rocky reefs occur worldwide. They may rival coral reefs in the striking colors of their inhabitants and are exceptional in the diversity of life forms present.

Kelp Beds

Kelp beds (Figure 33-4) occur worldwide through temperate and polar coastal waters. Together with coral reefs, they are the most biologically productive habitats on Earth per unit of surface area. They provide important and essential habitat for an array of marine vertebrates and invertebrates, and influence local oceanographic processes. The kelp are generally members of the order Laminariales (Chapter 31). The most familiar are species of *Macrocystis*, *Pelagophycus*, *Nereocystis*, *Cystoseira*, and *Egregia*. *Macrocystis* is famous for 60 cm of growth per day under ideal conditions!

■ 33-4 Kelp Beds ≈ Kelp beds lie just offshore in Southern California. (A) This kelp bed is seen from the air, at an altitude of several hundred meters. *(continued)*

■ **33-4 Kelp Beds** ≈ *(continued)* (**B**) This kelp bed is viewed from a 10 m sea cliff. (**C**) The kelp bed is home to a wide array of invertebrate and vertebrate species.

Mangroves

Mangroves dominate the world's tropical coastlines (Figure 33-5). They are limited to tropical and, to a limited extent, subtropical shorelines of the earth. They form thick, wooded areas that provide food and shelter for a host of estuarine, littoral, nearshore sublittoral species, and the young of oceanic organisms. Mangroves stabilize coastal sediments and disperse the force of waves while capturing organic rich sediments and extending shorelines. Approximately 54 plant species occur nearly exclusively in mangrove forests, but the diversity in a particular mangrove forest tends to be low.

■ **33-5 Mangroves** ≈ (**A**) The seaward edge of a mangrove thicket forms a nearly impenetrable barrier in this estuarine environment along the Gulf Coast of southern Florida. (**B**) Established mangroves have a distinct zonation of mangrove species with red mangroves, *Rhizophora mangle*, dominating the lower levels. (**C** and **D**) Mangrove seedling production results in rapid reestablishment of mangroves damaged by storms as shown on St. Thomas Island in the U.S. Virgin Islands. (**E**) Further inland, the root pneumatophores of this black mangrove, *Avicennia germinans*, provide an avenue of gas exchange between the aerial plant parts and those submerged in the anaerobic muds below.

Fouling Communities

Fouling communities (Figure 33-6) are formed on objects placed into the marine environment. They can include pier pilings, floats, boats, trash, and a host of other objects. If remaining in place for years, these objects may serve as protection, and artificial reef-type communities result. The actual fouling community results from populations of encrusting organisms attached to an artificial substrate. Sessile organisms include sponges, tunicates, polychaetes, sea anemones, bryozoans, mussels, sea stars, molluscs, and a variety of other invertebrates, both chordates and nonchordates.

Splash
Isopods
Barnacles

High-tide
Barnacles

Mid-tide
Gooseneck
barnacles

Low-tide
Mussels
Seaweeds
Seastars

Sublittoral

1. Gooseneck barnacle   2. Mussels   3. Ochre stars

■ **33-6 Fouling Communities** ≈ (A) Many artificial objects, such as these pier pilings, placed in the ocean are in the intertidal zone. The result is established fouling communities that are accessible during low tides without getting wet. (B) The abundance of prey species such as these goosenecked barnacles, *Pollicipes polymerus,* and mussels, *Mytilus californianus,* results in the appearance of predators such as these ochre stars, *Pisaster ochraceus.* (C) Subtidal portions of pier pilings in lagoons and bays may show distinctly different communities from intertidal portions. (D) Fouling communities (here on a concrete pier piling) established in high wave-energy areas (as in A) are significantly different in species composition from those established in bays and lagoons. (E) Pilings and horizontal portions of piers provide protection and cover for fish.

Sea "Grass" Communities

Sea grass beds occur from low tide to depths up to 15 m (Figure 33-7). They do best in depths above 5 m and are found in all latitudes. Surfgrass, *Phyllospadix* (Figures 33-7A and 32-28B), and eelgrass, *Zostera* (Figures 33-7B and 32-28A), are the most common grass-like species in temperate latitudes of North America. Ironically, none are true grasses. Each species differs in its habitat preference. In southern and tropical latitudes, turtle grass, *Thalassia testudinum* (Figures 33-7C, 33-7D, and 32-25), dominates from southern Florida to the Gulf of Mexico, the Caribbean, Central America, and Venezuela. In both latitudes, other species are variously important.

Surfgrass

Eelgrass

Turtle grass

Turtle grass

■ **33-7 Sea "Grass" Communities** ≈ (**A**) Surfgrass, *Phyllospadix scouleri*, is a flowering plant common to rocky intertidal shores of the Eastern Pacific from Vancouver Island to Southern California. The five *Phyllospadix* species collectively are distributed along the coasts of Japan and North America as far south as Baja California. (**B**) *Zostera* occurs in sandy and estuarine habitats. They are widely distributed on temperate shores, including North America. (**C** and **D**) Turtle grass, *Thalassia testudinum,* is a tropical-to-low-latitude subtropical species.

Intertidal Habitats

Intertidal habitats vary in the specific physical conditions to which organisms must adapt. In most cases, the conditions vary widely between high and low tides and make life here challenging. If the challenges are met, the abundance of food allows adapted organisms to thrive.

The major physical environmental factors influencing each of these habitats include

≈ temperature extremes

≈ nature of the bottom materials (substrate)

≈ salinity changes

≈ exposure to sunlight

≈ wave shock and tidal surge

≈ drying action of air

The nature of the substrate is the principal determinant of the specific littoral (intertidal) habitat, and the substrate is in large part the consequence of local geology and shore wave-energy exposure.

Rocky Shore

The rocky shore habitat (Figure 33-8) is characteristic of **emergent** coastlines (where land has become uncovered by water as a result of plate tectonic emergence) and areas of high wave energy. Organisms within this habitat live on exposed rocks, or attached to and protected by rocks, and on various species of marine algae and surfgrass. A large number of inhabitants are free-swimming and only partially dependent upon the protective nature of the substrate. Very diverse communities live along rocky shores and there is an ongoing debate about mechanisms producing such a species rich community.

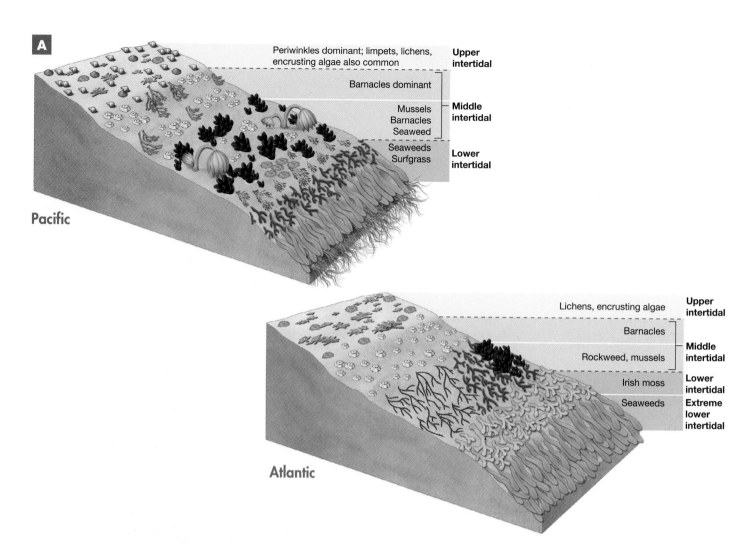

A — Periwinkles dominant; limpets, lichens, encrusting algae also common | **Upper intertidal**

Barnacles dominant

Mussels Barnacles Seaweed | **Middle intertidal**

Seaweeds Surfgrass | **Lower intertidal**

Pacific

Lichens, encrusting algae | **Upper intertidal**

Barnacles

Rockweed, mussels | **Middle intertidal**

Irish moss | **Lower intertidal**

Seaweeds | **Extreme lower intertidal**

Atlantic

■ **33-8 Rocky Shore Intertidal** ≈ (A) The zonation of rocky intertidal habitats differs in specific species depending upon latitude and geographic location. However, the same general microenvironment variables present on the Atlantic coast of North America are also present, for example, on the Indian Ocean coast of Africa. The result is differential distribution of species associated with tidal range. Historically, the stratification of organisms was first documented on the coast of the Pacific Northwest (B), although all emergent coastlines from Maine (C) to California (D) to New Zealand show the same phenomenon.

Sandy Beach

The primary feature of the sandy beach habitat is an unstable substrate (Figure 33-9). Although these habitats often offer an abundance of food in the form of drift, lack of stable substrate makes residence challenging. As a consequences, there is much less species diversity and successful forms are generally those that can burrow below the influence of wave action.

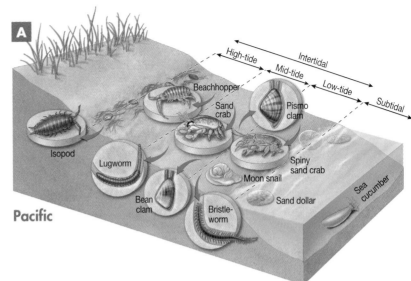

Pacific

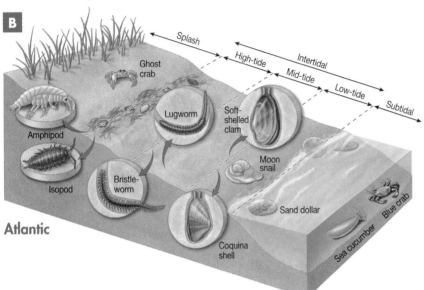

Atlantic

■ 33-9 Sandy Beach ≈ (A) The frequency of tidal coverage and retreat influence distribution of organisms in all littoral (intertidal) habitats, including a sandy beach. **(B)** While relatively low in species diversity, the sandy beach habitat has a distinct zonation, although the specific species composition varies with latitude and geographic location. **C)** The unstable substrate is associated with low primary productivity, but large amounts of organic matter are delivered as drift when storms break loose kelp and other autotrophic species and deposit the material on the beach. **(D and E)** Beach size depends upon a host of variables, including local bathymetry and topography, source of sand, exposure to wave energy **(F)**, and others. These may vary seasonally and result in large differences along the same beach. *(continued)*

■ **33-9** **Sandy Beach** ≈ *(continued)* A beach in summer when wave energy is low may be covered with sand (G) but lack sand during the winter (H) when wave energy is high. The shifting substrate favors organisms that can burrow into the sand quickly to avoid being washed away. The pismo clam, *Tivela stultorum* (I), can quickly go from the surface to buried (J) with only the siphons showing (K) in a matter of a few seconds.(L) The mole crab, *Emerita analoga*, is also able to quickly bury into the sand.

Estuaries (Salt Marsh)

The salt marsh habitat (Figure 33-10) is, like coral reefs and kelp beds, one of the most biologically productive habitats on Earth. Estuaries vary widely in their appearance and nature, depending upon the type of coast on which

they occur: **submergent**, in which the land has become covered with water as a result of plate tectonic **subsidence**, or emergent. Salt marshes of submergent coasts are broad and expansive, while those of emergent coasts are generally nestled in river-cut valleys where a river empties into the sea and land topography is nearly level with shoreline **bathymetry** (*bathy*—deep, *metry*—measure). Sandbars and cobble berms protect the salt marsh from wave action, and although the sand, silt, and mud substrates are easily moved, protected from wave action they are stable between storms. As a consequence of this stability and the delivery of nutrients by tidal fluctuations and river flow into the marsh each day, the salt marsh offers many advantages to the few organisms that are able to tolerate its physical conditions.

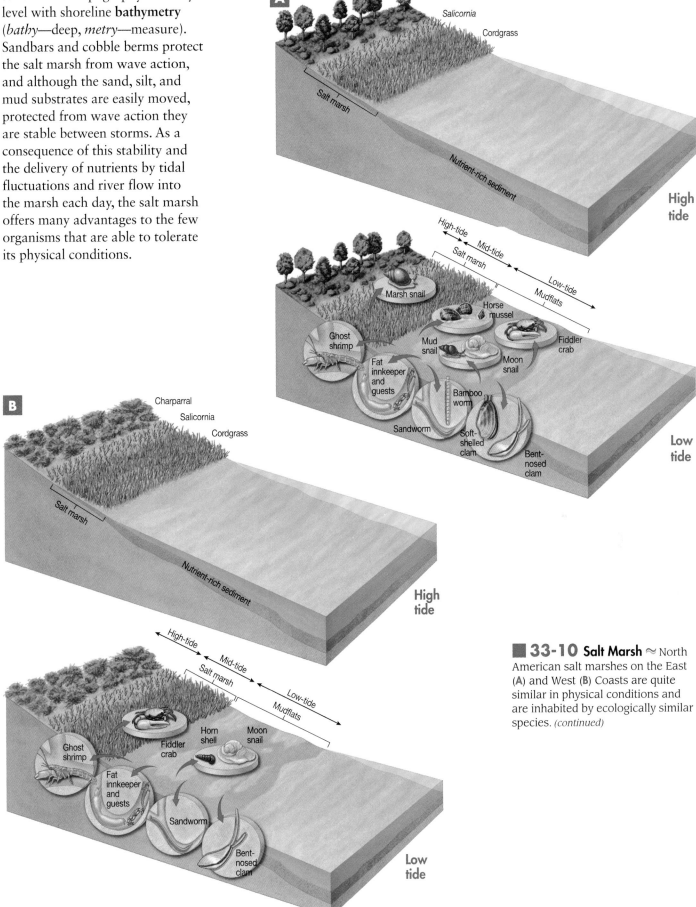

■ 33-10 Salt Marsh ~ North American salt marshes on the East (**A**) and West (**B**) Coasts are quite similar in physical conditions and are inhabited by ecologically similar species. *(continued)*

Pickleweed

California cordgrass

Ghost shrimp

Fiddler crab

California horn snail

■ **33-10 Salt Marsh** ≈ *(continued)* **(C)** Note the dark, nutrient-rich layer of mud (arrow), generally so rich in nutrients and micro-organisms (Chapter 2) that it is nearly black in color and devoid of oxygen. Some of the microorganisms that metabolize the nutrients produce hydrogen sulfide gas as a by-product. When the sediment is disturbed, the rotten egg smell of hydrogen sulfide is sometimes obvious and has been one of the reasons for them being considered places to fill in and develop into marinas or dumps. **(D)** The salt marshes of the emergent West Coast of North America are generally in narrow, river-cut valleys. The normal tidal flushing of these salt marshes, even when they have not been dredged for marinas or filled for development, is often threatened by other types of development. Notice in this Southern California salt marsh how the sandy beach barrier has been stabilized by the placement of a coastal highway and the marsh is transected by a railroad line (arrows). These not only influence normal tidal flushing, but also severely alter other physical factors and impact population size and composition. **(E and F)** The zonations pictured in **(A)** and **(B)** show this pickleweed, *Salicornia* (Chapter 32), at mid-tide to high-tide levels and California cordgrass, *Spartina foliosa,* at the mid-tide to upper low-tide zone. Common animals include ghost shrimp **(G)**, *Callianassa affinis,* the fiddler crab, *Uca crenulata* **(H)**, and the California horn snail, *Cerithidea californica* **(I)**. (For more information on these species, see Chapters 11 and 16.) *(continued)*

■ **33-10** **Salt Marsh** ≈ *(continued)* The presence of these organisms is generally obvious with the (**J**) telltale holes of the ghost shrimp visible at the surface, (**K**) balls of mud near the entrance to the fiddler crab's hole, and (**L**) the horn snails (arrows) present in large numbers at low tide.

Mudflats

Mudflats, or tidal flats (Figure 33-11), are generally next to salt marshes or other estuaries. Tidal ebb and flow once or twice per day floods and drains the flat. Typically, mudflats are very rich in organic matter, particularly **detritus** (*detritus*—wear away). This organic buffet means mudflats are biologically productive. Phytoplankton and zooplankton are abundant, as are animals such as mud snails that feed upon the detritus and benthic plankton. Filter-feeding animals such as oysters and clams are abundant because plankton and organic matter are plentiful in the water. At high tide, fish and crabs move through the flats. Birds and other animals visit mudflats to prey upon other animals that reside there. Most of the permanent animal residents live in the mud, which is anaerobic due to microbial activity. Burrowing clams, worms, and crustaceans are abundant, and many have evolved tubes that allow them to obtain oxygen from the surface (Figure 11-9A).

■ **33-11** **Mudflats** ≈ Mudflats are low-tide areas generally neighboring estuaries, including salt marshes (Figures 33-10A and B). They may take the form of narrow channels called sloughs (**A**), or be very broad (**B**).

Mangroves

Many mangroves are also important estuarine, intertidal habitats (See page 291 for a description.)

Sand Dunes

Although not a marine habitat, sand dunes (Figure 33-12) are part of the supralittoral habitat and are strongly influenced by the marine environment. Dunes form where there is a supply of rock particles in the range of 0.2–2.0 mm. The critical factor is a beach large enough for sand to deposit and for sand to dry during low tides. Vegetation also plays an important role in the growth and formation of dunes. Dunes occur on many coastal strips and in temperate locations.

■ **33-12 Sand Dunes** ≈ Sand dunes form when a combination of sand availability, sand size, and beach size combine in the correct proportions for sand to accumulate. Vegetation also plays an important role in dune formation. Common sources of sand are estuaries and offshore sandbars, and the sand is deposited on the beach by wave action. Dunes are perhaps the most fragile and dynamic habitats on Earth, forming where sand accumulates around objects on the beach. Dunes generally have two to three sets of parallel dunes with the youngest closest to the ocean. The oldest is generally covered with plants and is therefore the most stable.

Definitions of Terms and Taxa Used in Figure 1-1

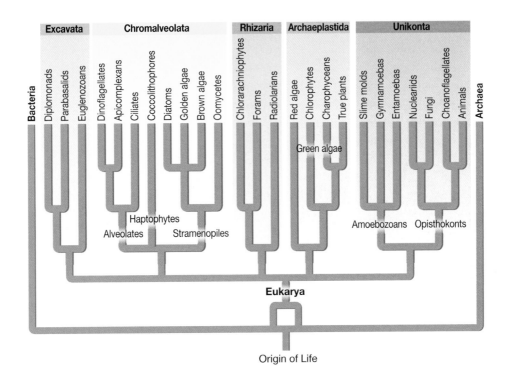

Origin of Life

Group names and taxa are listed in the order they occur from left to right in Figure 1-1 beginning with the bottom lines and working up the figure. (Archaea is an exception, as they are considered together with the Bacteria.)

The groupings in Figure 1-1 are provisional and based on current evidence. Biologists are more certain of some than others, but all are subject to revision as new evidence becomes available and differences of data interpretation resolved.

≈ Bacteria and Archaea

Bacteria and Archaea constitute two of the three known taxa placed at the level of Domain, the most inclusive of all categories. All other names and taxa in the figure are in the third Domain: Eukarya.

The cells of Bacteria and Archaea lack a membrane enclosing their hereditary material (DNA) and therefore do not have a true nucleus. They differ in a number of ways, including whether a particular protein type is associated with their DNA, number and type of chemical tools used to process their DNA, and the chemicals used to form a wall around each cell. Although Bacteria and Archaea were formerly considered to be closely related taxa, current data support the notion that Archaea and Eukarya are more closely related than either is to Bacteria. See Table 2.1.

≈ Eukarya

The most obvious unifying feature of organisms in Eukarya is the presence of a membrane enclosing their hereditary material and forming a nucleus. This taxon includes all familiar organisms, including you.

Excavata

A number of unique features are seen in some members of this group, but the single characteristic that unites them is the presence of certain sequences of DNA not seen in other groups. The name is derived from a feeding groove present on one side of the cell in some species, but not common to all members of this group. This grouping is controversial, and will most likely be modified as new data are examined.

Only Euglenozoans are covered in the *Atlas*. The others are listed in this figure for completeness.

Chromalveolata

This is an extremely diverse group, with unique characteristics present in one subgroup and absent in all others. Some species are single-celled while others are multicellular. Based upon molecular and cellular data, species share a common plastid origin and pigment structure, and cellulose cell walls.

All Chromoalveolate subgroups are discussed in the *Atlas* except Apicomplexans and Oomycetes.

• Alveolates
A common feature of this clade is the presence of membrane-enclosed spaces beneath the cell membrane called alveoli. The name is derived from the presence of these structures.

• Haptophytes
Members of this clade have a haptonema, a unique cellular structure resembling a flagellum, but differing in both structure and function. The name is derived from this structure.

• Stramenopiles
A common feature of this clade is the presence of tubular hair-like structures covering one of their two flagella (called a "tinsel flagellum"). The name is derived from these structures.

Rhizaria

Comparative DNA data support the notion that this is an important evolutionary group. Although diverse, many species (not all) have thread-like cytoplasmic extensions. This grouping is controversial.

The Forams (Foraminiferians) and Radiolarians are presented in this *Atlas*.

Archaeplastida

Based upon comparative molecular and cellular structural data, members of this group share a common ancestor. Another diverse group and one that contains plants. All subgroups are covered in this *Atlas* except for the Charophyceans.

• Red Algae
Red algae form a monophyletic clade. Most are multicellular and marine. They have chlorophyll *a*, but also have large amounts of the pigments phycocyanin and phycoerythrin, which give them their distinctive red, brown, and purple colors. No flagellated cells have been found in red algae. Life cycles in some are very complex.

• Green Algae
This name refers to the bright green color of a pigment within the photosynthetic structure called a chloroplast. The pigment is common to these organisms. You can see in Figure 1.1 that "green algae" is used here as a descriptive term and not a clade.

• True Plants
True plants are paraphyletic with the green and red algae. They are multicellular and have chlorophyll *a*. All exhibit life cycles with alternation of generations where the fertilized egg develops into a multicellular embryo within protective cells on the female plant.

Unikonta

Molecular data support the hypothesis that this diverse collection of organisms should be placed in a single group. It is the least controversial of the groups presented.

Animals are the only subgroup covered in this *Atlas*.

• Amoebozoans
Amoebozoa as a clade is based principally upon comparative molecular data. Members vary widely in morphology. The name is derived from their ability to change shape and form and is from the Greek *amoeba*—change.

• Opisthokonts
Comparative molecular and cellular morphology data support the Opisthokonts as a clade. The name is derived from the common feature of a flagellum, when present, being located at the "rear" of a moving cell (*opisthios*—rear, posterior, *kontos*—pole).

Definitions of Terms, Clades, and Taxa Used in Figure 1-2

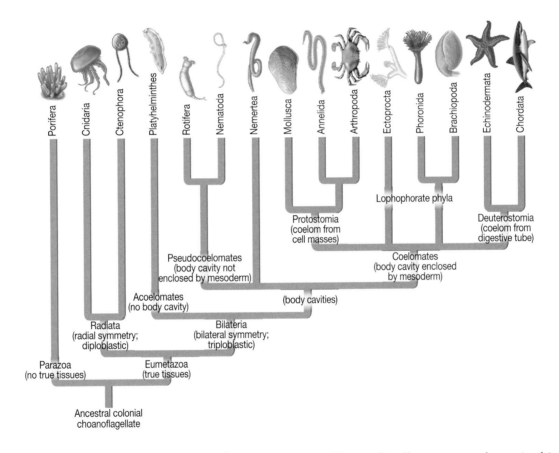

Clades and taxa are listed in the order they occur from left to right on Figure 1-2 beginning with the bottom lines and working up the figure.

∼ Choanoflagellates

These are single-celled or colonial organisms in the clade Unikonta (See Figure 1-1). Molecular and cellular morphologies support the hypothesis that choanoflagellates are in a clade with all multicellular animals (metazoans). Morphologies of colonial choanoflagellates match the requirement of one of the competing hypotheses describing the origin of the Metazoa: the colonial flagellate hypothesis.

Choanoflagellates are not shown in this *Atlas* (though cells resembling them are found in sponges).

∼ Parazoa

The organisms included in this group do not have **true tissues** (See Eumetazoa). However, parazoan's structural organization shows a definite pattern, and that pattern is often one of layers.

∼ Eumetazoa

These organisms have true tissues. A true tissue is defined as a group of cells, generally having the same morphology and organized in such as way as to perform a common function.

≈ Radiata

Radiatans show radial symmetry (Figure 1-4B) or some variation of radial symmetry. They are also diploblastic, meaning that only two layers of cells form in the developing embryo. All adult radiatan cells are derived from one of these layers (Figure 1-9).

≈ Bilateria

These organisms show bilateral symmetry (Figure 1-4C) or some variation of bilateral symmetry. They are also triploblastic, meaning that three layers of cells form in the developing embryo. All adult bilaterian cells are derived from one of these layers (Figures 1-8, 1-9, and 1-11).

≈ Acoelomates

Any organism that is bilaterally symmetrical, triploblastic and does not have a body cavity is an acoelomate (Figures 1-8, 1-9, and 1-11).

≈ Pseudocoelomates

Organisms that are bilaterally symmetrical, triploblastic, and have a body cavity that is *not* entirely lined with cells from the mesoderm are placed in this group (Figures 1-8, 1-9, and 1-11).

≈ Coelomates

The organisms included in this group are bilaterally symmetrical, triploblastic, and have a body cavity that *is* entirely lined with cells from the mesoderm (Figures 1-7, 1-8, 1-9, and 1-11).

≈ Protostomia

These organisms are bilaterally symmetrical, triploblastic coelomates in which the mesoderm (middle tissue layer) originates from cells near the blastopore (Figure 1-10).

≈ Lophophorates

Three animal phyla have developmental and molecular characteristics that are ambiguous. They possess characteristics of both Protostomia and Deuterostomia. Their placement in Figure 1-2 is highly controversial and since all possess a feeding structure called a lophophore, they are labeled Lophophorate (consistent with traditional classifications).

≈ Deuterostomia

These organisms are bilaterally symmetrical, triploblastic coelomates in which the mesoderm (middle tissue layer) originates from cells at the end of the primitive gut opposite the blastopore (Figure 1-10).

Definitions of Terms and Taxa Used in Figure 1-3 and Elsewhere

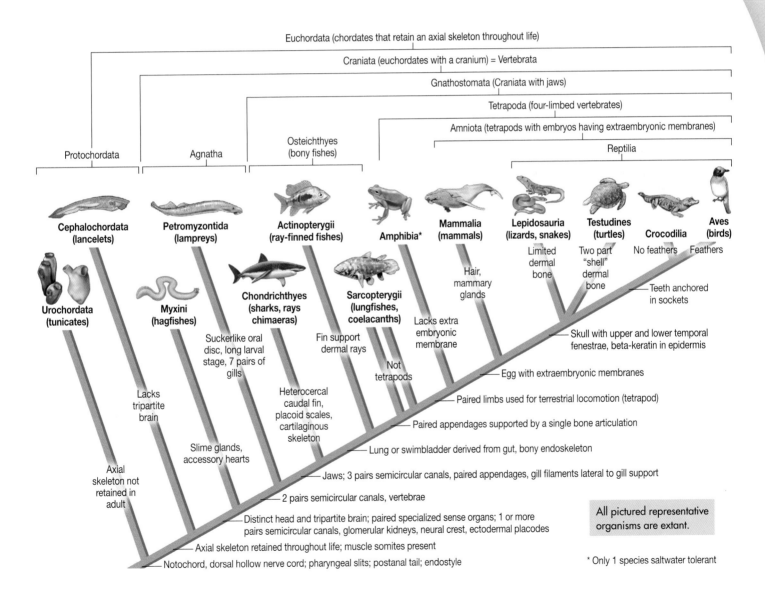

Euchordata (chordates that retain an axial skeleton throughout life)

Craniata (euchordates with a cranium) = Vertebrata

Gnathostomata (Craniata with jaws)

Tetrapoda (four-limbed vertebrates)

Amniota (tetrapods with embryos having extraembryonic membranes)

Reptilia

Protochordata

Agnatha

Osteichthyes (bony fishes)

Cephalochordata (lancelets)

Petromyzontida (lampreys)

Actinopterygii (ray-finned fishes)

Amphibia*

Mammalia (mammals)

Lepidosauria (lizards, snakes)

Testudines (turtles)

Crocodilia

Aves (birds)

Limited dermal bone

Two part "shell" dermal bone

No feathers   Feathers

Hair, mammary glands

Teeth anchored in sockets

Urochordata (tunicates)

Myxini (hagfishes)

Chondrichthyes (sharks, rays chimaeras)

Sarcopterygii (lungfishes, coelacanths)

Lacks extra embryonic membrane

Skull with upper and lower temporal fenestrae, beta-keratin in epidermis

Suckerlike oral disc, long larval stage, 7 pairs of gills

Fin support dermal rays

Not tetrapods

Egg with extraembryonic membranes

Lacks tripartite brain

Heterocercal caudal fin, placoid scales, cartilaginous skeleton

Paired limbs used for terrestrial locomotion (tetrapod)

Paired appendages supported by a single bone articulation

Axial skeleton not retained in adult

Slime glands, accessory hearts

Lung or swimbladder derived from gut, bony endoskeleton

Jaws; 3 pairs semicircular canals, paired appendages, gill filaments lateral to gill support

2 pairs semicircular canals, vertebrae

Distinct head and tripartite brain; paired specialized sense organs; 1 or more pairs semicircular canals, glomerular kidneys, neural crest, ectodermal placodes

All pictured representative organisms are extant.

Axial skeleton retained throughout life; muscle somites present

Notochord, dorsal hollow nerve cord; pharyngeal slits; postanal tail; endostyle

* Only 1 species saltwater tolerant

Terms are listed from top to bottom and from left to right.

≈ **Euchordata** means "true" chordate (*eu*—good, *chorda*—string).

≈ **Craniata** is a proposed clade that includes animals with a hard (cartilage or bone) skull.

≈ **Gnathostomata** is a proposed clade that includes organisms with opposing jaws, teeth, paired appendages, and other anatomical and physiological features in common.

≈ **Tetrapoda** are vertebrates with four limbs. Tetrapoda includes Amphibia, Reptilia, Aves, and Mammalia.

≈ **Amniota** is a tetrapod clade. They have membranes surrounding their egg or developing embryo and lack a larval stage (that is, they have direct development).

≈ **Protochordata** are the nonvertebrate chordates.

≈ **Agnatha** is a paraphyletic clade of jawless fish and excludes all vertebrates with jaws. Extant species known as cyclostomes are monophyletic.

≈ **Osteichthyes** are generally considered to be the bony fish and include the Actinopterygii, which is monophyletic, and the Sarcopterygii, which is monophyletic and includes the tetrapods.

≈ **Urochordata** through **Aves** are major animal clades and are covered in separate chapters in this *Atlas*.

≈ The **axial skeleton** is made of the bones along the central axis of the body and consists of the skull (including middle ear bones in some chordates), the hyoid bone of the throat, the rib cage (may include the sternum), and the vertebral column.

≈ The **tripartite brain** is one that consists of the forebrain, midbrain, and a hindbrain, which are associated with specific gene expressions.

≈ **Dermal rays** (skin rays) are dermal bone (membrane bone) that support the fins.

≈ The **extraembryonic membranes** include the amnion, yolk sac, chorion, and the allantois. These membranes surround the embryo and are present in reptiles, birds, and mammals.

≈ The **notochord** is a mesodermally derived flexible, rod-like structure in all chordates located ventral to the hollow nerve cord. It is replaced by the vertebral column in the vertebrates.

≈ The **dorsal hollow nerve cord** is ectodermally derived nervous tissue located dorsal to the notochord. As embryonic development proceeds, anterior portions develop into the brain. Posterior to the brain, it develops into the spinal cord.

≈ The **pharyngeal slits** are structures formed by *evagination* of the endodermal lining of the pharynx and *invagination* of the ectoderm of the pharynx (pharyngeal grooves). They are common to the ancestors of echinoderms (but are subsequently lost), hemichordates, cephalochordates, urochordates, and vertebrates (contested in some clades).

≈ A **post anal tail** consists of somatic musculature and a notochord extending the body beyond the anus.

≈ The **endostyle** resides in the pharyngeal floor. It secretes mucus used in trapping small food particles. A derivative is the thyroid gland. The thyroid is present in adult lampreys and all other vertebrates.

≈ **Somites** are muscles arranged in segments and occur in the chordates, annelids, and arthropods.

≈ The **semicircular canals** are three, fluid-filled, half-circular interconnected tubes lined with cilia. The cilia respond to the movement of the fluid and act as receptors for detecting body position and movement.

≈ A **glomerular kidney** is one that contains a capillary bed called a glomerulus involved in the first step of blood filtration. It is surrounded by a hollow capsule called Bowman's capsule.

≈ The **neural crest** is located near the developing dorsal nerve cord and consists of cells unique to vertebrates, which give rise to a variety of tissues including cartilage, bone, smooth muscle, and nerve cells.

≈ **Ectodermal placodes** are thickenings of embryonic ectoderm. They contribute to the cranial sensory system of vertebrates. It is unclear if they are homologous across taxa.

≈ The **temporal fenestrae** are holes in the temporal bone (bones of the side and base of the skull). They are spaces that allow passage of chewing muscles.

≈ **Beta-keratin** is a fibrous protein important in the component of reptilian skin, by adding strength and preventing (minimizing) water loss. It also is structurally important in forming bird beaks, claws, and feathers.

Photo Credits

Morton Publishing expresses thanks to the following aquaria and zoos for allowing our authors access to their facilities to take the photographs reproduced within the pages of this Atlas:

Aquarium of the Pacific, Long Beach, CA: Fig. **6-11D**, p. 56; Fig. **6-11J**, p. 57; Fig. **6-12O**, p. 61; Fig. **11-8B**, p. 88; Fig. **16-14A**, p. 128; Fig. **16-16C**, p. 129; Fig. **16-16N, O**, p. 131; Fig. p. 137, **top left**; Fig. **18-9C**, page 143; Fig. **23-15B**, p. 177; Fig. **23-16**, p. 177; Fig. **23-17B**, p. 177; Fig. p. 179, **top right**; Fig. **24-15D**, p. 186; Fig. **24-22C**, p. 190; Fig. **25-20B**, p. 205; Fig. **25-21**, p. 206

Birch Aquarium at Scripps: Fig. **6-12I**, p. 59; Fig. **6-12N**, p. 60; Fig. **6-18A left, right**, p. 64; Fig. **7-4**, p. 69; Fig. **11-8E**, p. 90; Fig. **11-8F left**, p. 90; Fig. **11-9G right**, p. 94; Fig. **11-11A right, center**, p. 96; Fig. **12-10C**, p. 106; Fig. **16-16E**, p. 129; Fig. p. 159, **top right**; Fig. p. 169, **top left, right**; Fig. **24-7**, p. 184; Fig. **24-14**, p. 186; Fig. **24-16B**, p. 187; Fig. **24-20B, C, E, F**, p. 188; Fig. **24-21A**, p. 189; Fig. **24-22A, B, D**, p. 190; Fig. **24-23A**, p. 190; Fig. **24-23E**, p. 191; Fig. **24-24D, E, F**, p. 192; Fig. **24-24M**, p. 193

Cabrillo Marine Aquarium, City of Los Angeles Recreation and Parks: Fig. **11-11O**, p. 100

Chula Vista Nature Center: Fig. p. 169, **top left**; Fig. **23-19A, B**, p. 178; Fig. **26-14B**, p. 220

Denver Museum of Nature & Science: Fig. **11-8F**, page 90; Fig. **26-5M, N**, p. 212; Fig. **26-10A, B**, p. 216; Fig. **26-10A, B, C, D**, p. 216

Denver Zoo: Fig. p. 119, **top right**; Fig. **24-11A**, p. 185; Fig. **24-24K, N**, p. 193; Fig. **26-6A, C**, p. 213; Fig. **26-15V**, p. 225

Downtown Aquarium, Denver, CO: Fig. **6-12J center**, p. 60; Fig. **11-9G left**, p. 94; Fig. **16-14B**, p. 128; Fig. **16-16J, K**, p. 130; Fig. **18-8C**, p. 141; Fig. **18-11D**, page 145; Fig. **22-11C**, p. 166; Fig. **23-9A**, p. 174; Fig. **23-12A**, p. 175; Fig. **23-13C**, p. 176; Fig. **23-14 A**, p. 176; Fig. p. 179, **top left**; Fig. **24-11C**, p. 185; Fig. **24-20D**, p. 188; Fig. **24-23B**, p. 190; Fig. **24-24A, B**, p. 191; Fig. **24-24G**, p. 192; Fig. **26-15E**, p. 221; Fig. **31-24C**, p. 272

Monterey Bay Aquarium: Fig. **6-14A, B, C, D**, p. 62; Fig. **23-3 B**, p. 172; Fig. **23-11**, p. 175; Fig. **23-13A**, p. 176; Fig. **24-12A**, p. 186; Fig. **31-24A**, p. 272

Oregon Coast Aquarium: Fig. **6-9**, p. 55; Fig. **16-10B**, p. 126; Fig. **21-2A**, p. 157; Fig. **24-21B**, p. 189; Fig. **26-15A**, p. 221

Oregon State University Hatfield Marine Science Visitor Center: Fig. **21-2B**, page 157

Oregon Zoo: Fig. **28-5**, p. 246

San Diego Natural History Museum: Fig. **26-4**, p. 210; Fig. **26-16**, p. 226; Fig. **27-11J**, p. 237

Santa Monica Pier Aquarium: Fig. **16-10C**, p. 126; Fig. **18-11A**, p. 145

Sea World San Diego: Fig. p. 1, **top right**; Fig. p. 151, **top left**; Fig. **23-12B**, p. 175; Fig. **24-9A**, p. 184; Fig. **24-11D**, p. 185; Fig. **25-20C**, p. 205; Fig. **26-6B, D, E**, p. 213; Fig. **27-2C**, p. 239; Fig. **27-6A, B**, p. 233; Fig. **27-7**, p. 233; Fig. **27-8A, B, C**, p. 234; Fig. **27-9A, B**, p. 234; Fig. **27-15A, B, C, D**, p. 240; Fig. **27-16A, B, C, D**, p. 240; Fig. **27-19A, B**, p. 241; Fig. **27-22A, B, C, D**, p. 242

Shark Reef Aquarium, Las Vegas: Fig. **23-10**, p. 174

Ty Warner Sea Center, Santa Barbara, CA: Fig. **16-16**, p. 128

Morton Publishing expresses thanks also to the following sources for allowing us to use their photos:

≈ *A Photographic Atlas for the Zoology Laboratory*, 6th Ed.: Fig. **6-15**, p. 63; Fig. **6-16A**, p. 63; Fig. **22-2A**, p. 160; Fig. **24-25**, p. 194; Fig. **25-4**, p. 199; Fig. **25-8A, B**, p. 200; Fig. **26-2**, p. 210

≈ *Comparative Anatomy*, 2nd Ed.: Fig. **22-2B**, p. 161; Fig. **23-2 A, B**, p. 172; **Fig. 23-2B**, p. 172

≈ George D. Lepp / Photo Researchers: Fig. **22-6, right**, p. 162

≈ Comstock Images: Fig. **23-18**, p. 178

≈ Fuse: Fig. **23-20**, p. 178

≈ Tom McHugh / Photo Researchers: Fig. **23-21**, p. 178

≈ Tony Camacho / Photo Researchers: Fig. **25-14**, p. 204

≈ Gilbert S. Grant / Photo Researchers: Fig. **26-5K**, p. 212

≈ M. Philip Kahl / Photo Researchers: Fig. **26-9A, left**, p. 215

≈ Julie Demansky / Photo Researchers: Fig. **26-9A, top center**, p. 215

≈ James H. Robinson / Photo Researchers: Fig. **26-9A, right**, p. 215

≈ Dennis Flaherty / Photo Researchers: Fig. **26-9A, bottom center**, p. 215

≈ Art Wolfe / Photo Researchers: Fig. **26-9B, left**, p. 215

≈ Adam Jones / Photo Researchers: Fig. **26-9B, right**, p. 215

≈ Peter Chadwick / Photo Researchers: Fig. **26-12B**, p. 218

≈ Millard H. Sharp / Photo Researchers: Fig. **26-12D**, p. 218

≈ Connie Bransilver / Photo Researchers: Fig. **26-12I**, p. 219

≈ J.-L. Klein and M.-L. Hubert / Photo Researchers: Fig. **27-10A**, p. 235

≈ Dan Guravich / Photo Researchers: Fig. **27-10B**, p. 235

≈ John Shaw / Photo Researchers: Fig. **27-10C**, p. 235

Plumbaginaceae, 278, 285
pneumatocyst, 246, 270
Poaceae, 280, 288
Poales, 280
Podicipediformes, 209, 214
Podilymbus podiceps, 214
pogonophorans, 101
polar bears, 162, 235
pollinators, 277
Pollycipes polymerus, 126, 292
polychaetes / Polychaeta, 101–105, 108
Polygordius, 105
Polyphyllia talpina, 61
Polyorchis penicillatus, 64
Polyplacophora, 83, 86, 87
polyps, 49, 62, 64, 65, 66
polyribosomes, 9
Polysiphonia lanosum, 252, 254, 255
porcupinefish, 189
Porifera, 41, 43
Porites porites, 61
Porphyra, 251
Porphyridium purpureum, 249, 250
porpoises, 239
Portuguese man-o-war, 64
Postelsia / Postelsia palmaeformis, 273, 274
Prasinophyceae, 33, 34
prawn, 131
predators and predator anti-feedants, 43, 68, 88, 96, 98, 101, 119, 124, 139, 155
birds as, 207, 216
primary endosymbiosis, 33, 35
primrose. *See* evening primrose
Prionitis lanceolata, 258
Pristiformes, 170, 177
Pristiophoriformes, 170
Pristis zijsron, 177
proboscis, 147
Procellariiformes, 209, 216
prokaryotes, 9
protandric
bivalves, 91
hermaphrodite species, 139
protein / protein synthesis, 9, 44, 166
Protista, 30
protochordates, 156
Protoeaster nodosus, 141
protostomes / Protostomia, 6, 78, 122, 133, 134, 135, 304
annelid, 105, 110
coelomate, 102
developmental pattern, 85
pseudocoelomate, 114
versus deuterostome development, 7
protozoea, 127
Pseudoceratina crassa, 48
pseudocoelomates, 8, 78, 113, 114, 121, 304
Pseudocolochirus violaceus, 145
Pseudoplexaura, 57
pseudopods / pseudopodia, 27, 31, 32
Pseudopterogorgia bipinnata, 56
pterobranchs / Pterobranchia, 147, 148
Pterocladia, 251
Pterois volitans, 190
Pterygophora, 248, 273, 274
Ptilosarcus gurneyi, 55
puffins, 221
pycnogonids / Pycongonida, 119, 120, 122, 124
Pycnopodia helianthoides, 142
Pygoscelis papua, 213
pyrenoid, 33

queen angelfish, 192
queen conch, 98
queen triggerfish, 189
quorum sensing, 17

Radiata, 304
radiolarians / Radiolaria, 27, 28, 32, 302
radula, 84, 98, 99
ragwood, 283
rails, 220
Rajiformes, 170
Ralfsia, 270, 271
Rallus longirostris levipes, 210, 220
Rana cancrivora, 161, 201
Rana catesbeiana, 199
raphe, 37
ratfish, 178
ratites, 207
ravens, 226
ray-finned fish, 183
rays, 174, 177
Recurvirostra americana, 221

red algae, 35, 243, 244, 249, 255–258, 302
red-lined worm, 107
red tides, 30, 27, 36
reefs, marine, 289–290
remipedia, 124
Renilla reniformis, 55
reproduction / reproductive cycles, 4, 5
reptiles / Reptilia, 153, 195–196, 198, 203–205
circulatory system, 205
marine, 205
nonavian, 196
scales, 204
reticulopodia, 31
Rhincodon typus, 178
Rhinobatus productus, 177, 178
Rhizaria, 27, 28, 30–31, 302
rhizomes, 281
Rhizophorales / Rhizophoraceae / *Rhizophora mangal*, 279, 281, 285
rhodophytes / Rhodophta / Rhodophyceae, 28, 33, 243, 245, 249, 250, 251, 253, 258
rhopalia, 62
ribosomes and ribosomal RNA (rRNA), 9
Riftia, 21, 23, 24
rockfish, 191
rockweed, 246, 247, 248, 269, 270
rocky shore habitat, 293–294
roundworms, 8, 113
Rush Family, 280, 288
Rynchops niger, 226

Sabellastarte magnifica, 106
Saccharina latissima, 273
Sagittoidea, 136
saddle anemonefish, 192
salamanders, 201, 202
Salicornia, 281, 284, 286
Salmoniformes, 180
Salpa aspera, 155
salps, 151, 158
saltbush, 284
salterns, 26
saltgrass, 288
salt heliotrope, 286
salt marshes, 280, 281, 283, 284, 287, 288, 296–299
saltwort, 278, 283
sand dollars, 137, 142–144
sand dunes, 300
sandpipers, 221, 224
sandy beach habitat, 295–296
Sarcophyton, 60
Sarcopterygii, 153, 179, 181, 182, 194, 195, 196
sardines, 186
Sardinops sagax, 186
Sargassum, 270, 271
sawfish, 177
scallops, 90
scales
fish, 204
placoid, 173
reptilian, 204
types of, 183
scaphopods / Scaphopoda, 83, 94–95
scavengers, 90, 139, 167
Scirpus species, 287
Scomber japonicas, 163, 182
Scorpaena plumieri, 191
Scorpaeniformes, 181, 190, 191
scorpionfish, 190, 191, 179
scrawled filefish, 189
scutes, 204
Scypha, 44, 45
scyphistomae, 62
Scyphozoa, 49, 52, 62–63
Scytosiphonales / *Scytosiphon lomentaria*, 270, 272
sea anemones, 4, 49
sea apple, 145
sea arrowgrass, 286
seablite, 284
sea comb, 244, 258
sea cows, 230
sea cucumbers, 137, 144–146
seadragon, leafy, 188
sea fig, 283
sea fungus, 265
sea gooseberry, 67, 68, 69
sea grass beds, 293
sea hare, 100
seahorses, 188
sea jellies, 62–63
sea lavender, 285
sea lettuce, 259, 260
sea lilies, 146

sea lions, 231, 233
seals, 231
elephant, 231–233
fur, 233
harbor, 162, 231
sea otters, 233, 234
sea pansies, 55
sea pen, 55
sea plume, 56
sea rod, 57
sea sacs, 256
sea slugs, 100
sea snake, 206
sea spiders, 119, 122
sea squirts, 151, 155, 157, 158
sea stars, 137, 138, 139–142
sea turtle, 195, 204, 205
sea urchins, 137, 142–143
seaweeds, 243, 244, 245–246, 248, 252, 257, 272, 290
Sebastes mystinus, 191
Sebastidae, 191
Secernentea, 116
secondary endosymbiosis, 35
sedges, 280, 287
seed shrimp, 125
Sepia officinalis, 90
Sepioteuthis sepioidea, 89
shapes / symmetry, 4
sharks, 166, 174, 175, 176, 177, 178.
See also dogfish shark
shearwaters, 216
shipworms, 90
shorebirds, 221
shore grass, 288
shovel nose guitarfish, 177, 178
shrimp, 124, 125, 128, 131, 298
Silvetia / Silvetia compressa, 269, 270
silversides, 187
siphonophores, 49, 64, 65
siphons, 157, 158
sipunculids / Sipuncula, 84, 109–111
Sirenia, 227, 228, 230
skates, 174, 177
skimmer, black, 226
skin, tetrapod, 201
skull, amniote, 203
Smithora naiadum, 252
snails, 83, 96, 97–99
snakes, 199, 205, 206
soda straws (algae), 272
Solanales, 279
Somateria mollissima and *spectabilis*, 212
southern elephant seal, 232
Sparisoma viride, 193
Spartina / Spartina foliosa, 280, 288, 298
speciation, 2
Sphacelariales, 266, 267, 269
Spheciospongia vesparium, 47
Sphenisciformes, 209, 213
Spheniscus demersus, humboldti, and magellanicuis, 213
Sphyraena barracuda, 192
spicules (sponge), 43, 44
spiracles (example), 178
spirilla / spirillum, 16
Spirobranchus giganteus, 101, 103
spirochaetes, 16
Spirorbis, 108
Spirulina, 21
Spisula solidissima, 91
sponges, 41, 42, 192, 290
body morphology, 43–44
Demospongiae, 46
reproduction, 44–45
Synconid, 44
taxonomy, 45
spongin, 44
spongocoel, 44, 45
spoonbills, 218
spoon worms, 103
spores, 245
sporophytes, 270, 273
spotted trunkfish, 189
Squalus, 172, 173, 174
Squamata, 196, 205, 206
Squatiniformes, 170
squid, 83, 88, 89
squirrelfish, 187
Staphyloccus aureus, 12
Staurozoa, 49, 52
Steller sea lion, 233
Stenolaemata, 75, 77
Stenoplax conspicua, 87
Sterna
antillarum, elegans, and *maxima*, 225
caspia, 224

stilt, black-necked, 221
stingray, 174, 175, 177, 178
stomates, 281, 282
stomatopods / Stomatopoda, 120, 127
Stramenopile / stramenopiles, 35, 36–37, 38, 265, 266, 302
strobilation, 62
stromatolites, 21, 22
Strombus / Strombus gigas, 95, 98
stoneworts, 33
stoplight parrotfish, 193
storks, 218
Stronglyocentrotus droebachiensis, 142
purpuratus, 143
sturgeon, 184
Suaeda, 284
succulence / succulent leaves, 280, 281, 283, 284
sugar kelp, 273
sulfur-oxidizing bacteria / sulfur-reducing bacteria, 21, 23, 24
sunflowers, 278, 283
surfgrass, 287, 293
swans, 211
Swiftia, 57
swim bladder, 182
Symbiodinium species, 36
symmetry, 4, 138, 145, 304
symplesiomorphies, 2
synapomorphies, 159
Synapsida, 203
Synapta maculata, 145
Synechococcus, 21, 22
Syngnathiformes, 180
Syngnathus leptorhynchus, 188
Syringodium filiforme, 287
systematics, 4, 6

Tabellaria, 39
Taeniura lymna, 177
Taliepus nuttali, 129
Tantulocarida, 125
tapeworms, 71
Tardigrada, 117–118, 121
tarpons, 185
tar spot (algae), 272
taxon / taxa, 2
Taxonomy, 7
Tegula funebralis, 96
teleost fish skeleton, 200
temnospondyls, 198
tentacles, 80
Tentaculata, 67, 69
Terebratalia, 80
Terebratulida, 79
terns, 221, 224, 225
terrestrial environment, 195–196, 198, 202, 203
Testudines, 3, 4, 196, 206
Tethya aurantia, 46
tetrapods, 194, 195, 196, 197
avian, 212
eggs, 199
head movements, 200
skeleton, 200
skin, 201
Tetraodontiformes, 180, 189
Thalassia testudinum, 286, 293
Thaliacea, 155, 156, 158
thallus (seaweed), 245
thecae, 30, 36
Themiste alutacea and *pyrodies*, 112
thermophiles, extreme, 25
Thermotoga maritima, 20
theropods, 207
Thiobacillus, 21
Thiothrix, 21
Thor amboinensis, 131
tidal flats, 299
tidepool sculpin, 191
tiger cowry, 99
Tintidium, 29
tintinnids, 29
Tivela stultorum, 92, 296
toads, 201
Tonicella lineata, 87
topsmelt, 187
Torpediniformes, 170
Torrey pine tree and cone, 276
totipotent, 42
toxins, 95
Trematoda, 71, 73
Triakis semifasciatum, 175, 176
Trichecus manatus latirostris, 230
trichomes, 21
Tridacna
derasa, 94
gigas, 91, 94
Tripneustes ventricosus, 143

trochophore, 78, 84, 94, 95, 105
Trochozoa, 78, 81
trophosome, 24
true plants, 302
trumpetfish, 188
tubeworm, 23
tun, 118
tunicates, 158
turbellarians / Tubellaria, 71–74
turbot, diamond, 190
turnstone, ruddy, 224
Tursiops truncates, 239
turtle(s), 3, 4, 162, 199, 203, 205–206. *See also* sea turtle
turtle grasses, 286, 293
tusk shells, 94, 95

Uca crenulata, 129, 298
Ulothrix, 261
Ulotrichales, 259, 260, 261
Ulvales / *Ulva*, 259, 260, 261, 271
intestinalis, 261
Ulvophyceae, 245, 259, 260
Umbelliferae, 278, 282
Unikonta, 302
Uria aalge, 221
Urobatis halleri, 174, 175, 178
urochordates / Urochordata, 151, 153, 155, 156, 158, 159
Urodela, 196, 202
Urosoidea, 228
Ursidae, 228, 235
Ursus maritimus, 1, 235
Urticina crassicornis, 54

vascular plants, 275–276, 279, 281
vegetative cells, 12
Velella velella, 64, 65
veligers, 84, 89, 91, 94, 95
velum / velarium, 62
verbenas, 284
Verongula
gigantea, 46
rigida, 48
vertebrates / Vertebrata, 158
epidermal derivatives, 162
epidermis, 201
fertilization / copulatory organ, 199
skeleton, 160
vertebral column, 161
vibrios / *Vibrio*, 16, 17, 20
violet fan nudibranch, 100
viviparity, 177
Vorticella, 27
vultures, 218

walruses, 231, 233, 234
water bears, 117–118
watercress, 262
water fowl, 211
water molds, 36
waterweed, 280
western gull, 154
whales, 151, 235–242
whimbrel, 224
White Cliffs of Dover, 31
whitetail dascyllus, 192
willets, 221, 224
Winogradsky column (Sergei Winogradsky), 24–25
wireweed, 271
worms
arrow, 133, 135, 136
red-lined, 107
segmented / polychaete, 101, 107
spoon, 103

xerophytes and xerophyte adaptations, 281
Xestospongia muta, 46
xylem, 275–276

yarrow, 283
yellowhead jawfish, 193
yellow tang, 192

Zalophus californianus, 233
Zebrasoma flavescens, 192
Ziphiidae, 229, 239, 242
zoea, 127, 132
Zonaria / Zonaria farlowii, 266, 268
zooecium / zooids, 76, 105, 148
Zooplanktors / zooplankton, 27, 67, 125, 299
zooxanthellae, 52, 55, 71, 90–91, 94
Zosteraceae and *Zostera marina*, 280, 282, 287, 293